# JOE LEDGER
## THE OFFICIAL COMPANION

## DANA FREDSTI & MARI ADKINS

### WITH THOMAS C. RAYMOND, BRIAN L. BIRD, KELLY POWERS, BABETTE RAYMOND AND BEN RAYMOND

**JOURNALSTONE**
YOUR LINK TO ARTIST TALENT

JournalStone books may be ordered through booksellers or by contacting:
JournalStone
www.journalstone.com

The views expressed in this work are solely those of the authors and do not necessarily reflect the views of the publisher, and the publisher hereby disclaims any responsibility for them.

Photo Credits:
Cover Image: DVARG/Shutterstock.com
p.13: © Macmillan Publishing; p17: © Bruce Press; p.18: public domain; p.27 (hazmat): © Martinlisner, Dreamstime; p.27 (biohazard): © Dreamstime; p.31: © Thomas C. Raymond (thanks given to Josh at The Outdoorsman of Santa Fe and his boss Bill Roney); p.32: © Thomas C. Raymond; p.45 © Blackstone Audio; p.60: © Jonathan Maberry; p.64 © David Naughton-Shires; p.66: © Thomas C. Raymond; p.67: © Jonathan Maberry; p.68: © BenilliUSA.com; p.72: © Remington.com; p.93 & 94: © Thomas C. Raymond; p.96: © Vinella Olp, mommabearpics.com; p.97: courtesy of Southport Atkinson Art Gallery; p.99: © Sara Jo West; p.100: photo by Robert O'Brien, © Jonathan Maberry; p.101: © Jonathan Maberry & Sara Jo West; p.104: © Macmillan Publishing; p.105: © Lee Hartnup; p.111: © Oleg Zabielin, Dreamstime; p.113: Paperback editions courtesy Pinnacle Books, hardcover editions courtesy JournalStone Publishing, Audiobooks courtesy Blackstone Audio; p.114 (top): © Macmillan Publishing; p.114 (bottom): Alslutsky, Dreamstime; p.116: © Lockheed-Martin; p.117: © Jonathan Maberry; p.119: Unicorn—©Marbenzu, Dreamstime, Nazi photo—©Steve Allen, Dreamstime, Neanderthal—© Slawek Kozakiewicz, Dreamstime; p.123: © Macmillan Publishing; p.124: © Boeing Rotorcraft Systems; p.125: © Emily Meghan; p.126 (selkie): public domain; p.127: © Yana Ermakova; p.129: public domain; p.130: public domain; p.133: © Macmillan Publishing; p.135: © Municipality of Damascus; p.137: public domain; p.138 (Entry of the Crusaders into Constantinople): Gutav Dore; p.138 (bottom): © Jonathan Maberry; p.139 (top): public domain; p.139 (bottom): Gustav Dore; p.141: © Catherine Scully; p.142: © Liars Club Logo designed by Michael Miller, used by permission of The Liars Club; p.143: © Macmillan Publishing; p.146: public domain; p.147 (top): public domain; p.147 (bottom): © Fernando Gregory, Dreamstime; p.148: public domain; p.149: © United States Air Force; p.150 (top): © U.S. Coast Guard; p.150 (bottom): © Jonathan Maberry; p.152: © Macmillan Publishing; p.153: © Jonathan Maberry; p.154: © Oleg Zabielin; p.155: Model: Lasse Antaro, photo by Mads Schmidt; p.156: © Sara Jo West; p.158 (top): © JournalStone; p.158 (bottom): public domain; p.159 (top): © Ryan Brown; used by permission of IDW Publishing; p.159 (bottom): © Macmillan Publishing; p.160: © Oleg Zabielin; p.162 (top): © Thomas C. Raymond; p.162 (bottom): © Valentin Gaina, Dreamstime ; p.168 (top): © Macmillan Publishing; p.168 (bottom): © David Naughton-Shires; p.169: © Greg Chapman; p.170: © Robert Elrod; p.173: © Spectral-design, Dreamstime; p.177: © Macmillan Publishing; p.178: © CDC.gov; p.179: © Pogonici; p.182: Dreamstime Images; p.183: © TexasWarhawk/Wikimedia Commons; p.184: © Stuman1/Wikimedia Commons; p.188 & 189: © Robert Reed Murphy; p.190 (top): © St. Martin's Griffin; p.190 (bottom): © Simon & Schuster Books for Young Readers; p.191 (top): *Dead of Night* and *Fall of Night* covers used by permission of St. Martin's Griffin; *Dark of Night* and *Still of Night* covers used by permission of Journalstone; p.191 (bottom): © Rachael Lavin; p.193: © Jonathan Maberry; p.194: © IDW Publishing; p.195: © Travis Hodges; p.197: © Sara Jo West; p.200: © Charles C. Pinckney, model: Dyana Postelle; p. 203: © Moonshine Team;

ISBN:    978-1-942712-70-1    (sc)
ISBN:    978-1-942712-71-8    (ebook)
ISBN:    978-1-942712-72-5    (hc)

JournalStone rev. date: August 25, 2017

Library of Congress Control Number: 2017948071

Printed in the United States of America

Cover & Interior Design: Jess Landry
Edited by: Aaron J. French

*"I'm doing what I believe is in the best interests of the American people."*
—Joe Ledger, *Deep Dark*


Mari: For Tommy.

Dana: This one's for all the readers out there who've happily lost themselves in the world of Joe Ledger.

## ACKNOWLEDGMENTS

Special thanks to Michael Homler and the good folks at St. Martin's Griffin and Macmillan Audio. Thanks to Jason Pinter for being Joe's first godfather. Thanks to Sara Crowe of Pippin Properties, Inc and Dana Spector of Paradigm. Thanks to Tony Eldridge of Lone Tree Entertainment. Thanks to Javier Grillo-Marxuach for Department Zero. Thanks to Blackstone Audio. Thanks to Christopher Payne at JournalStone Publishing.

Thanks to Kelly Littleton for introducing us to the DMS historian.

Special thanks to Catherine Scully, Robert Elrod and Greg Chapman for their marvelous renderings of Cthulhu.

Thanks to Josh at "The Outdoorsman of Santa Fe" and his boss Bill Roney for their graciousness in giving access to their stock for photographing.

Thanks to David Fitzgerald for helping give structure to chaos.

# JOE LEDGER
## THE OFFICIAL COMPANION

# CONTENTS

# ABOUT THIS BOOK

*"I washed my face, rinsed my mouth out with handfuls of tap water, pasted on my best I-didn't-just-kill-a-zombie expression, and left with my coffee."*
—Joe Ledger, *Patient Zero*

The information presented in this book is meant to supplement the Joe Ledger novels, as written by Jonathan Maberry and published by St Martin's Griffin. Any and all omissions are those of the authors and various field agents. Characters' first appearances as indicated are in chronological order based on the events in the books and stories rather than by publication date. Fans of Joe Ledger, consider this companion a valuable field guide of background information about the characters, the science, and the technology used in the series.

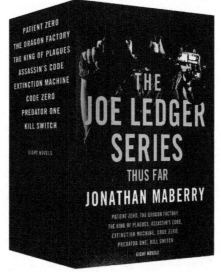

# ABOUT THIS BOOK

# PREFACE

## JONATHAN MABERRY

*When you have to kill the same terrorist twice in one week, then there's either something wrong with your skills or something wrong with your world.*
*And there's nothing wrong with my skills.*

That's how I opened the first Joe Ledger novel, *Patient Zero.*

It was kind of flip, kind of smartass. But then again, so is Joe. Though, I didn't know who Joe was when I first met him.

Here's what happened. I was sitting at the Red Lion Diner—a true classic American diner, in Willow Grove, Pennsylvania—working on a nonfiction project, *Zombie CSU: The Forensics of the Living Dead.* That book was scheduled for release from Citadel Press, as a kind of companion to a series of nonfiction occult/paranormal books I was writing for them. It was to be sandwiched in between the Bram Stoker Award-winning *The Cryptopedia* and *They Bite*, both co-written with my longtime friend, David F. Kramer. At the time of that writing I was also working on *Bad Moon Rising*, the third and final volume in my Pine Deep Trilogy. *Bad Moon Rising* was my third novel and I wasn't yet sure what I would do next.

> "Jonathan Maberry's *Patient Zero* strips today's headlines and offers a frightening tale of how far extremists will go to succeed. Brilliant, shocking, horrifying, it puts the terror back in terrorist."
> —James Rollins, *New York Times* bestselling author of the *Sigma Force* series

So, I was sitting there drinking way too much coffee, eating eggs, and editing interviews from various experts for *Zombie CSU*. That morning I'd come from a session with a SWAT team in Philadelphia, where the snipers and team members showed me how they would reclaim a city street from zombies, even if the zoms were fast runners (as in the 2004 remake of *Dawn of the Dead* or the infected-but-not-really-a-zombie flick *28 Days Later*).

While I was editing two voices began talking in my head. If you're not a writer, this is an obvious cry for help. It's when you call your doctor and put him on combat pay because it's going to be a bumpy ride. However, if you *are* a writer, this is the sort of thing that happens. Characters who have been looking for their voice suddenly find it and a scene begins playing. We don't always know who these people are, what their story is, or much of anything else. Novels, you see, often float around in the subconscious like bits of debris and they are not really a cohesive story until something happens and some of that debris coalesces into a story, or a scene. That's what happened that day.

The conversation was between a snarky pain-in-the-ass of a cop and an enigmatic and somewhat threatening director of some kind of black ops group. As is my habit when such things happen, I turned to a fresh page in my notebook and began writing down the conversation. And, as also happens, I took control of it and shaped it, and in doing so, became more fully aware of what the story was and who these two guys were.

If you've read *Patient Zero*, this is the scene where Mr. Church interviews Joe Ledger for the first time and they talk about a recent joint police/Homeland raid on a terrorist cell in Baltimore. The conversation kept my interest and I put *Zombie CSU* aside for the rest of the day, went home to type up the scene. I expanded it and fleshed out the characters. The boss man was always Mr. Church, right from the beginning, though I knew it wasn't his real name. The hero was not yet named Joe Ledger. That came two days later when my wife, Sara Jo, and my son, Sam, and I were making an Italian dinner together. I explained what I had of the story and we knocked around character names. I had originally planned to call my protagonist 'John Book,' but then realized that was Harrison Ford's character in *Witness*. Book became Ledger (thanks thesaurus) and John became Joe. I liked the three-syllable name. It scanned well.

I wrote out an outline and some sample pages and gave them to my agent, Sara Crowe. It was not another horror novel, as were the Pine Deep books. This was a mainstream science thriller that happened to have some horror elements—zombies. However, I decided to go the extra yard and make sure there was good, solid real-world science to explain how the zombies were created, and why. I reached out

> "Great characters we immediately come to care about, a plot that grabs you by the collar on page one. Written like a combination of the best of Tom Clancy, Ian Fleming and Len Wein, *The Dragon Factory* is a visual thriller, presenting a page-turning plot with all the twists of a great science-fictionesque spy story."
>
> **—Story Time**

to some world-class scientists—many of whom I'd already interviewed for *Zombie CSU*. I also spoke to the cops and a bunch of military experts, psychologists, medical doctors, and more.

I kind of expected my agent to balk at me taking a new direction with my fiction, but this was one of many times Sara Crowe surprised me. She loved the new idea, loved the story and characters, and decided to shop the book as a mainstream thriller, and to take it to a new house. She landed it at St. Martin's Griffin, with editor Jason Pinter. By now the book's title had undergone three or four changes. It was originally *Code Zero*, but I decided that *Patient Zero* had more punch, since we start the zombie thing from the very first infected person.

Shortly after Pinter bought it, however, he landed a contract to go off and write his own thrillers. I was orphaned, as they say in the business. But not for long. A newbie editor, Michael Homler, grabbed *Patient Zero* and proved at once that he was the perfect editor for the book. He bought *Patient Zero* and asked for two more in the series.

Which was a bit of a shocker. I thought this was going to be a one and done thing. A standalone thriller. I mean, once they dealt with the zombies what was next?

Between the time my agent told me we had an offer and when Homler called me—let's call it forty minutes—I came up with ideas for books 2 and 3. It wasn't actually even a stretch. Writers often have ideas banging around in their heads and I grabbed at some of the cooler (and weirder) ideas that I'd toyed with.

I'm a bit of a science junkie anyway, so I started thinking about what was being discussed in the news, and in the science trade journals I like to read. Transgenics was breaking big, and so were post-9/11 conspiracy theories. So, I decided to do one transgenic novel, *The Dragon Factory*, and a novel about a cabal of super-rich bad guys who 'borrow' the mythology of groups like the *Illuminati* and so

---

### FRIENDS IN THE INDUSTRY:
### DR. JOHN M. CMAR

Dr. John M Cmar is an Infectious Disease Specialist in Baltimore, Maryland. He graduated with honors from University of Cincinnati College of Medicine in 2001. Having more than 16 years of diverse experiences, especially in INFECTIOUS DISEASE AND INTERNAL MEDICINE, Dr. John M Cmar affiliates with Sinai Hospital Of Baltimore, and cooperates with other doctors and specialists in medical group Sinai Hospital Of Baltimore, Inc. Call Dr. John M Cmar on phone number (410) 601-6207 for more information and advises or to book an appointment.

> "*Patient Zero* is a well written, often insanely paced and utterly compelling piece of entertainment."
> —*Death Ray Magazine*

on, and use that as a front for influencing the stock market by exploiting market shifts following terrorist attacks. That one was *The King of Plagues*. Not sure that one's all fiction.

The books did well. Very well.

By the time I started writing *Plagues* St. Martin's asked me for the next two. And I was off and running. Building the organization headed by Mr. Church, *The Department of Military Sciences*; staffing it with characters I found fascinating; cooking up new threats; and expanding on the life of Joe Ledger.

One side note, I've discovered while writing the Ledger novels that he is substantially funnier than I am. Not sure how that works.

While writing the novels I was also tapped by various anthology editors and magazine editors to write short stories featuring Joe Ledger. The first was "Zero Tolerance," which remains a favorite, because it allowed me to re-visit a plot element I'd deliberately left hanging in *Patient Zero*. I did that again with *The Dragon Factory*, by following it with a short story, "Dog Days," that not only tied up a thread but introduced Joe's combat dog, Ghost.

Ghost, by the way, gets a ton of fan mail. Yes, my fictional hero's fictional dog gets fan mail. (I love my readers because they're as batshit crazy as I am!)

The ninth Joe Ledger novel, *Dogs of War*, debuted in April 2017. At this writing, I'm deeply into the 10th book, *Deep Silence*. There is a collection of the Ledger stories available, *Joe Ledger: Special Ops*; another in the works; and an anthology, *Joe Ledger: Unstoppable*, which features original Ledger fiction

> "Ledger is an unstoppable force, and in his universe there are no immovable objects. Yet although he's the ultimate bad-ass fighting machine, he's written with sensitivity, humor and style. That's what makes the Joe Ledger series so compelling."
>
> —Tim Lebbon, *New York Times* bestseller and 4-time British Fantasy Award-winning author of *The Silence* and *Relics*

**PULP MAGAZINE COVERS**

The Joe Ledger thrillers are cutting-edge science blended with military action, but they owe a great debt to the pulp thrillers of the 30s and 40s. Author Jonathan Maberry grew up reading the reprints of Doc Savage, The Spider, The Shadow, G8 and his Battle Aces, The Avenger, and dozens of others. Many of those stories featured wild 'science fiction' devices that have since proved to be real and viable, like retina scanners, jets, lasers, jetpacks, computers, rockets, and more.

by some of my 'friends in the industry,' including Aaron Rosenberg, David Farland, James A. Moore, James Ray Tuck, Steve Alten, Javier Grillo-Marxuach, Jennifer Campbell-Hicks, Jeremy Robinson, Joe McKinney, Jon McGoran, Keith R.A. DeCandido, Larry Correia, Nicholas Seven, Seanan McGuire, Scott Sigler, Weston Ochse, Bryan Thomas Schmidt, GP Charles, and Dana Fredsti. Quite a lineup.

And, also at this writing, the Joe Ledger novels are under option to Hollywood producer Tony Eldridge of Lone Tree Entertainment. Tony is a producer on the wonderful *Equalizer* flicks with Denzel Washington. And he's also partnered with Janet Zucker of Zucker Productions for *Mars One* and my Monk Addison short stories.

Of every character I've created for my novels—and the book I'm writing is my 30th—as well as characters from my hundred-plus short stories and many comics, Joe Ledger is my favorite. I can drop him—willingly or unwillingly—into any situation and he will bring serious game. He's fun to write about, though sometimes what happens in his stories breaks my heart.

Later on in this book I'll talk about the 'expanded Joe Ledger universe,' because he is too restless to remain in his own stories. That's fun, too, especially when someone reads one of my *Rot & Ruin* stories or a Sam Hunter short story and meets Joe for the first time and then is surprised to learn there's a lot more Joe out there.

---

## FRIENDS IN THE INDUSTRY: KEITH R.A. DECANDIDO

Keith R. A. DeCandido is a second-degree black belt in karate (he both teaches and trains) and has spent an inordinate amount of time in Key West. Other tales of his taking place in the Keys include "We Seceded Where Others Failed" in *Altered States of the Union*, the Mack Bolan, Executioner novel *Deep Recon*, "Raymond's Room" in *Doctor Who: Missing Pieces*, and a series of stories featuring Cassie Zukav, weirdness magnet, in the anthologies *Apocalypse 13*, *Bad-Ass Faeries: It's Elemental*, *A Baker's Dozen of Magic*, *Out of Tune*, *Tales from the House Band*, vols. 1 and 2, and *TV Gods: Summer Programming*, the online zines *Buzzy Mag* and *Story of the Month Club*, and the collections *Ragnarok and Roll: Tales of Cassie Zukav, Weirdness Magnet* and *Without a License: The Fantastic Worlds of Keith R. A. DeCandido*. Other recent work includes the *Marvel Tales of Asgard* trilogy, featuring Thor, Sif, and the Warriors Three; *Stargate SG-1: Kali's Wrath*; *Heroes Reborn: Save the Cheerleader, Destroy the World*; *A Furnace Sealed*; *Mermaid Precinct*; three novellas in his *Super City Cops* series; and stories in *Aliens: Bug Hunt*, *Baker Street Irregulars*, *Limbus Inc. Book III*, *Nights of the Living Dead*, *V-Wars: Night Terrors*, *The X-Files: Trust No One*, and others. Find out less at his cheerfully retro website, www.DeCandido.net. Read his action-packed story "Ganbatte" in *Joe Ledger: Unstoppable*.

"Joe Ledger is one of my finest possessions. No, I didn't write him, I didn't create him. But I was there, hanging on the edge of my seat from the first book, and I have been a loyal reader ever since. It's like when you discover a band while they're young. Nobody knows about them. You're the one telling all your friends they have to check this out. That was me with *Patient Zero*. I'm proud to say the series just keeps getting better and better. Joe Ledger is part James Bond, part Jason Bourne, part snark master, but he is 100% great entertainment. When people ask me who I should be reading, I always mention Jonathan Maberry's Joe Ledger series. This is the new standard, the new true American badass."

—Joe McKinney, Bram Stoker Award-winning author of the *Dead World* and *Deadlands* series

Oh, and yeah…cosplay? The first time people showed up dressed as Joe Ledger and Echo Team at a comic con it freaked me out. Since then I've encountered other characters from the Ledger books, including a slew of "Mother Night" cosplayers from *Code Zero*.

I have no intention of giving Joe and his companions a rest. I have more Ledger novels and short stories planned; I'm in discussions for a Joe Ledger comic; and there's the movie in development. Who knows where Joe will go next, who or what he'll fight, or what sacrifices he'll be called on to make to keep this weird old world spinning on its crooked axis. Joe will be there in the thick of the fight, though, and I can't wait to find out what happens next.

## FRIENDS IN THE INDUSTRY: JOE MCKINNEY

Joe McKinney has his feet in several different worlds. In his day job, he has worked as a patrol officer for the San Antonio Police Department, a DWI enforcement officer, a disaster mitigation specialist, a homicide detective, the director of the city of San Antonio's 911 call center, and a patrol supervisor. He played college baseball for Trinity University, where he graduated with a bachelor's degree in American history, and went on to earn a master's degree in English literature from the University of Texas at San Antonio. He was the manager of a Barnes & Noble for a while, where he indulged a lifelong obsession with books. He published his first novel, *Dead City*, in 2006, a book that has since been recognized as a seminal work in the zombie genre. Since then, he has gone on to win two Bram Stoker Awards and expanded his oeuvre to cover everything from true crime and writings on police procedure to science fiction to cooking to Texas history. The author of more than twenty books, he is a frequent guest at horror and mystery conventions. Joe and his wife, Tina, have two lovely daughters and make their home in a little town just outside of San Antonio, where he pursues his passion for cooking and makes what some consider to be the finest batch of chili in Texas. You can keep up with all of Joe's latest releases by friending him on Facebook. His short story "Rookie" can be found in *Joe Ledger: Unstoppable*.

# INTRODUCTIONS
## MARI ADKINS & DANA FREDSTI

*"I reloaded and took up a defensive position to one side of the door in case they ambushed me.*
*The doors opened. They ambushed me."*
—Joe Ledger, *Extinction Machine*

## THE BIRTH OF A BOOK

*"My copy of the Geneva Convention got burned up in a fire."*
—Mr. Church, *Patient Zero*

The two FBI thugs at my front door didn't really surprise me. Not after the Kentucky Brawl bombing and all the local and national controversy and social media fallout that followed. At least I thought they were FBI thugs. Why? Because I know that look. After all the reading I've done, all the *X-files* episodes I've seen, how can I not? Tall, dark hair, dark sunglasses, dark suits, beefy jock types with expressionless faces. As if everything that made them human had been sucked right out of them. For all I know, maybe it had. At the same time, I knew they weren't FBI thugs. What did surprise me was that it had taken them a year to get to me. After all, I've lived in the same place a whole seven years now. That's almost stable. And it's not like I hide my online presence—not that they couldn't have dug me up if I did hide.

> "If Stephen King were to get hold of Vince Flynn's Mitch Rapp, you'd have an idea of what Jonathan Maberry has accomplished with the Department of Military Sciences' uber-agent Joe Ledger. *Patient Zero* is a frightening tale that injects a new level of horror into the already terror-filled post-9/11 world. A bio-terror weapon that raises the dead? In Maberry's masterful hands, you will believe!"
>
> — Ken Isaacson, author of *Silent Counsel*

I stuck my head around the doorframe, and—sure enough—the ubiquitous Escalade, blacked-out, sat in the parking lot. Just as I opened my mouth to speak, the coffee maker in the kitchen gurgled to a halt and made a loud click. Startled, I let out a squeaky noise. I swear one of the FBI thugs almost smiled. Almost. My voice still squeaked when I asked, "Can I help y'all?"

"Ms. Adkins?"

"Moonshine Team?" I extended my right hand.

The FBI thug on the right choked on his own spit and covered up a laugh behind a closed fist. So much for cool and poised.

I tried again. "Coffee?"

The FBI thug on the left made a motion toward the open door with his hand.

Oh, yeah. I stepped back and let them in and guided them to the kitchen table and offered them seats. I asked if I could get them some fresh coffee, which they declined. Even so, I got myself a cup, took a drag off my e-cig, and joined them. "So," I asked, "what brings you out on this lovely day?" I exhaled a small cloud of clove-scented vapor…

…It could have happened that way.

In a different life under a different set of circumstances.

Maybe.

I joined the Joe Ledger fandom a little late. But the more I heard about the stories, the more curious I became, and you know what is said about curiosity. Thank goodness satisfaction brought me back, otherwise I'd have never gotten the chance to put this companion together. When I started reading, I picked up *Patient Zero* and read straight through to the end of *The King of Plagues*. Time was on my side,

### FRIENDS IN THE INDUSTRY: JENNIFER CAMPBELL-HICKS

Jennifer Campbell-Hicks's work has appeared in *Clarkesworld, Nature: Futures, Raygun Chronicles: Space Opera for a New Age*, and many other anthologies and magazines. She is a journalist who was on the Pulitzer Prize–winning staff of the *Denver Post* and lives in Colorado with her husband, her two children, and her dog. Visit her blog at www.jennifercampbellhicks.blogspot.com, and read her short story "Three Times" in *Joe Ledger: Unstoppable*.

though, and I only waited a small handful of months for the release of *Assassin's Code*. I assure you that the yearlong wait for *Extinction Machine* was difficult. Totally worth it, but difficult. I couldn't—and still can't—wait to see what possible global catastrophe Echo team thwarted next.

So what exactly about these stories and characters hooked me? Like some things in life, it's one of those things that's not easy—if at all possible—to pin down. *Je ne sais quoi*. What draws anyone to anything? I could go into a long, boring explanation of the particular psychiatry involved, but I won't. If Rudy Sanchez were here, I could have him do that for me, but he isn't. Thank me later.

Curious to find out what other people thought of the Joe Ledger books, I googled. A common theme appeared almost right away. Most people find that the stories:

- have a fast-paced narrative
- that is sometimes disarming
- but filled with high tension
- with skillful storytelling
- and solid research merged shrewdly
- into intelligent, mature writing

My favorite description? "Unputdownable."

> A soldier is nothing without his gear and that is very true for Joe, Echo and the DMS. Having the right gear will change a battle faster than all the ammo in the world. For instance: An "ALICE" (All-purpose Lightweight Individual Carrying Equipment) pack (worn by Echo Team in "Zero Tolerance" from Special Ops) is a standard backpack worn by the U.S. Army since 1973 until recently. It consists of the following standard items: The field pack itself, an equipment belt (also known as a WEB-belt), Suspenders (for the belt), a foldable shovel, first aid kit, ammunition cases that clip onto the belt, and a canteen with cover that also clips onto the belt. The pack is designed to carry fifty pounds or more of gear, but it fits snugly on the body when worn correctly.

Graphic details? Oh, there are plenty. Thanks to Jonathan's background in the martial arts, he's able to write fight and combat sequences ranging from a quick, powerful knockout to hyper-violent, full-on carnage. Yet, he manages this in tolerable doses; these displays are neither too long nor too short, nor are they difficult to follow, whether this be realistic combat with weaponry or hand-to-hand. As well, readers won't find any Hollywood bullets in these stories; once guns are empty, plenty of clips start flying around.

The narrative comes to readers in two ways. Both first and second person point of view. The main storyline is told by Joe Ledger with stinging humor and vivid detail. The second person parallel storyline is a variety of other characters—usually someone inside the DMS but with the majority being "the bad guys." The antagonists in the stories are generally involved in complicated relationships—with each other and often with various lovers. The characters for the most part:

- are imperfect and vulnerable
- can be outsmarted by the enemy
- can be emotionally broken

But there's so much more.

The best things about the Joe Ledger stories? Jonathan's writing style with his keen sense of detail mixed with his vivid descriptions that draw the reader into the stories in such a way that it keeps them engaged and thoroughly entertained. Beyond that, what keeps the reader reading is the in-depth character development of those dealing with the psychological effects of combat—including certain ethical

> "This is the coolest book I've read since discovering *Covert One*. With this new series, Jonathan Maberry becomes my generation's Robert Ludlum. Joe Ledger is a hero for the new millennium—tough as nails, sharp as a whip, and up for anything. He's a man who puts honor before his own self-preservation, who rides the edges and isn't afraid to go down fighting. The story is absolutely riveting, and the scariest concept to come down the pike in a long while. I want Ledger to fight all my battles. I dare you to put this book down before the endgame plays out. I dare you."
>
> —JT Ellison, author of *All the Pretty Girls*

issues—which advances throughout the series. This is seen through the personal introspection of Joe Ledger's interior monologue as well as peppered throughout with realistic, mature dialogue that is underscored with just the right amount of well-placed humor.

The stories are something of a diverse fusion of action-adventure, horror, science-fiction, and military thriller. They are crafted with hard science with no diluted jargon but written in clean, clear language. Readers are exposed to zombies, aliens, vampires, viruses, and plagues all created by mad scientist types, some with suspicious ties to pharmaceutical entrepreneurs. Nothing is safe. By incorporating cyberterrorism, bioterrorism, and conspiracy theories (some that date back hundreds, even thousands of years), readers continue to turn page after page to find out who or what or where blows up next.

And that's the thing.

Jonathan's brilliant storytelling skillset includes tapping into that one underlying thing that terrifies all of us, especially now in our post-9/11 world. The probability of "what if." Jonathan manages with a strange straightforwardness to produce convincing bad guys—terrorists, counter terrorists, corrupt government officials. He cleverly taps into an already somewhat unsettled state of mind that often leaves the reader overwhelmed.

This entire series leaves the reader thinking, "What if someone really could and *did* do X, Y, or Z?"

### FRIENDS IN THE INDUSTRY: TIM LEBBON

Tim Lebbon is a *New York Times*-bestselling writer from South Wales. He's had over thirty novels published to date, as well as hundreds of novellas and short stories. His latest novel is the supernatural thriller *Relics*, and other recent releases include *The Silence*, *The Family Man*, and *The Rage War* trilogy. He has won four British Fantasy Awards, a Bram Stoker Award, and a Scribe Award, and has been a finalist for World Fantasy, International Horror Guild and Shirley Jackson Awards.

The movie of his story *Pay the Ghost*, starring Nicolas Cage, was released Hallowe'en 2015, and several other novels and screenplays are in development. Find out more about Tim at his website www.timlebbon.net

What if some marginalized part of the population is influenced into acting in degenerate ways under the right conditions and guidance?

What if an organization or government—or both—is masterminding to produce pathogens and financing scientific feats that could destroy millions?

So. After saying all that, I can safely say that this whole companion project got started with one innocuous question and a brief message exchange between Jonathan and myself. It all got started because I asked my husband if he'd ever seen a Joe Ledger companion anywhere. He hadn't, and I couldn't turn one up, either. The lack of a companion gnawed at me. The books had grown so convoluted by that point that I felt the need for flowcharts and sticky notes to read through one book. I had several, "But didn't X do X in book X?" moments. Months later, I contacted Jonathan and inquired about a companion—had I missed the existence of one; was one forthcoming? The ensuing discussion led to the volume you, reader, are now holding.

One of the best parts of this project was that I was able to go back and revisit all the wonderful, exciting adventures of Joe Ledger and Echo Team, and other often mysterious characters. Due to the nature of building the companion, I was able to connect the dots between stories and characters in a way that I hadn't before. It was fascinating to untangle all of these Gordian knots and put them into what I hope are logical orders and categories. My hope is that this is a book that inspires readers to do their own underlining, as well as write their own notes in the margins as they make their own connections, making this reference as personal an experience as possible.

And most of all, have as much fun reading it as I've had putting it all together.

*Mari Adkins*
*Lexington, Kentucky*
*February 2017*

## WHAT MARI SAID.

No, seriously.

The original idea for this book was all Mari's. A labor of love thought up by someone who loves this world as much as I do. When I first read her introduction, I was amazed how articulately she'd summed up so much of how I feel about the Joe Ledger series and Jonathan Maberry's writing in general. And when faced with writing my own intro, I thought, "What can I possibly add to this?"

When I first read *Patient Zero*, I wrote one of my very rare fan letters (or email, to be precise). I tend to be very shy when it comes to talking to other writers I admire. But I fell in love with *Patient Zero* for a number of reasons—not the least that it took the zombie genre and did something new with it. It also introduced the coolest protagonist since F. Paul Wilson's Repairman Jack. I was also a relatively new author with a zombie series coming out and I thought, "Wouldn't it be cool to see if the guy who wrote *Patient Zero* might read and blurb my book?"

He did and it was.

I have since read pretty much anything Jonathan has written. An entire bookshelf is filled with his novels, and I'm gonna have to start a second shelf pretty soon. The eighth Joe Ledger novel, *Kill Switch*, helped me get through the last weeks of my mom's life. I'd read a little bit each night and escape from a pretty screwed up reality into the world of Joe Ledger—with a helping of Cthulhu on top of the usual hi-tech, kickass action one expects from the series. Can't ask for more from a book than that level of escapism.

Fast-forward a few months when Jonathan asked if I would be interested in jumping in on a project in progress to help out, I was inclined to say "yes" even before I knew what the project was about. Then I found out it would be working on a companion book for the Joe Ledger series, and that it would entail re-reading all of the books again, plus require me to read an advanced copy of *Dogs of War*…

Oh noes! Please don't throw me in that briarpatch!

Writing tends to be a solitary profession. We spend a lot of time in our own heads, sometimes so deeply that inter-action with anyone we haven't made up is an unwelcome intrusion. Other times, however, collaboration is the key. I mean, sure, Joe is kickass on his own. But part of the rea-son he's been able to overcome incredible odds and save the world time and time again, are his teammates.

One of the highlights of this project—aside from reread-ing all of the Joe Ledger novels—has been working with and getting to know Mari. She's a talented nut with a sharp sense of humor.

## FRANKENSTEIN'S LEGACY

There is a lot of weird science in the Joe Ledger novels. I would love to say that all, or even most of it, is fictitious, but that's not the case. Most of the science in my novels is real. The stuff that's false is in the minority. Scary, I know.

There is an old conman's saying: Use nine truths to sell one lie. It's a practical approach. When I was writing about the *Seif al Din* pathogen in *Patient Zero*, I based most of the science on the very real and tragic forms of spongiform encephalopathy, otherwise known as 'mad cow disease.' That's a very scary prion disorder that creates horrific diseases including 'fatal familial insomnia.' My mad science tweak was to greatly speed up the infection rate and to have the disease married, through transgenic science, with other kinds of aggressive parasites. While the actual disease known as '*Seif al Din*' is fake, its development, structure, research and field testing are all based on practices that have been part of international bioweapons testing protocols.

I can't say enough nice things about working with Jonathan. But I can never make up my mind if he's more Joe Ledger or Mr. Church. I suspect he bounces back and forth, depending on the need at hand. I have never, however, seen him snacking on vanilla wafers. I'm with Joe on that one, by the way. So many cookies in the world; why the hell would anyone choose vanilla wafers?

Anyway, I digress.

I've also enjoyed working with what I call our SIDEBAR Team: Thomas, Babette, Kelly and Ben.

"This book KICKS ASS! I read the whole thing with a big crazy grin of pure delight on my face, and I haven't stopped smiling yet. Zombies! Terrorists! Mad Scientists! Heavy Weapons! Stuff Blowing Up! And in the middle of it all, Joe Ledger, one truly badass action hero for the new millennium. You want to know what this book is? It's pure distilled essence of fun. Take a big ol' swallow of it and hang on tight, 'cause you ain't sleeping 'til it's done with you. But you are gonna love the trip."

—JD Rhoades, author of *Safe and Sound, Good Day in Hell* and *Hellhound On My Trail*

## HAZMAT SUIT

Hazardous Materials Suits come in all shapes, sizes and degrees of protection, from simple biological filters to full protection against even the deadliest pathogens.

The same is true for the computer hacking in the various books, the manipulation of the stock market in *The King of Plagues*, the autonomous drive system hacking in *Predator One*, the limited-field power disruption in *Kill Switch*; and the robotics, AI and nanotechnology in *Dogs of War*. Nearly all of it is real.

Of course I take greater liberties with things like Majestic Three and the development of the T-craft or Prospero Bell's God Machine. But exactly where the line between fact and fiction is drawn...well, I'll let the reader figure that out.

## CAUTION
## POTENTIAL BIOHAZARD PRESENT

## BIOHAZARD SIGN

It is reasonable to believe that the next great wars will not be fought with tanks and bombs but with digital data and microscopic organisms.

Their commitment to the job and willingness to go above and beyond have been a gift. And I so appreciate my husband Dave lending his organizational skills.

In summation, this has been a challenging and ultimately satisfying project. I hope that all of the Ledger fans out there enjoy the results.

Just remember...

Ahead there be spoilers!

*Dana Fredsti*
*San Francisco, CA*
*April, 2017*

# FOR THE RECORD...

## TRANSCRIPTS AND FIELD NOTES FROM DR. JAYDEN SUMMERSTONE
## OFFICIAL HISTORIAN OF THE DEPARTMENT OF MILITARY SCIENCES

The historian showed his identification at the gate and was passed through to the inner security at The Pier. Once out of sight of passersby on the street or the surrounding beach, the historian was instructed to park in the underground garage, hand over his keys, and go through a much more rigorous process to verify who he was and why he was there. He placed his left hand on a geometry scanner that measured the landscape of his palm and fingers to a microscopic degree, and also recorded his fingerprints. He peered into a retina scanner, breathed into a vapor scanner, stood while a laser ran up and down his body to measure everything from exact height—adjusted for shoes—to the shape and orientation of ears, nose, mouth, jawline and thirty-eight other specific points. A high-res picture of the historian appeared on an LED screen, and he studied himself. Tall, with slanted eyes that looked almost Asian, but were not; skin the color of polished teak, without mark, scar or flaw; a full-lipped and unsmiling mouth, tapered jaw and very short hair touched—but lightly—with gray around the ears. He wore one of his best suits today, a double-vented Kiton Dark Blue Shadow Plaid suit with a two-button jacket and pick stitch detailing. Instead of trousers he wore a kilt in matching fabric. Everything, including his John Lobb weird paneled leather Oxford shoes, were hand-sewn. From the calculating look in the security officer's eyes, the historian guessed—and rightly so—that the officer could price it all down to the last penny.

The historian's briefcase was given a thorough search that included various electronic scanners. It was not immediately returned but remained open on the security desk while the officer studied the scanner results on a MindReader substation. When everything checked out, he asked the historian four questions.

"What is your name?"

"Jayden Summerstone," said the historian. "Professor of Science History at Berkeley."

"Thank you, professor. What is the day code?"

"'The lunatics are in my head,'" said Summerstone and he had to stop himself from citing the source. That was a professional habit, but he knew from past experience that it came off as pedantic.

"Thank you," said the officer. "What is the nature of your business with us today?"

"I am conducting interviews of senior staff," said Summerstone. "I am writing a complete history of the Department of Military Sciences."

The officer nodded. "And what is the name of your sponsor?"

Summerstone smiled. "My sponsor is Aunt Sallie."

"Thank you."

"And, for the record," said Summerstone, "she actually is my aunt."

The bland mask of the security officer's face did not flicker. Much. He closed the professor's briefcase and handed it back.

A moment later a section of wall behind the officer opened to reveal an elevator car, from which an attractive Latina emerged. She was short, round, and pretty; dressed in a dark blue sweater with a plunging neckline over tights and low-heeled shoes. She smiled a dazzling smile and extended her hand.

"Dr. Summerstone?" she said. "I'm Lydia Rose, Captain Ledger's assistant."

"It's professor, actually," said Summerstone.

---

## FRIENDS IN THE INDUSTRY: STEVE ALTEN

Steve Alten is the *New York Times* and International best-selling author of sixteen thrillers, including the *MEG* series, about Carcharodon Megalodon, the 70 foot, 50-ton prehistoric Great White shark, set to be released in theaters in 2018. Steve is also founder and director of Adopt-an-Author, a nationwide free teen reading program now being used by thousands of secondary school teachers to entice even the most reluctant readers to read. Steve's new thriller, *Undisclosed*, debuts June 6, 2017. His short story "The Honey Pot" appears in *Joe Ledger: Unstoppable*.

The most common weapon found and used by both villain and hero is the Handgun. While there are other weapons that may have superior firepower, range and killing ability, it is hard to conceal an AK-47 or large combat shotgun when all you are doing is knocking on someone's door to ask questions. Handguns really break down into two models: semi-automatic with "clips" or magazines that hold the ammo and usually slide into the handle of the gun, or the revolver (five shot wheelguns and six shooters) that have chambers where ammo is loaded and then rotates as it is being fired.

Most handguns are very similar to each other in design and function. The modern semi-automatics consist of the grip (where the clip is inserted), the barrel, a racking slide system that slides off the barrel and rechambers a round, a trigger with guard, an ejection port for spent ammo and a sighting system. The revolvers only difference is the revolving chambers and length of the barrel. EVERY handgun has a safety built into the weapon. However, not all handguns have an external safety.

- Handguns also have the most options when it comes to ammo, the common ones being:
- .22: the "assassin's" bullet because it doesn't always exit and will bounce around inside a body (or the brain of a zombie).
- .40: standard issue for many SWAT officers.
- .45: for when you want to stop someone, quickly. Joe prefers the .45 when he begins his adventures with the DMS
- 9mm: most commonly used round in today's handguns.

The rarer rounds found in the Ledger Universe are:
- 10mm: used by various DMS teams. It is larger than the .45 cal and will put a hurt on anyone who gets in its way.
- .25: used most notably by Nadja of the Sabbatarians and Dr. Pharos, it is an antiquated round that is hard to find (I know, I tried.)
- .38: also known as the cop's best friend since it is usually their back-up piece found on their ankle. Joe's dad is carrying one in *Predator One*.

**SIG SAUER P226 9MM**

Joe's P226 is a .45 cal weapon that was modified by one of Mr. Church's "Friends in the Industry." Normally, the P226 has 4 configurations: .22, .9mm, .357 (if you REALLY want to knock someone out) and .40. Harry Bolt's P220 is another upgraded firearm that many would love to have (it normally comes in 10mm and .45, but the .9mm makes it more versatile for finding ammo).

Lydia Rose's smile did not flicker. "Of course, honey. Whatever you say. We have a room set up for staff interviews. There's coffee, fruit, protein bars, sandwiches, and anything you might want to drink."

She gestured to the elevator and they got on. The indicator lights said that they were going to sub-level four, which meant that it was well below sea level. That made Summerstone a bit nervous because this was California and he had an East Coaster's fear of earthquakes. He did not mention this, however, and kept his face blank, avoiding small talk.

Lydia Rose never stopped smiling as she led him through a maze of corridors and finally into a well-appointed conference room. It was stocked with enough provisions to allow him to survive the end of the world. There was a large oak table, a dozen very good quality leather chairs, soothing indirect lighting, and rather good artwork on the walls. Lydia Rose left him alone for ten minutes, during which he prowled the room, studied the art—a Yayoi Kusama, a Stephen Bauman, and a seascape that looked to be an original Jan van de Cappelle. The collection, small as it was, represented both good taste and very deep pockets. The van de Cappelle had to be worth a few million.

"Wow," he said aloud.

"You know art?" said a voice behind him and Summerstone jumped, spinning to see a tall, rough-looking blond haired man standing in the doorway. He had not heard the door open.

"Ah," said Summerstone, slapping his composure into place. "Captain Ledger, I presume?"

"Or a workable clone," said Ledger, coming over and offering a big, callused hand. They shook. The DMS field team chief wore a Hawaiian shirt with a print of topless Hula dancers over raggedy jeans and flip-flops. His hair looked like it had fallen out of love with its favorite comb, and there was three days' worth of golden-blond fuzz on the man's jaws. Summerstone thought Ledger looked like Matt Damon after several days in a small town Mexican jail.

"Thank you for being so accommodating, captain," said Summerstone. "These interviews will—"

Ledger held up a hand. "Let me stop you right there, chief. First, I didn't agree to this. It came down as an order to all staff. Your being the nephew of Aunt Sallie, I assure you, does not stoke the fires of my enthusiasm."

Summerstone smiled. "Yes, I've gotten the impression that there is no real love lost between you and my aunt."

"She has threatened to kneecap me on at least eight separate occasions," said Ledger.

"She does that."

"She meant it," insisted Ledger.

"Yes," agreed Summerstone. "She's always been rather forthright."

"'Forthright?'" Ledger tasted the word, amused by it. "Okay. She also considers me a mouth-breathing, muscle-bound nonintellectual whose best qualities are that I might be a useful human

**GLOCK .45**

Glock is an Austrian company that came into prominence in 1980 when the Austrian Military wanted a new handgun to replace the World War 2 German guns they were using. Glock originally designed their weapon to fire .9mm rounds, but have since expanded to be able to fire seven different types of ammo. In the Ledger Universe, only three types of ammo are used: .40 for SWAT, .45 for Joe himself, and the .9mm used by Kingsmen, and Top.

Sig Sauer is an American company that was originally created in Germany. It was originally known as SIG and added the Sauer when they bought the J.P. Sauer and Sohn company. According to SIG Sauer, one-third of US police use their firearms. All SIG Sauer handguns start with the "P" designation. They can be purchased in several ammo sizes, but are most often .9mm being originally German in origin. Grace Courtland's P239 is configured for .9mm, standard for a British SAS agent.

The three manufacturers of handguns that are most commonly cited are: Beretta, Glock, and Sig Sauer.

Beretta is an Italian company with a solid history for making handguns that shoot straight, have little recoil and deliver good stopping power. It is one of the most common guns used by police forces around the world and within the U.S. The Beretta family of handguns today uses .9mm ammo exclusively.

shield."

"Ah," said the professor.

"She blames me for every bad thing that has ever happened. And not just since I've been here. I'm pretty sure she thinks that it's my fault cancer hasn't been cured and for the Black Death outbreak of the thirteen-hundreds. She is not my biggest fan."

"From your tone, sir, I believe it's clear that the sentiments go both ways."

"I wouldn't accuse her of causing the Black Death," admitted Ledger, "but she may be the actual antichrist. Jury's still out."

"Ah," said Summerstone again.

"Wanted to make sure that was on the table before we had our little chat." Ledger poured coffee for them both. They sat on two sides of one corner of the table. "Now, tell me why exactly we're both wasting our time with this bullshit?"

"What part of it is unclear?"

"The 'why' of it. As I understand it, your history of the DMS is only for our internal records."

"Yes."

"We actually already know the history. Ask anyone. There's a kind of indoctrination phase where we tell people who come to work for us who the fuck we are and why the fuck we do what we do."

"Yes, and that's useful, I'm sure," said Summerstone, trying to keep the stiffness out of his tone. "But given the nature of what this organization does, it is not reasonable to assume that there will be an

### FRIENDS IN THE INDUSTRY: SCOTT SIGLER

Number one *New York Times* bestselling author Scott Sigler is the creator of fifteen novels, six novellas, and dozens of short stories. His works are available from Crown Publishing and Del Rey Books. In 2005, Scott built a large online following by releasing his audiobooks as serialized podcasts. A decade later, he still gives his stories away—for free—every Sunday at www.scottsigler.com. His loyal fans, who named themselves "Junkies," have downloaded more than forty million individual episodes. He has been covered in *Time, Entertainment Weekly, Publishers Weekly, The New York Times, The Washington Post, the San Francisco Chronicle, the Chicago Tribune, Io9, Wired, the Huffington Post, BusinessWeek,* and *Fangoria*. Scott is the co-founder of Empty Set Entertainment, which publishes his *Galactic Football League* YA series. He lives in San Diego, California, with his wee little dog, Reesie.

unbroken chain of information from one generation to the next. You were hired, I believe, to replace a team that had been killed during the *Seif al Din* matter. None of those people survived to pass on their knowledge. Colonel Samson Riggs, who I believe was widely regarded as your 'hero,' died in Atlanta during the *Mother Night* affair, and he took with him a great deal of information that might be useful to DMS members who will have to follow in his footsteps. History teaches us perspective, captain. We learn from it and by doing so we learn to avoid repeating mistakes and we learn to make better choices. We learn to survive because others were unable to do so. We become a more effective organization by constantly being the sum of all of our experiences and our shared knowledge."

Ledger sipped his coffee and then leaned back and frowned up at the ceiling. "Balls," he said after a while.

Summerstone opened his briefcase and removed a small recorder, a leather-bound notebook and a Mont Blanc pen. "Shall we begin?"

# TRANSCRIPT OF INTERVIEW WITH CAPTAIN JOSEPH LEDGER

## (PARTIAL)
## CONDUCTED AT THE PIER
## DMS SPECIAL PROJECTS OFFICE
## PACIFIC BEACH, SAN DIEGO, CALIFORNIA

SUMMERSTONE: At the risk of going all Spock here, when and how do you decide when the needs of the few or the one outweigh the needs of the many? Or is it always a matter of the "many" coming first?

LEDGER: That's one of those questions you can't answer until you're ass-deep in the shit.

SUMMERSTONE: Try.

LEDGER: There is no straight answer to it. That's what I mean. I suppose it's an 'eyes-on-the-prize' approach in most cases. If it's just cleaning out a nest of bad guys and there's no clock ticking down

"*Patient Zero* is a feast for thriller lovers! It's a delicious and diabolical stew of genres and traditions. With a pinch of forensic procedural, a dash of hard-boiled noir, a sprinkle of medical thriller, and a tincture of apocalyptic zombie epic, Jonathan Maberry cooks up a succulent meal of mayhem that slyly comments on our paranoid times. The hard-shelled hero, Baltimore shamus Joe Ledger, deserves to stand alongside F. Paul Wilson's Repairman Jack in the pantheon of genre icons. Highest recommendation!"

—Jay Bonansinga, Best-selling author of *The Walking Dead* novels (with Robert Kirkman)

to boom time, then a lot of your focus is on the guys to the left and the right of you. In a lot of firefights politics go right out the window in favor of you and your buddies coming home alive. Sometimes that even means letting an asshole slip the leash if it means saving the lives of your team. We can usually hunt the cocksucker down later on and spank him. But given the fact that the DMS doesn't roll for, say, a bank robbery or a home invasion, the stakes are often a lot higher than any of us on the line. Sometimes we have to allow the meat-grinder to chew us up if that's what it'll take to save a whole city. Or the country. Or the fucking world, for that matter.

SUMMERSTONE: How do you cope with that?

LEDGER: It's what a soldier does.

SUMMERSTONE: I'm sorry, captain, but that answer seems disingenuous.

LEDGER: (sighs) Yeah, maybe it is. It's the company line for anyone who puts on the uniform—literally or metaphorically. How do we cope? There's no way to answer that. We cope. We find a way to process it. Sometimes that means spending a shit-ton of hours on the couch with Rudy Sanchez. Sometimes you sit around with anyone who survived and you talk it out. Or you sit together and don't talk at all. Sometimes you drink alone. Sometimes you go home and hug your loved ones. Sometimes you go to the gym and work out until the lactic acid is screaming in your muscles and you can barely breathe. Sometimes none of that works because you've seen too much, done too much, gave too much and lost too much.

SUMMERSTONE: What happens then?

LEDGER: Go to the cemetery and ask the dead.

SUMMERSTONE: Ah. I see. Let's switch gears. Tell me about Ghost.

LEDGER: Sure.

SUMMERSTONE: I've seen a lot of working canines before, but would

There are three other manufacturers that are mentioned by name in the Ledger Universe that are still being manufactured now: H&K (a German manufacturer), Ruger, and S&W (Smith and Wesson).

H&K is mentioned for their Mark23 .45 used by Joe and Echo Team at the vault. Heckler and Koch are based out of Germany. It was started in 1948 and produces weapons for both the military/police forces of the world and sport shooters everywhere.

Rugers are used by several characters, from Violin with her Mark III .22, the SR22 used by "Jacob and Mason," and the "Blackhawk" used by a Berserker (which was probably a .57 magnum, but could have been any of 15 different styles of ammo). Ruger is an American company that primarily markets sporting rifles and handguns. It was started in 1949 in the U.S.A.

I be going out on a limb to assume there's something special about him?

LEDGER: First off, I have to admit that before Ghost I was a card-carrying cat person. I have an old marmalade tabby named Cobbler. He's getting on in years now, but we've been together for a long, long time. There are times I cared more about him than anyone else. I actually disliked dogs.

SUMMERSTONE: What changed?

LEDGER: Church bullied me into accepting a combat dog for missions where canine senses would increase the likelihood of successful completion and decrease the danger to human lives.

SUMMERSTONE: And...?

LEDGER: And I agreed to giving it a try. Under protest and with zero expectations of success. I figured that by the end of the first week either I'd be in the hospital being treated for dog bites and rabies or he'd be buried in my yard where no one could find him. And it started with those kind of feelings being clearly mutual. But...after a few days of training we started developing a kind of rhythm. Ghost is smart as fuck. Almost spooky smart. And, before you say anything, I know that pet owners tend to ascribe human perceptions and emotions to their animals, blah blah blah. It's not the case here. The more we trained, the more we just knew what the other was going to do, or not do.

SUMMERSTONE: How long did it take to train him?

LEDGER: I'm still training him. Just like I'm still training myself. It's not a smartass answer, professor. This is a reality of special ops. We're always training, always learning, improving, refining. That goes for individual skills as much as it goes for team-building. Ghost and I are a team. We have to make sure that the team works at peak efficiency in the largest possible variety of situations.

SUMMERSTONE: What type of training did he undergo? What did you do together to build this kind of rapport?

LEDGER: There are standard obedience drills, bonding exercises, and like that. That's how you start. The dog has to accept you as the alpha of your pack of two. That has to be absolutely established, and it's built as much on drills as it is on trust. You can't be a weak or hesitant leader or you lose the respect of the pack, which decreases both the pack's efficiency and your overall chances of survival. Sloppy packs die. Or they get other people killed. So, we started there. Then Ghost had to learn combat skills, including tracking, verbal and hand signs, threat assessment, and lethal and nonlethal responses for a variety of situations. Then there are extended pack exercises. Ghost needed to learn how to accept other members of the DMS as members of my pack, but not to defer to them instead of me. Top and Bunny can give Ghost a few commands when I'm not around, and he'll obey because he's done so much training with them and because we've all gone into battle together. But if I told Ghost to attack one of them, he would do it without question.

SUMMERSTONE: That's rather appalling.

LEDGER: It's natural law. It's also practical. What if a DMS team member, even someone on Echo Team, turned out to be a double-agent? What if one of my guys went bugfuck nuts and started shooting everyone? What if one of them fell under some kind of mind control?

SUMMERSTONE: I'm sorry, captain, but 'mind control?' That's a joke, right?

LEDGER: Look me in the eye and tell me if I'm joking.

SUMMERSTONE: But—

LEDGER: You need to read up on my cases. Have you gone through the after action reports for the *Kill Switch* matter? No? Do it and then tell me if I'm joking about mind control. We live in a strange damn world and my crew at the Special Projects Office are the point of the spear when it comes to probing the outer edges of 'oh fuck!'. Ghost has been with me since right after Grace Courtland died. He was with me when I tracked down the son of a bitch who murdered her. I buried him under rocks and we both stood there and pissed on the grave. Yeah, I love my dog. He's been through the valley of the shadow with me.

SUMMERSTONE: What's the most difficult decision or choice you've had to make?

LEDGER: Ever? Shit, that's tough. Getting up and going to work every day. That's really tough. Staying home and not going to work would be tougher, though.

SUMMERSTONE: Let's play the Bachelor. If you had to choose between taking Ghost, Bunny, or Top on a mission, who'd get the rose, so to speak?

LEDGER: You're hilarious. I've done gigs with all three and with each of them. I take whoever is best suited to the job. Hypotheticals don't really work with the kind of stuff we do.

SUMMERSTONE: This may not be a fair question, but if there's one person you could have saved or outcome you could have changed in your years at the DMS…who or what would it be?

LEDGER: If you read my file, then you know that there are two people I feel that I've failed. When I was fourteen my girlfriend, Helen, and I were attacked by older teens. I was beaten nearly to death and she was raped and brutalized. We technically survived the event, but not in any genuine way. Helen kept going away from me, deeper into psychosis and self-hatred. I guess it's textbook, but we both blamed ourselves for what happened. Victims often do. It fucked us both up. I had some psychological issues of my own and, before you ask, no I'm not going to tell you about them. If someone else already has, do yourself a favor and don't push that button, *capiche*?

SUMMERSTONE: Understood, captain. But you said you have regrets. You could not have overcome those older boys. I know from your file that you didn't start studying martial arts until you were fifteen, and I believe it was four or five to one?

LEDGER: Are you asking me for a rational threat assessment and response evaluation for a life-changing trauma? If so, please go and fuck yourself.

---

## FRIENDS IN THE INDUSTRY: NICHOLAS STEVEN

Nicholas Steven is the new action-adventure pen name of a bestselling ghostwriter. If you ask him his real name, he'll give you the old "I could tell you, but then I'd have to kill you" line, and he'll say it just ominously enough that you won't ask again. He'll then give you a charming smile that's at odds with the unnerving hold his steely eyes have on you, and he'll strongly suggest you take note of his alias so you don't miss any of his future publications, which he promises will be killer reads. His story "Confusion" appears in *Joe Ledger: Unstoppable*.

SUMMERSTONE: I'm just saying…

LEDGER: And I'm saying that guilt is not logical or reasonable and no amount of therapy or distance changes the ache I feel for not having been able to protect Helen. She committed suicide a few years after that and I was never able to get useful information on the guys who attacked us.

SUMMERSTONE: I'm very sor—

LEDGER: If you say that you're sorry, doc, I'll bring Ghost in here and let him chew on your nutsack. Sound fair?

SUMMERSTONE: Very well. However, that attack happened many years before you joined the DMS. Any regrets from your years *in* the DMS?

LEDGER: (a very long pause) If I could somehow go back in time and save Grace Courtland's life, I would. Even if it would mean that I'd be dead instead of her. I'd do it.

SUMMERSTONE: Even though you're involved with Junie Flynn?

LEDGER: Yes. End of discussion. Pick a new topic.

SUMMERSTONE: How do you separate the people in your life from your job, especially when they work with you? To clarify, how do you choose when doing a job means risking the welfare or lives of those you love?

LEDGER: Except for my dad, my brother, and his family, everyone I know is in the game. Home life and work life are part of the same cycle, and that makes it okay. When I go to war I'm fighting for my family. Every single day. I don't know if I can make it more clear than that.

SUMMERSTONE: What's the craziest thing you've seen over the course of your various missions?

LEDGER: A pencil neck asking stupid questions while the world is probably burning down.

# PART ONE

## WHO IS JOE LEDGER?

*"I had a sick dog, a dead man's gun, a stolen briefcase, a vampire hunter's stake in my belt, and a cell phone; and I was walking down a street in Tehran less than a day after breaking three political prisoners out of jail."*
—Joe Ledger, *Assassin's Code*

### JOSEPH EDWIN LEDGER

**RANK:** Captain
**CALL SIGN:** Cowboy
**FIRST APPEARANCE:** *Countdown / Patient Zero*
**BIO:** Before the DMS, Joe served in the Army and then with Baltimore Police. He fell onto the DMS radar after working a Joint Task Force attached to Homeland Security. When in the heat of combat, Joe helped save the lives of several men because of his ability to act without hesitation.

Church originally brought Joe into the DMS because he needed a leader for Echo Team. His hope was that Joe would make a "great terrorist." He also sees Joe as a "thinking weapon," which is a more than fair assessment. Joe speaks several languages, has extensive training in Jujutsu, is lighting quick with his hands or a knife, and a deadly shot with a firearm. He has a strong understanding of the underlying workings of politics and years of investigative field work. Also, while Joe excels at dismantling an enemy, he extracts as much information as he can before removing a threat. With all these attributes, Joe is tailor-made for the DMS, the perfect person to head a team of special operators against terrorists with cutting-edge bioweapons.

The victim of childhood trauma that eventually took the life of his girlfriend, Joe is a dangerous but badly damaged man, with three separate and very distinct, personalities living inside his head:

- The Civilized Man: the idealistic and moral side of Joe;
- The Cop: the "in-control" investigator;
- The Warrior, a.k.a. "The Killer": the savage and unforgiving man. This is what answers the call to violence in Joe's world.

With help from his doctor and friend, Rudy Sanchez, Joe has been able to control his aspects and apply them to any given situation.

Joe is also a professional—and world-class—smartass.

**IMPORTANT CONNECTIONS:** Joe and Rudy Sanchez are best friends. Rudy, as a young psychiatrist, was assigned to Joe and Joe's former girlfriend, Helen. Helen's death traumatized Rudy and created a deeper bond—one of shared pain—between them.

### JONATHAN MABERRY ON CASTING THE JOE LEDGER NOVELS

Building a cast of characters for any novel is a challenge. You need to construct characters who suit the story, have a reason to be there, *deserve* their spots, are nuanced enough to come off as real, and who are different enough from each other that they are uniquely individual. Doing that in a single novel is tough enough, but when crafting characters who will be riding with you for years, that's something else again.

Characters need growth. They should not be exactly the same at the end of a novel as they are at the outset. In *Patient Zero* I based Joe on a lot of different people, including some aspects of myself. Joe shares my core values and he's suffered some of the same childhood traumas as I did. Not exactly the same, but close enough. He's more emotionally damaged than I am (thank god!) but also thinner, younger and better looking. So there's that.

However, Joe's personality also draws on several professional law enforcement and military persons I've had the pleasure to know over the years. The professionalism, the high degree of competence, the good nature beneath the warrior's façade, the insight—those are qualities I admire in other people and wanted to instill in Joe.

The other characters are also based, in whole or part, on real people. Many characters, like Top and Bunny, are true amalgams, cobbling together elements from folks I've known or met. Some are people who have won placement in the Joe Ledger cast of characters. Brendan Tate, Steve Duffy, and others are real people, and I hope that I've done them justice in the DMS versions of them.

The villains of my novels are particularly fun to create. I hate two dimensional villains. I hate villains who are not self-aware enough to understand what they are and who they are becoming. I was inspired by the complex villains of the Travis McGee novels by John D. MacDonald and the nuanced characters in John Sandford's Lucas Davenport and Virgil Flowers books. And, I suppose, by the whole cast of gray-area characters that populate the novels of James Lee Burke. Villains do not appear in whole form, thoroughly evil, and with no inner conflict. Characters like Sebastian Gault, Hugo Vox, the Jakoby Twins, Artemisia Bliss and, of course, Toys, are wonderfully challenging to write because even I don't always know what makes them tick. I discover it as I write scenes in which they have to confront their own worldview.

That's really the core of each character: how do they act based upon their perceptions of the world and the feelings that oblige them toward certain courses of action. If you can crawl into the interior logic of each character, then what they do makes sense and it is part of a pattern of action unique to each player.

# TRANSCRIPT OF INTERVIEW WITH DR. RUDY SANCHEZ

## (PARTIAL)
## CONDUCTED AT THE PIER
## DMS SPECIAL PROJECTS OFFICE
## PACIFIC BEACH, SAN DIEGO, CALIFORNIA

PROFESSOR JAYDEN SUMMERSTONE: If you could change one thing about Captain Ledger to make your job easier, what would it be?

DR. RUDY SANCHEZ: That's a complex question, professor. It may also be unfair.

SUMMERSTONE: Indulge me.

SANCHEZ: What might I change about Joe Ledger? Hm. Perhaps I would like to see him retire and let someone else take up the fight.

SUMMERSTONE: Why? Do you think he is past his peak efficiency?

SANCHEZ: Did I imply that? No? Why then do you infer it? My comment was made entirely out of admiration for what he has accomplished and compassion for what he has sacrificed. Your aunt may have small regard for Captain Ledger, but let me assure you that as much as I respect Auntie's views on many topics, she is wrong about Joe and she is unfair to him. He is the very best of us, and if it wasn't for him you would not be sitting there in your trendy five thousand dollar suit. You would be dead. As would I. As would most or all of our eight billion fellow citizens. Am I being hyperbolic? No, I am being precise. Next question.

SUMMERSTONE: You seem to care very much for your colleagues and humanity in general. Do you ever regret your decision to work for—and stay with—the DMS?

SANCHEZ: Do I regret doing my part to help the brave men and women of the DMS save the world? Really? That's a serious question?

SUMMERSTONE: I'm looking for views, Dr. Sanchez, and insights. Consider these 'leading questions' in order to—

SANCHEZ: Yes, yes, I know what you're doing. (sighs) I'm being cranky because I feel there is an antagonistic subtext to your questions about Captain Ledger. Am I wrong?

SUMMERSTONE: I…do admit to having a certain slanted view of who and what he was before coming here.

SANCHEZ: Because of your aunt.

SUMMERSTONE: Because of my aunt.

SANCHEZ: And now?

SUMMERSTONE: I'm an academic, doctor. I should never fall into the trap of prejudice in advance of the facts.

SANCHEZ: Because…?

SUMMERSTONE: It steers me toward subjective rather than objective assessment.

SANCHEZ: Ah.

SUMMERSTONE: I will consider my wrist slapped.

SANCHEZ: Good. What's your next question?

SUMMERSTONE: If you had to choose between saving a friend or colleague and saving the world, which would it be?

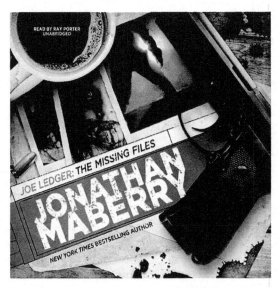

*Joe Ledger: The Missing Files*

SANCHEZ: The question is unfair, but I'll answer it. The world comes first, but only if there is no option for both to survive. Any rational person would give you the same answer.

SUMMERSTONE: Fair enough. So, you're a doctor, and your main goal is the preservation of life, right? So what would you do if faced with the choice of killing someone or losing someone you love?

SANCHEZ: You are aware, I hope, that doctors are not actually required to swear by the Hippocratic Oath. That is an urban myth. The Hippocratic Oath, as written, requires that a person swear by the god Apollo, and by Asclepius, and Hygieia and Panacea and all the other benevolent gods and goddesses. It was briefly used—in modern terms, if you will—in 1508, as part of the graduation ceremonies at the University of Wittenberg. It was also used in 1804 as part of graduation ceremonies in the medical school in Montpellier, France. It is not a requirement for doctors in *this* century. I am a Catholic, which means that I could not and would not swear by ancient Greek gods. There are codes of conduct for medical doctors but we do not swear an oath not to take a life. That is a myth. That said, it is contrary to our beliefs as doctors to want to end life when we strive to preserve it. However, I am not a Quaker and although I chose not to train and serve as a soldier, if it became necessary to take a life in order to preserve the greater good or save the innocent, then of course I would make a practical decision.

SUMMERSTONE: Have you ever—?

SANCHEZ: Next question.

# PART TWO

## INSIDE THE DEPARTMENT OF MILITARY SCIENCES

*"Worst-case scenario is pretty much our job description."*
—Bunny, *Predator One*

## THE MISSION OF THE DMS

The Department of Military Sciences is tasked with searching out and responding to terrorist threats involving cutting-edge science.

## THE ORGANIZATION & ITS HISTORY

Mr. Church hates red tape. He hates when political agendas and party politics are more important than the practical needs of the country. He originally approached the United States government to create a small rapid-response unit in the days following 9/11, around the same time as Homeland Security was chartered. Congress rejected the Department of Military Sciences project as too expensive and unnecessary. No one at the time considered terrorists capable of creating advanced bioweapons. But MindReader, a piece of analysis software, changed their mind.

> Devotion, Integrity, Service, Excellence, Honor, Respect, Loyalty, Semper Fidelis "Always Faithful," and Semper Fortis "Always Courageous" are a few of the core values of our military forces. During my time with the DMS we display two above all others: Semper Vigilans "Always Vigilant" and Semper Gumby: "Always Flexible."
>
> —Birddog

He originally took the plan to the United Kingdom, where he had old friends, and shared his model with them, resulting in the creation of Barrier. When Barrier proved to be not only workable but highly effective, Mr. Church again applied to the U.S. government and was given a developmental budget.

The DMS charter comes from Executive Order-9166|DMS of the President of the United States. By definition, the DMS is an autonomous enigma which exists only as far as the POTUS and one congressional subcommittee are concerned. Even so, the DMS operates with shared authority alongside the military and law enforcement. The ultimate mission was described by Joe Ledger in *Dogs of War* as, "...working schlubs like us...clean up the mess when it goes wrong."

However, the DMS charter has been rescinded at least twice, first time by the Vice-President, who wanted the DMS shut down so that he could get control of MindReader. If he got hold of the computer, he'd have access to everything inside of it—all of the software and all of the hardware. Also, the DMS would lose tactical analysis on forty-six terrorist-related database searches. The Secret Service would go blind, as would a good chunk of the DEA, CIA, FBI, ATF, and Homeland. The DMS would lose their data sharing with MI6 and Barrier along with certain agencies in Germany, Italy, and France.

The charter was rescinded the second time by POTUS during the events of *Kill Switch*.

The DMS scouts possible recruitments from the SEALs, Delta Force, and other groups, but always from those who are the best at their jobs. As a result, those employed by the DMS have higher than average IQs.

## FIELD OFFICES & TEAMS

The Department of Military Sciences operates out of regional field offices, currently of which there are seventeen that run thirty-six active teams.

### THE WAREHOUSE

Location: Easton, Maryland

Headed by: Mr. Church

Mr. Church never wanted a Washington D.C. base because of the local politics and the horrendous traffic congestion. However, he did want to be close enough for his people to reach the capitol in a hurry.

Easton was the most useful spot that would allow access to Washington D.C., Virginia, and the transportation hubs of Baltimore, which in turn extended to Philadelphia. This location gave the DMS ready access to highways, boating routes, and a good airport.

Church took this particular warehouse because it had been commandeered by the government and was, essentially, free at exactly the right time for the establishment of a Maryland base of operations. Plus, it meant that all the records, specimens, and other materials from the terrorist cell attack with the *Seif al Din* during the events of *Patient Zero* were already on-site.

"Jonathan Maberry has created a new genre. Mixing technology, thrills, chills, and procedural noir, Maberry shows why he is one of the freshest voices in fiction. Every reader will want to ride shotgun on Joe Ledger's adventures."

—Scott Nicholson, author of *The Skull Ring*, the *After Post-Apocalyptic* series and the *Next* series

While technically in Easton, on a portside dock at the end of the Perapasco River, everyone refers to the larger metro area as Baltimore.

This field office was home to Joe Ledger and Echo team from *Patient Zero* through *Code Zero*. Sadly, the original Warehouse was destroyed by the terrorist Erasmus Tull during the events of *Extinction Machine*, taking with it the lives of nearly two hundred agents. Ledger took initiative in the days following that disaster to create a Special Operations field office in San Diego, California.

The heavily-guarded Warehouse was situated in a building labeled Baylor Records and was wrapped by a heavy-duty gated chain-link fence topped with razor wire. Between the building and the first fence wound a second fence wearing signs warning intruders of high voltage. Inside, workrooms, office suites, small apartment suites, and storage rooms had been built. The main warehouse floor, though, had been left open and was large enough should someone need to park an airplane.

## THE HANGAR

Location: Brooklyn, New York

Headed by: Aunt Sallie

The Department of Military Sciences was first founded, by Mr. Church, at The Hangar at Floyd Bennet Field in Brooklyn, New York, making this their main headquarters. The operation is based in an old, decrepit, abandoned-looking, cavernous airplane hangar that hides the most sophisticated counterterrorism organization on the planet.

Inside, the walls were built with steel-reinforced concrete, and the place was packed with sensors, alarms, and secreted guard posts. This area was mostly used as a parking garage. The real meat of the operation was underground. Outside, the laborers restoring the building were, in fact, disguised perimeter guards; most of these were former field-team shooters who were either too old for active fieldwork or who had been injured on the job and could no longer do that work for the DMS.

The Hangar supports four field teams: Broadway, Liberty, Metropolis, and Gotham.

## DEPARTMENT ZERO

Location: Los Angeles

Headed by: As of *Dogs of War*, the second largest DMS office, Department Zero in Los Angeles is run by Major Tanure Solanke. This office runs four teams and does collaborative jobs with Mexican authorities.

Not yet detailed in any of the Joe Ledger series of books. It is the second largest DMS field office, with the Hangar being the largest.

Teams operating out of Department Zero are: Hollywood, Malibu, Burbank, and Sandshark.

"Wow! From the first page of *Patient Zero* you know you're in the hands of a master. Maberry has created a brave, bruised, wisecracking hero destined to rub shoulders with the likes of Jack Reacher and Harry Bosch. This is high-concept with brains, action with soul and fast paced tension with psychological insight. The brilliant beginning to a series destined for success."

—M.J. Rose, international bestselling author of *The Reincarnationist* and *The Collector of Dying Breaths*

## THE PIER: SPECIAL PROJECTS OFFICE

Location: Pacific Beach, San Diego, California

Headed by: Joe Ledger

The DMS's latest field office, built on a San Diego pier after the events of *Code Zero*. This is a Special Operations office and supports Echo, Slingshot, Deep Six, and Kraken teams.

## THE ROOKERY

Location: Denver, Colorado

Headed by: Captain Jericho DeRosa

Teams operating out of The Rookery include Mile High, Bighorn, Puma and Black Diamond.

## THE SPEAKEASY

Location: Chicago, Illinois

Headed by: Lt. Colonel Bess Morganstern

Teams operating out of The Speakeasy include Gangbusters, The Untouchables, and Black Hats.

## THE BARN
## DMS SPECIAL TEAMS FIELD OFFICE

Location: near Houston, Texas, former dairy farm recommissioned by the DMS

Headed by: Captain Dell Parker

Teams operating out of the Barn include Shockwave & Longhorn

Designation: Under the directorship of the late Colonel Samson Riggs, the Barn was the home of the DMS Special Projects Office. Following the deaths of many of the team members during Mother Night's destruction of the Centers for Disease Control, the Barn went through a reorganization. The Pier in San Diego was designated as the new Special Projects Office and the Barn, now under new command, overseas DMS operations in Texas and the Gulf of Mexico.

# TRANSCRIPT OF INTERVIEW WITH MR. CHURCH

## (PARTIAL)
## CONDUCTED AT THE HANGAR
## DMS HEADQUARTERS
## FLOYD BENNETT FIELD, BROOKLYN, NY

PROFESSOR JAYDEN SUMMERSTONE: Why did you start DMS? I realize that 'how' is also an important question, but I think a lot of people would really like to know why.

DMS DIRECTOR MR. CHURCH: I saw a need and addressed it. There was a noticeable open slot in a crucial gap between the intelligence networks and the special operations response groups, and there was far too much red tape and interjurisdictional infighting. I am frequently disappointed by those who place personal or political agendas ahead of national security.

SUMMERSTONE: Given the tendency for career politicians and bureaucrats to focus on self-interest, how did you ever get permission and funding to start the DMS?

*"Patient Zero* is a riveting page-turner. Cool stuff! Hooray for Jonathan Maberry. Please give us more Joe Ledger right now!"

—Victor Gischler, author of *Shotgun Opera, Go-Go Girls of the Apocalypse* and *A Fire Beneath the Skin* trilogy

MR. CHURCH: I created the organization apart from government oversight, established its policies, hired the right people, and secured operational financing before I offered it as a whole package to the president.

SUMMERSTONE: And he accepted it? Just like that?

MR. CHURCH: Nothing is ever simple, Professor Summerstone. However, I have found that, given time and the correct resources, anyone can be brought to a point of understanding.

SUMMERSTONE: There are rumors that you used MindReader to obtain information useful in, shall we say, encouraging cooperation.

MR. CHURCH: I will not comment on the substance of rumors.

SUMMERSTONE: How would you describe your career path to Director of the DMS?

MR. CHURCH: Complicated.

SUMMERSTONE: Can you be a bit more specific?

MR. CHURCH: Of course.

SUMMERSTONE: *Will* you?

MR. CHURCH: No.

SUMMERSTONE: Very well. There's a lot of speculation as to your occupation before the DMS came into existence. Would you be willing to talk about any of it?

MR. CHURCH: No.

"The magic of Joe Ledger for me is that his physical indomitability is counterbalanced by the deeply affecting internal hurdles he has to overcome. Ledger's limitations are emotional and psychological, and that makes him a compelling human character, even when he's performing near superhuman feats in the heat of the action. He's a badass with a psychiatrist and problems with rage and grief, and the cumulative effects of the things happening around him (and to people he cares for) are wearing on him. While he has the Bond/Bourne qualities that make his stories an exciting ride, it's his psychological vulnerability after the fight that I think sets him above his remorseless, unflappable counterparts in adventure fiction."

—Bracken MacLeod, author of *Stranded* and *Come to Dust*

SUMMERSTONE: How about an 'out of left field' question. What's with the cookies? Seriously, why vanilla wafers?

MR. CHURCH: Surely you have more relevant questions.

SUMMERSTONE: Ooo-kay. What would you do if the DMS was ever officially shut down for good? No executive order, no official sanctions. How would you handle that?

MR. CHURCH: If I found it necessary to conduct off-book operations, I would.

SUMMERSTONE: Have you ever done that before?

MR. CHURCH: Have a cookie.

SUMMERSTONE: How many people were part of the original incarnation of the DMS? Was Aunt Sallie one of them?

MR. CHURCH: The first iteration of the DMS was built as a small group. Aunt Sallie was there at the beginning, as was Major Courtland. Bug and Dr. William Hu were the next to join. After that we selected twenty-four field operatives from the various branches of the military and from law enforcement, and eighty support staff.

SUMMERSTONE: But you knew my aunt before the DMS?

MR. CHURCH: We have been friends and colleagues for a great many years. Aunt Sallie is one of the very few people in whom I place my full trust. There are good reasons for that. Even though you are her nephew, I doubt she will be entirely candid about her life prior to the DMS. There are reasons for that, too.

"Bunny—real name, Harvey Rabbit—is the sort of big, jovial, utterly dependable man that I recognize instantly, because he makes up a good percentage of the men in my family. They're soldiers and football players and mountains that move, and it's such a joy to see that in fiction. Bunny is an endlessly dependable ally, always ready to wade into the fight for the sake of what's right and in the service of Echo Team. Joe would have a much harder time without him. I hope he never has to find out how hard."

—Seanan McGuire, *New York Times* award-winning author of urban fantasy and biomedical science fiction (as Mira Grant)

SUMMERSTONE: A big part of what makes the DMS so effective is MindReader. What would you do if you suddenly lost access to all that information? How would you keep the organization going without it?

MR. CHURCH: If MindReader was destroyed, I would rebuild it. If it became obsolete, as it very nearly did, I would endeavor to replace it with something better.

SUMMERSTONE: I heard that it went through a recent upgrade.

MR. CHURCH: Yes. We were fortunate enough to obtain a functional prototype for a true quantum computer. Bug and his team were given the challenge of integrating it with the older version of MindReader and then taking it to the next level of tactical efficiency.

SUMMERSTONE: And he did?

MR. CHURCH: Ask him.

## JONATHAN'S COMMENTARY

*Encountering Mr. Church while writing* Patient Zero *was a distinct pleasure. He's a fascinating character and I actually know more about him than I do any of the other players, including Ledger. Mr. Church sprang wholly formed into my head and he whispered his extensive back story to me. I know his secrets. I know secrets that even Aunt Sallie doesn't know. One of these days I'll probably break down and tell the long, complex and deeply weird life story of the Deacon. He's a mighty spooky cat.*

# MINDREADER

## MINDREADER

*Ultra-classified elite supercomputer system; the primary weapon and cornerstone of the DMS.*
MindReader, Church's own proprietary computer system, is the key weapon used by the DMS. An enormously powerful and sophisticated cybernetic system, MindReader is several generations ahead of anything else known to exist. It is a master key system that can analyze data on any platform, in any machine or human language. Everything the DMS does and supports is built around the precision of the intelligence of the software and the speed of its response.

Computers have provided an almost endless stream of data. Data does not necessarily equal knowledge. The key here is how data is interpreted. Knowledge is power. This is where data analytics comes in. Data analytics is exactly what it sounds like, the analysis of data to find patterns and forecast trends. It is vital in modern warfare. Those who can quickly and accurately analyze data are in the position of having power because "knowledge is power."

The highly dangerous system is Church's sole property. No one outside of a select few DMS senior staff has access to it; and no one has full access except Church, who jealously guards it.

## ORIGIN OF MINDREADER

Prior to the formation of the DMS, Church was involved in various operations with a covert team of special agents from different countries, code-named the List. Their primary goal was to tear down the Cabal, a group of rogue scientists who had built very advanced systems using illegal technologies first initiated by the Nazis. The Cabal capitalized on the work of an Italian computer scientist named Antonio Bertolini, one of the most brilliant computer engineers of the 20th century. Bertolini developed a search-and-destroy software package for the Italian government, but before he could deliver it he was murdered and his system stolen.

The program, known as Pangaea, was decades ahead of its time. Before its retrieval, the Cabal used Pangaea with great success to steal bulk research material from laboratories, corporations, and governments worldwide. This allowed the criminal organization access to a frightening range of cutting-edge science. They had no need to do research: they simply stole the information, combined it to form a massive database, and then went straight into development. Finally, the system was recovered during a raid on the Pangaea lab, and the List put it to better use: searching down and destroying all of the information the Cabal had amassed.

At this time Church was already supporting the development of a similar computer system called Oracle (a system that Church would later give to Lilith and the women of Arklight). Oracle was good, but it wasn't Pangaea. Nevertheless, Church and his team were able to combine the best elements of both systems into a new generation, originally designated as Babel. But even that was insufficient for what he believed was needed to create an organization like the Department of Military Sciences. Church scouted for the very best software engineers who were also insightful into the current and future needs of cyberwarfare. This team wrote the master programs for what became MindReader.

Today, MindReader bears little resemblance to Pangaea except in overall design theory. Both computers were designed to intrude into any hard drive and, using a special series of conversion codes, learn the language of the target system in a way that allows them to act as if they are the target system. And both systems exit without leaving a trace.

The similarities end there. Pangaea's footprint, though very light, can be detected by a few of the world's top military-grade systems, but even then it often leaves the appearance of a computer error rather than computer invasion.

Pangaea was a system with ultra-sophisticated intrusion software. This initial system was named after the original landmass that eventually broke up into the seven separate continents (masterful foreshadowing by Maberry). Pangaea has multiphasic pattern-search capabilities, that had a subroutine that was designed to erase any trace of its footprint after it hacked into other systems. It intruded where it did not belong and destroyed things that were too valuable to let stand. For Pangaea the path of destruction was through the memory banks of other computers. It sought certain information and retrieved it, often deleting the information on the target mainframes, then it deleted all traces of its own presence. A subroutine called "Kreskin," which was designed to search for patterns and collate any relevant information into a set of projections that were as close to human intuition and guesswork as a binary computer mind could achieve.

MindReader is many thousands of times faster, has a different pattern recognition system, clones passwords, and rewrites the security code of the target system to leave no trace at all of having been there. This includes tweaking time codes, logs of download time, and all other aspects of the target system's memory.

## SYSTEM CAPACITIES

MindReader is the fastest computer on the planet, housed in the basement of the Hangar, in a cold room lined wall-to-wall with a supercomputer cluster. Prior to the events detailed in *Dogs of War*, the primary computer block is made up of three thousand premarket upgrades of the Tianhe-1A system operating at a speed of 2.507 petaflops; over thirty percent faster than the Cray XT5 Jaguar. Although the MindReader system incorporates a variety of functions, two primary and overlapping functions stand out and make it the most valuable tool in the DMS intelligence arsenal.

First, MindReader continually sifts through the data on an endless hunt for terrorist activity. The system collates intelligence using an elegant pattern-recognition software package designed to look for trends and very carefully crafted to take into account factors that might otherwise be missed. It is capable of factoring in input from different operating systems, different languages—both computer and human—different cultures, time zones, currency rates, units of measure, routes of transport, and so on. MindReader cuts through all these variables and more.

Although no computer can generalize or make intuitive leaps, MindReader's cascading analytic system comes remarkably close, designed to recognize patterns by drawing on information culled from an enormous number of sources from all major intelligence networks. These targeted systems include all domestic law enforcement and intelligences services, as well as those from trusted international allies, including many that refuse to share their intel with the DMS, and many others the DMS was not officially allowed to access.

Often, different agencies will have glimpsed hints of nefarious developments brewing or obtained scattered bits of covert information, but MindReader sorts through all the pieces of the puzzle and begins assembling fragments into whole, actionable pictures. This capacity gives the DMS an invaluable advantage over other covert special ops units.

The other primary function is actually its most frightening aspect: MindReader is an intrusion weapon. Its super-intrusion software package, the only one of its kind, can hack its way into virtually any known computer system without tripping alarms. Once in, it can poke around, take what it wants, and then rewrite the target's security software and memory to erase all traces of its presence, leaving behind absolutely no record of the intrusion. All other intelligence software leaves some kind of detectable scar on the target system; MindReader is a ghost.

Unfortunately, over time the bad guys learned to adapt to MindReader's capabilities.

Zarathustra, for instance, is a system that was specifically designed to protect data against all forms of intrusion, particularly MindReader.

To combat this, the next system that will surpass

> From MindReader, Haruspex was designed and used by Artemisia Bliss (aka Mother Night). She stole the master plans for Pangaea and created Haruspex specifically to be invisible to MindReader. A haruspex, in terms of ancient Etruscan and Roman culture, was a person who could divine the future and unlock the mysteries of the fates by reading the entrails of sacrificed sheep.

MindReader will use quantum technology. Designed by Dr. Aaron Davidovich, and adopted by the DMS, a quantum computer has quantum bits (qubits). A single qubit can represent a one, a zero, or any quantum superposition of these two qubit states. In other words, they can be both values at the same time. Quantum computers have the potential to perform certain calculations significantly faster than any silicon-based computer.

# PART THREE
## THE GOOD GUYS

*"I saw Echo Team standing apart from the activity, looking like a biker gang that had crashed a women's empowerment meeting."*
—Joe Ledger, *Assassin's Code*

## COMMAND

### MR. CHURCH

Real Name: Classified. Also known as Elder; Mr. St John; Mr. Deacon; Mr. Pope; Mr. Christian; Colonel Eldritch; The Sexton; Dr. Bishop

Rank: Director

Call Sign: Deacon

First Appearance: *Patient Zero*

Bio: The enigmatic man known by well over a dozen names is the founder and director of the Department of Military Sciences. Brilliant, cold, and dangerous, Church brings enormous financial and technological resources to bear in his crusade against terrorism. He is apolitical, and though he is a big-picture humanist, he is also ruthless and well-connected. The running bet is that he's a former Cold War era special ops shooter. But that might be simply another layer of cover. He's

Brick and I once accompanied Mr. Church to oversee a sensitive logistics transfer between the DMS and Joint Task Force 2, the Canadian special operations force. During this mission, the team leader Lt. Colonel Steve Hunter kept referring to Church as Mr. Christie. We learned later on that it is short for Christian, another of his aliases, and not surprising the brand name of vanilla wafers manufactured by Kraft Canada.

—Birddog

past sixty but looks somewhere in his forties and is especially fit. The average person finds it difficult to imagine him ever losing any kind of confrontation. He's detail-oriented, vicious, and unsympathetic, and keeps the facts of his life beyond the DMS to himself. Very few people know that the terrorism analyst who works for him, Dr. Circe O'Tree-Sanchez, is actually his daughter. Church keeps that a secret (Joe is one of the few who know this) in order to protect her. In the later books it becomes apparent that Church has some kind of love-hate relationship with Lilith, head of Arklight. Church is also well-known for his love of vanilla wafers.

**IMPORTANT CONNECTIONS:** Mr. Church is the father of Dr. Circe O'Tree and the father-in-law of Dr. Rudy Sanchez. He has a connection (as yet unknown, even to his friends) with Lilith. There is a possible family connection with Lilith and Violin.

## AUNT SALLIE

Real Name: Classified
Call Sign: Auntie
Rank: DMS Chief of Operations, Director of Field Operations
First Appearance: First mentioned in *Patient Zero*
Bio: Only Mr. Church knows who Aunt Sallie really is. And, though she could pass for Whoopi Goldberg's twin sister, she has none of the actress' charm and compassion. A former field agent and assassin, Aunt Sallie is the only person who knows Mr. Church's secrets. The two share a long, colorful history that dates back to the Cold War. She runs the Hangar, the DMS headquarters located at Floyd Bennett Field in Brooklyn.

**IMPORTANT CONNECTIONS**: Auntie has held a secret love for Mr. Church her whole life, but it has never been shared with him.

### THE COOKIE CODE

A lot of people ask if there is some kind of code tied to the way Mr. Church eats cookies, offers them, handles them, and so on.

The short answer is: yes. There is a Cookie Code. And, yes, nearly everything tied to those cookies has some layered meaning. And there are even clues as to who Mr. Church is.

The code has not (so far) been cracked by any of the readers, though some folks are getting close. Jonathan Maberry promises a big prize for whoever solves the Mr. Church Cookie Code.

The DMS staff have a running bet that there is a secret code to Mr. Church's vanilla wafer fetish.

The one percent of Aunt Sallie that gives a shit is spent on notifying a fallen operative's next-of-kin.
—Birddog

## JONATHAN'S COMMENTARY

*Yes, I really would like Whoopi Goldberg to play Aunt Sallie. And, no, if I found out that Whoopi is actually a retired spy and assassin I'm not sure I would be totally surprised.*

# COMPUTER SCIENCES DIVISION

## JEROME LEROY WILLIAMS

Rank: Director of Computer Sciences, Deputy Director of Field Support

Call Sign: Bug

First appearance: *Patient Zero*

Bio: Bug is the heart of the DMS. His genius with computers brought him to the attention of Mr. Church, who hired him to manage the supercomputer MindReader.

**IMPORTANT CONNECTIONS:** Bug's mother was murdered by a bomb drone in *Predator One*.

## OTIS CARLISLE

Rank: Senior Technician, DMS Communications Systems

Call Sign: Genius Bar

First Appearance: *Kill Switch*

Bio: Otis is a former Apple technical support employee recruited by Bug to help upgrade and manage the DMS communications systems, including adapting technologies stolen from Hugo Vox and Mother Night.

## NIKKI BLOOMBERG

Rank: Senior Technician, DMS Computer Sciences Division

Call Sign: Zelda

First Appearance: *Code Zero*

Bio: Nikki is a dedicated computer engineer whose primary function at the DMS is to oversee pattern analysis.

"Jonathan Maberry has created and crafted vivid, flawed, complex characters and thrown those poor bastards into terrifying-yet-potentially-realistic apocalyptic scenarios that keep me burning through pages faster that burning fire that engulfed the Royal Hospital of London at White Chapel. With each book, Jonathan Maberry has explored and expanded the character's personalities, especially Joe Ledger. A complex, conflicted, yet a caring soldier of badass-dom, that could give Batman a warm-wee-wee stain in his Bat-skivvies. This is the true power of such engaging stories and characters. The images of the team tactically clearing out new, dark places fill my mind. I can almost feel the cold metal of the weapon in my hands and the see the soft green glow of the IF goggles. The hair on my arms raise and when the 'monsters' rush out of the darkness, I am strongly considering wee-weeing my own skivvies."

—Thom Erb, author of *Heaven, Hell, or Houston, Tones of Home* and the upcoming novel, *The Last in Line-Eternal Flame Trilogy*-book one

## YODA HAN DUNMAN

Rank: Senior Technician, DMS Computer Sciences Division
Call Sign: Jedi Reptile
First Appearance: *Extinction Machine*
Bio: Yoda (real name) is a socially inept computer expert who was a gray hat hacker until he was recruited by Bug for the DMS. He oversees the software systems for MindReader. He is also point man for cyberintrusion.

# INTEGRATED SCIENCES DIVISION

*"Mr. Church always makes sure we have the best toys."*
–Joe Ledger

## DOCTOR WILLIAM HU

Rank: Science Director
Call Sign: Dalek
First appearance: *Patient Zero*

> He'll deny it, but Dr. Hu has an extensive Tamagotchi collection.
> —Birddog

Bio: Doctor Hu is one of the most brilliant scientists in the world—proof that Mr. Church never hires second best. He runs the advanced sciences division of the DMS and oversees research and development. He and Joe Ledger have failed to bond on a spectacular level.
Final Appearance: *Kill Switch*
**IMPORTANT CONNECTIONS:** Dr. Hu was responsible for scouting and vetting Artemisia Bliss, and they were briefly lovers.

## JOAN HENRIETTA 'DOC' HOLLIDAY

Rank: Director of Integrated Sciences for the DMS
Call Sign: Huckleberry
First Appearance: *Deep Silence*
Bio: Descended from the noted gunslinger Doc Holliday and prostitute Big Nose Kate. Doc Holliday is a brilliant, brash, aggressive scientist with a weird sense of humor and a flirtatious sense of fun. Her core discipline is biomechanical engineering, but she also has deep knowledge of medicine, physics and other disciplines. She has unspecified ties to Arklight. Aunt Sallie has expressed concerns that Doc Holliday is an Arklight spy. The two powerful DMS women are often at each other's throats.

---

## JONATHAN'S COMMENTARY

*Dr. Hu started out as a likeable guy. For about five minutes. He and I share some of the same pop culture sensibilities, but as I wrote him I realized that I—like Joe—couldn't stand the little bastard. Joe may be sarcastic but he isn't mean-spirited about it; Hu is. Despite being deeply brilliant and capable of running point for the DMS Integrated Sciences Division, Hu is a caustic, petty, nasty little S.O.B. The fact that his scientific knowledge has saved the world as often as all of the DMS field teams combined did nothing to put Hu's ego in check.*

**IMPORTANT CONNECTIONS:** Doc Holliday beat Dr. Hu to patent filing three times, and is the only known person to have scored higher than Hu on the Rand-Cunningham Esoteric Intelligence test.

# EXECUTIVE SECURITY

## BRICKLIN 'BRICK' ANDERSON

Rank: Gunnery Sergeant, U.S. Army

Call Sign: Stonewall

First Appearance: *The Dragon Factory*

Bio: Brick Anderson is a former DMS field

> Most recent acquisition has been Brick's new carbotanium artificial leg from the Italian car maker, Pagani. —**Birddog**

agent who lost a leg in combat. He originally ran the Field Support team for the Hub, the Denver Field Office, then worked out of the Warehouse before becoming Mr. Church's personal assistant and bodyguard after Gus Dietrich's death at the Warehouse. He's not quite as tall as Bunny, but he has bigger arms and a broader chest.

**IMPORTANT CONNECTIONS:** Brick is the only living person who has total access to Mr. Church, and serves as bodyguard, personal assistant, valet, and confidant.

## GUS DIETRICH

Rank: Command Sergeant Major, retired; US Army

Call Sign: Bulldog

First Appearance: *Patient Zero*

Bio: Retired Command Sergeant Major Dietrich was Mr. Church's personal assistant, aide and bodyguard. Bulldog tough and fiercely loyal, Dietrich was one of the few people Church trusted completely.

Final Appearance: *Code Zero*

**IMPORTANT CONNECTIONS:** Fully cognizant of the dangers of his job, Gus Dietrich took the time to prepare a kind of 'how to' manual for whomever might one day need to replace him. That manual was entrusted to Brick Anderson. Not even Mr. Church knows what is contained in it.

# ECHO TEAM

*"My daddy wanted me to stay in Force Recon. Worst that could happen there is I get shot."*
—Bunny, *Deep Dark*

Joe Ledger's group of first-chair shooters. This SpecOps team has logged more field time than any other DMS unit; and they've tackled some of the most dangerous threats to humanity imaginable. Their specialty is investigation, apprehension, and some field work also done at the warehouse.

## BRIAN BIRD

Rank: Logistics Specialist
Call Sign: Birddog
First Appearance: *Extinction Machine*
Bio: Birddog works closely with Brick, making sure that the field teams get all the hardware they need to get the job done.

## OLIVER 'OLLIE' BROWN

Rank: 2nd Lieutenant, U.S. Army
Call Sign: Scarface
First appearance: *Patient Zero*
Bio: Ollie Brown was one of the first people chosen as possible team leaders for Echo Team in the desperate days following the first outbreak of *Seif al Din*. Brown was a caustic, bitter man who was largely unlikeable. He was also a superb soldier, a locksmith, and a hero.
**IMPORTANT CONNECTIONS:** Until Skip Tyler was revealed as the traitor in Echo Team, Ollie was Joe Ledger's number one suspect.

## PETE DOBBS

Call Sign: Prankster
Rank: former Army Ranger (staff sergeant) and sergeant from Kentucky State Police
First Appearance: *Extinction Machine*
Bio: Shooter recruited from ATF team working War on Drugs in Appalachia.
Final Appearance: *Extinction Machine*

> Unless it's covered in tactical gear and a field team is gearing up, you will never see more than four people gathered in or around a conference table. Nobody at the DMS enjoys meetings..
> —Birddog

# STERCUS FIT

*"If it's weird and pissed off—we shoot it"*—found scribbled around the new Echo Team logo, possibly by Bunny

---

**BODY ARMOR**

Kevlar: we have all heard of it, but what is it? It was created by Stephanie Kwolak at DuPont in the 1960's. It is a synthetic fiber that is five times stronger than steel and it has many uses. For the military, they weave the fibers into sheets and then stack those sheets on top of each other.

"Dragon Skin" battle armor is a lightweight battle armor used by the public, law enforcement and the U.S. military. Made of overlapping one-quarter inch by two inch disks encased in a fiberglass panel. A single panel is eleven-one-half inches by thirteen-one-half inches and weighs around six pounds. First mentioned in *Patient Zero*.

Spider Silk Kevlar and vests are being worked on now for the U.S. military. Spider silk is five times as strong as steel with one-sixth the density. This means that if you have one-hundred pounds of spider silk and steel, the silk would be one-sixth the size. It is first mentioned in *The King of Plagues*.

## SPYDERCO AUTONOMY KNIFE

The Autonomy by SpyderCo is a quick release knife that, up until recently, was exclusively manufactured for the United States Coast Guard to meet the demanding mission requirements of rescue swimmers. It features an oversized quick release button for one handed deployment while wearing gloves and a serrated sheep's foot blade designed for cutting rope.

Birddog prefers the knife in its tactical diamond like carbon (DLC) coating for its non-reflective black surface and for its versatility in also cutting cargo netting and, when needed, heavy cable or wire.

First American knife made with non-corroding H-1 steel.

## STEVE DUFFY

Call Sign: Spartan
Rank: Staff Sergeant, US Air Force
First Appearance: *Dogs of War*
Bio: Duffy was hired by Sam Imura as a security officer at The Warehouse and moved up to field team operator. While working for Sam he received advanced training as a sniper and soon demonstrated an extraordinary talent for this kind of work. Following the events of *Dogs of War*, Duffy was hired by Ledger as a full member of Echo Team.

**IMPORTANT CONNECTIONS:** Real-world good guy Steve Duffy won an auction to have a character named after him as part of the Pixel Project, a global nonprofit doing important work to stop violence against women.

## NOAH FALLON

Rank: Sergeant
Call Sign: Gandalf
First Appearance: *Code Zero*
Bio: Noah was one of several new recruits brought on during the *Code Zero* case. A quiet, introspective man, Ledger was never sure if Fallon was cut out for the horrors of the DMS world.

## ROBERT "BIG BOB" FARADAY

Rank: former ATF
Call Sign: Slim
First Appearance: *Zero Tolerance*
Bio: Big Bob Faraday, a former ATF agent, stands six foot five inches and is built like the Sears Tower. A man with a gentle heart, he was almost killed by Russians in *The Dragon Factory*. Due to the injuries he sustained, he was left unable to perform field work but helped create "The Shop," a sort of annex of The Warehouse, where he works with Mike Harnick and Brian "Birddog" Bird.

## HELICOPTERS

A helicopter is an aircraft that utilizes revolving rotors (or blades) to create both lift and propulsion. It has the ability to move both vertically and horizontally depending on the direction of the blades. Usually ranked by size: light, for passenger, reconnaissance, or short travel. Medium for supply missions, fire and rescue, and ambulance. And large for transporting troops, weaponry, or cargo.

Unlike airplanes, helicopters have the advantage of being able to hover in place which is why they are used in several professions in civilian life. Weather/traffic reporters for news stations, firefighters, police, tourism, and of course the travel industry are all businesses that benefit from the use of helicopters.

Military helicopters are similar in design as their civilian counterparts, but with some notable differences. Among those being: they're larger, they have the ability to carry and fire weapons, and they're usually heavily armored. Helicopters can be used in several areas of the military including: medical evacuation, troop transport, air-to-ground support, supply drops, coastal patrol, water and fire rescue, and aerial reconnaissance.

## GHOST

Rank: Sergeant

Call Sign: Ghost

First Appearance: *Dog Days*

Bio: A big, strong, occasionally goofy and entirely dangerous white shepherd who is partnered with Joe Ledger. He has been awarded official rank as a sergeant in the DMS. Ghost's favorite toy is a stuffed cat with Dr Hu stitched on its chest. The dog is a picky eater in that he likes to separate his food and eat it all one piece at a time, even if that means disassembling an entire hotdog. Ghost was trained at The Warehouse by Zan Rosin and Joe Ledger and almost right away chose Rudy as his most favorite person.

**IMPORTANT CONNECTIONS:** Ghost and Rudy Sanchez's dog, Banshee, had a litter of very large puppies. Because Banshee had been bred by Lilith, the birth of mixed breed pups did not please the mistress of Arklight.

## RICKY GOMEZ

Rank: Sergeant

Call Sign: None assigned

First Appearance: *The King of Plagues*

Biography: From Brooklyn, Sergeant Gomez had been with Echo Team for over three months. He had a brother who played single-A ball for the Brooklyn Cyclones.

**M21**

In the Ledger Universe, there are only two snipers mentioned for Echo Team: John Smith aka "Chatterbox" and Sam Imura aka "Ronin." We never know what type of rifle John Smith uses, but we know that Sam Imura uses three different rifles: .408 Cheyenne Tactical, M110 SASS (Semi-Automatic Sniper System), and the M21 with a 20-round box magazine. The other sniper rifles mentioned are in the hands of Violin, a McMillan Tactical .50, and Ludo Monk, a Dragunov named "Olga." Monk also reminisces about using a Beretta .50 and a PSG1 (made by Heckler and Koch).

Sam's sniper rifles are all U.S. made, designed and tested. The M21 is actually an M14 with a sniper scope attached. It was first used in the Vietnam War and can be found today within the military community and private collections. It is one of the most accurate sniper rifles for a 7.62 ammunition from its time. The .408 Chey-Tac sniper rifle is a little bit of a misnomer. The .408 refers to the round that is fired from the weapon. The weapon itself is the M200 sniper rifle, considered to be the best sniper rifle in the world to date (Sam's has been modified to fire the .338 Lapua Magnum supersonic round). It has an effective range of 1.4 MILES. Think about that for a second, Sam Imura would not even have to be in the same general area as Echo Team to remove threats to them. The M110 SASS was one of the best sniper rifles in 2007, with the ability for ambidextrous use (good for lefties too), a 20-round magazine, and weighing only 16 pounds.

**COBBLER**

Unlike Ghost, Cobbler was a real cat and was part of Jonathan Maberry's family for twenty years. When he finally passed, Maberry decided to let Cobbler go live with Joe Ledger.

## SAM IMURA

Rank: Lieutenant, US Army

Call Sign: Ronin

First Appearance: *Extinction Machine*

Bio: Sam is one of the best snipers in the U.S. military. Cool and patient, he provides Echo Team with long-range punch. After being seriously injured during the *Kill Switch* matter, Sam opted out of field work and instead took over as commander for *The Warehouse*. Years later he would leave official military service and operate a crew of private contractors called 'The Boy Scouts,' doing scut work for various black operations groups.

**IMPORTANT CONNECTIONS:** Sam Imura is the older full brother of Tom Imura and half brother of Benny Imura (the *Rot & Ruin* novels). His Boy Scouts allied themselves with Dez Fox during the *Lucifer 113* outbreak. Although Sam was presumed killed in action and left behind by Dez Fox and her people (*Fall of Night*) Sam survived that battle and went off to work with teams trying to control the spread of the deadly pathogen ("Lone Gunman," published in *Nights of the Living Dead*, co-edited by Jonathan Maberry and George A. Romero).

## SNAKE HENDERSON

Rank: Sergeant

Call Sign: None assigned

First Appearance: *The King of Plagues*

Biography: (There are maybe five lines about Henderson and they are all: we barely knew him)

Final Appearance: *The King of Plagues*

## DUNCAN MCDOUGAL

Rank: Sergeant ATF agent

Call Sign: BadWolf

First Appearance: *Code Zero*

Bio: McDougal was a brawler from Boston who worked for Boston P.D., Massachusetts State Police, and the ATF before signing onto the DMS. Blunt, reliable, and practical, McDougall helped anchor Echo Team during the Mother Night attacks.

## MONTANA PARKER

Rank: FBI Special Agent (retired)

Call Sign: Stretch

First Appearance: *Code Zero*

Bio: Montana is a former FBI agent and the newest member of Echo Team. Tough, outspoken and reliable, she fit in well with the other top professionals on Joe Ledger's top squad. Montana was killed during the *Kill Switch* incident, along with many other DMS field agents.

Final Appearance: *Kill Switch*

### HARVEY "BUNNY" RABBIT

Rank: Master Sergeant, Marine Corps

Call Sign: Green Giant

First Appearance: *Patient Zero*

Bio: Bunny is a big, blond, former competitive volleyball player who joined the Marines and went from Force Recon to the DMS. He and Top are best friends, and they joined Echo Team at the same time as Joe Ledger. Bunny is a little over six-and-a-half feet tall and enormously strong. He, Top and Bunny have logged more combat time than anyone else in the DMS.

**IMPORTANT CONNECTIONS:** Bunny is involved with Lydia Ruiz, a former DMS agent who now runs security for FreeTech.

### SAMPSON RIGGS

Rank: Colonel

Call Sign: Big Kahuna

First Appearance: *Code Zero*

Bio: Sampson Riggs was a legendary DMS field agent, and until Joe Ledger came onto the scene, he had the highest case clearance record. Tall, strong, handsome, charming and wise, Riggs was the perfect leader and is responsible for saving the country and the world from several horrific threats.

Final Appearance: *Code Zero*

**IMPORTANT CONNECTIONS:** Sampson Riggs was Joe Ledger's personal hero and role model.

---

### BENELLI NOVA PISTOL GRIP SHOTGUN

Shotguns. Everyone knows what you mean when you say the word. The first thing that comes to mind is someone pumping the shell into the chamber with a distinctive "click-click" and then blowing large holes in things. So many movies have shown the "Sawed-off" shotgun that does massive damage to everyone in its path. But in truth, a shotgun is an almost useless weapon unless the person knows what they are doing, has the right ammunition for the job and has a target rich environment.

Combat shotguns, like those used in the Ledger Universe, are not like what you will buy for hunting or even home defense. Combat shotguns can look like your common shotgun, but are designed to hold more shells and have less recoil. Additionally, like Bunny's "Honey Boom Boom," many combat shotguns will have drum magazines and don't just fire the standard buckshot. From "Dragon's Breath" (magnesium loaded rounds that catch fire), shells that start with a slug, low level buck and then finish with LARGE buckshot, rounds that contain a tracer bullet (to better see what you are aiming at), flash bang ammo (when you just HAVE to get their attention), to "Shok-lock" rounds used by SWAT to breach locked doors; there is almost no limit to the damage a properly stocked combat shotgun can do.

## LYDIA RUIZ

Rank: Chief Petty Officer, United States Navy

Call Sign: Warbride

First Appearance: *Assassin's Code*

Bio: Apart from Top and Bunny, Lydia was the most experienced DMS field agent, formerly a member of the Navy's first covert group of female SEALs. Quick and ruthless in a fight, she's been on some of the most terrifying missions with Echo Team.

**IMPORTANT CONNECTIONS:** After the events of *Kill Switch*, Lydia resigned and took a job as head of security with FreeTech. She and Bunny live together in a small sea cottage.

## KHALID SHAHEED

Rank: Delta Force shooter and field trauma specialist; ex Navy SEAL

Call Sign: Dancing Duck

First Appearance: *The King of Plagues*

Bio: Khalid was a Muslim-American and former makeup artist who became one of Joe Ledger's most valuable team members. He was one of the most versatile members of Echo Team.

Final Appearance: *Assassin's Code*

## BRADLEY "TOP" SIMS

Rank: First Sergeant, Army Rangers

Call Sign: Sergeant Rock

First Appearance: *Patient Zero*

Bio: Top Sims is Joe Ledger's strong right hand and the most trusted field agent in the DMS. A former Ranger who came out of retirement after his son was killed and his daughter wounded in the early days of the Iraq War, Top now runs Echo Team. Top is the oldest field agent still active with the DMS, and along with Bunny has seen more action with Joe Ledger than anyone else.

**IMPORTANT CONNECTIONS:** Top Sims is estranged from his family and has adopted Bunny and the rest of Echo Team as his family.

The AH-64 (Apache) is the Army's large division/corps attack helicopter capable of rear, close, and shaping missions. It is also capable of deep precision striking that can provide reconnaissance during both day and night missions in all battlefield and weather conditions. The crew compartment has shielding between the cockpit areas that is in place so that at least one crew member can survive a heavy fire attack. Both the compartment doors as well as the rotor blades can sustain hits from 23mm rounds. The airframe of the helicopter includes two-thousand, five-hundred pounds of protection and a self-sealing fuel system to protect against ballistic projectiles. It incorporates a millimeter wave fire control radar, radar frequency interferometer, a "fire-and-forget" radar guided Hellfire missile, and cockpit management and digitization enhancements. The most distinguishing feature of the Apache is the Integrated Helmet and Display Sighting System (IHADSS) which enables the pilot or gunner to connect the helicopter's 30mm automatic M230 Chain Gun to his/her helmet. This allows the gun to track head movements so that it points in the direction that the soldier is looking. The M230E1 can also be fixed to a locked forward-firing position or controlled using the Target Acquisition and Design System (TADS). It has a standard performance of achieving at least one hit for every thirty shots fired at a wheeled vehicle at a range of eight-hundred and seventy to one-thousand, three-hundred yards.

## JOHN SMITH

Rank: Sniper

Call Sign: Chatterbox

First Appearance: *The King of Plagues*

Bio: John Smith was a man of very few words. His silence was indicative of a complex inner life that, alas, his comrades never got to know much about. He was one of the deadliest snipers in history and died in the service of his country.

Final Appearance: *Assassin's Code*

## PETER SMITH

Call Sign: Darth Sidious

Rank: Police Patrolman

First Appearance: *Dogs of War* (mention); *Deep Silence* (appearance)

Bio: Pete was a cop with Tate in Durham and when his friend decided to apply for federal work, Pete went with him. They were interviewed by Top and Bunny and went into training at The Pier in the days following *Dogs of War*. Pete is a well-rounded fighter, though he prefers sticks and fighting knives.

**IMPORTANT CONNECTIONS:** Real-world former cop Peter Smith was a close friend of Brenden Tate. Author Jonathan Maberry decided to sign him onto Echo Team so he could continue to serve with his late friend.

## BRENDEN TATE

Call Sign: Coffey

Rank: Crisis Intervention Officer, Durham Police Department, Durham, NC

First Appearance: *Dogs of War* (mention); *Deep Silence* (appearance)

Bio: As a utility infielder, Tate handles a lot of odd-jobs with competence, imagination and natural diligence. He's the gadget guy on Echo Team, and always has some nasty little device in a pocket, ready for special circumstances.

There is nothing deadlier in the world of firearms than a well-trained sniper. Given the time to find a stable place to fire from, they are truly the "Hand-of-God" when it comes to removing an enemy from the world.

Sniper rifles share several common characteristics: They have a stock that allows the sniper to snug the weapon into their body, the barrel tends to be the longest of any hand held weapon giving greater accuracy and range, a scope for determining distances and bringing their target to them, and a bi- or tri-pod for the front of the rifle so they do not have to hold the full weight of the weapon over long periods of time (most sniper rifles weigh in excess of fifteen pounds) and the ability to be broken down for transport. Sniper rifles will come in one of two styles: Bolt action, where the shooter manually ejects and chambers a new round every time, or magazine fed, where the weapon automatically expels the spent shell and loads a new one.

One final point about sniper rifles—you can look up any of these rifles online and get their specifications, but when you research snipers, you find that their weapons were usually a mix of parts: a barrel from one manufacturer, a stock from another, a scope from a third and bipod from a fourth. Each shooter will have his or her own special rifle that they have spent a long time modifying to be their baby and they know better than their own family.

Normally a dentist's mirror would not be considered a combat item, but leave it to the ingenuity of Top Simms in *Patient Zero* to use one while trying to see the enemy under a door.

**IMPORTANT CONNECTIONS:** Brenden Tate is named for a real-world police officer who died a few years ago. His fellow officers reached out to Jonathan Maberry to tell the author about Tate's deep love of the Ledger novels. Maberry was so touched that he decided to bring Tate into Echo Team.

## IVAN YANKOVICH

Rank: Sergeant, Detroit Police Department; SWAT
Call Sign: Hellboy
First Appearance: *Extinction Machine*
Bio: Ivan was a popular member of Echo Team who signed on shortly after the *Assassin's Code* matter in Iran. Tough, reliable, likeable, and dedicated, Ivan was the kind of operator that put everyone else at ease and was always ready with a joke.
Final Appearance: *Code Zero*

## SUPPORT STAFF

## LYDIA ROSE

Rank: Office Manager for The Pier
Call Sign: Crazy Panda
First Appearance: *Predator One*
Bio: Lydia Rose is the second Lydia in the DMS, but she is not a field agent. Lydia Rose is Joe Ledger's secretary and aide, and she runs the Pier operations with an iron hand but a radiant smile.

The AugustaWestlan helicopter is a light, twin-engine, eight-seat helicopter known for its speed, elegant appearance, and ease of control. It also has the distinction of being the first all-Italian helicopter to be mass-produced. Due to its use in emergency medical service, law enforcement, homeland security, search and rescue, maritime operation as well as for military functions, the AugustaWestlan was proclaimed in 2008 to be one of the industry's bestselling helicopters. It features various advanced avionic systems including a three-axis autopilot, and auto-coupled instrumental landing system, integrated GPS, moving map display, weather radar, and a traffic alerting system all designed to reduce the pilot workload. In case of single-engine failure, the AugustaWestlan has generous power reserve even on the single engine model. Some models feature a "quick convertible interior" which allows the cabin configuration to be quickly adapted for different roles. Mission specific equipment can also be installed in the expandable external baggage compartment. Optional military equipment for the AugustaWestlan include: dual controls, a rotor brake, fixed cargo hook, snow skis, wire-strike protection system, engine particle separator, engine compartment fire extinguishers, rappelling fittings, mounted machine guns, machine gun pods, 20mm cannons, rocket pods, and anti-tank and air-to-air missiles.

Although Lydia Rose is not a special operator, like all DMS personnel she is trained in various forms of armed and unarmed combat, as was demonstrated during the *Dogs of War* case, when she drove the Junkyard—the rolling armory designed by Brick Anderson and Mike Harnick.

**IMPORTANT CONNECTIONS:** Lydia Rose holds a secret animosity for the other 'Lydia'—Lydia Ruiz/Warbride—because they both like Bunny. Lydia Rose consoles herself by also lusting after Joe Ledger. In both cases her lust is (so far) unrequited.

## DR. RUDOLFO ERNESTO SANCHEZ Y MARTINEZ AKA 'RUDY SANCHEZ'

Rank: DMS Chief Medical Officer

Call sign: Aztec (honorary)

First appearance: *Patient Zero*

Bio: Mexican-born Rudy is now an American citizen and the Chief Medical Officer for the DMS. A psychiatrist specializing in post-violence trauma, Rudy was one of the doctors who helped Ground Zero workers cope with their experiences after 9-11. Since coming to work for the DMS, his job is to help the field teams cope with the horrors they encounter and the violence they're forced to commit.

**IMPORTANT CONNECTIONS:** He and Circe O'Tree met and fell in love during *The King of Plagues* affair, and have since married and had a child.

## JERRY SPENCER

Rank: Washington, D.C. Police Department, Forensics Expert

Call sign: Mr. Happy

First appearance: *Patient Zero*

Bio: In his fifties, after having worked with the Baltimore police for thirty years, Jerry Spencer gave up his retirement to take a position with the DMS; the move also netted him a nice raise in pay. Even so, he'd much rather be fishing. Jerry has an unsmiling face, iron grey hair, and dark eyes. Joe

**REMINGTON 870 PUMP SHOTGUN**

Now, a quick note about why a "sawed-off" shotgun is not really a killing weapon: The barrel of a shotgun allows the gases to build up behind the round and fire it at high rates of speed and lethal power. It also controls the scatter pattern of the buckshot coming out the end. When one cuts off the barrel, you lose a lot of that killing power, but do increase the scatter pattern. This is great if you are trying to wound many people in a small area, but it does not guarantee killing anyone.

One final thing: unless you are built like Bunny, don't try to fire a shotgun one handed and ALWAYS make sure the stock is snug against your shoulder. When you hear about people breaking and bruising their shoulders, it is usually because the butt of the weapon is not snug and the recoil tries to knock you on your butt. I talk from experience here.

—Thomas Raymond

Ledger describes him as "the best forensics man [I] ever met." Jerry was the oldest man on the task force at the Warehouse and escaped with a cracked sternum.

**IMPORTANT CONNECTIONS:** Jerry holds a grudge against Joe Ledger for talking him into coming out of retirement and going to work for the DMS.

## DEEDEE WHITMAN

Rank: Former military police; promoted to major within the DMS
Call Sign: Scream Queen
First Appearance: *The King of Plagues*
Bio: DeeDee is a former military police investigator who signed onto Echo Team prior to the *King of Plagues* matter. She is a tough, resourceful, easygoing operator who was on the fast-track to get her own field team before being critically injured by Rafael Santoro aboard the *Sea of Hope*. After that she spent time as the executive officer of The Warehouse. When Sam Imura took command of that facility, DeeDee was promoted to major and now serves as permanent liaison to Barrier, the British equivalent to the DMS.

# ALPHA TEAM

*"Unlike traditional branches of the military the DMS didn't use the standard A, B, C code names for all of the teams. They did originally, but as teams were wiped out they were replaced by teams with new names that started with the same letter. If Grace and I ever came up for air we were supposed to start building new B and C teams to replace the original Bravo and Charlie Teams massacred during a major terrorist action in late June."*
—Joe Ledger, *The Dragon Factory*

Headed by Grace Courtland
First Appearance: *Patient Zero*
Defeated at Blue Point Crab and Seafood Processing Plant, Crisfield, Maryland, when one of the team triggers an explosive booby trap.

## GRACE COURTLAND

Rank: Major, Special Air Service, UK
Call Sign: Amazing
First appearance: *Patient Zero*
Bio: Grace Courtland was the first woman to make it through the experimental program for women soldiers in the SAS. After distinguishing herself in that notorious boys' club, she helped Mr. Church form Barrier and later its American counterpart, the DMS. She and Joe Ledger became lovers for a brief time before Grace died a hero's death saving billions from ethnic genocide.

Interceptor Body Armor was used by U.S. military forces from the 1990's to the early 2010's. Unlike older Kevlar vests, these suits of armor cover the entire body and even have a flap for the groin area. It is first mentioned in *Patient Zero*.

Final Appearance: *The Dragon Factory*

**IMPORTANT CONNECTIONS:** Grace died in Joe's arms, and her killer, Conrad Veder, escaped the destruction on Dogfish Cay when the DMS took down the Dragon Factory. However Joe and Ghost hunted Veder down and executed him for her murder.

# FAMILY

## JAMES WOLCOTT LEDGER

Rank: Mayor of New Baltimore
First Appearance: *Patient Zero*
Biography: James Ledger stepped down the position of police commissioner to run for and win the election to become Mayor of Baltimore. He is very proud of his sons.

## SEAN LEDGER

Rank: Detective Two
First appearance: *Dogs of War*
Biography: Joe's younger brother outranked Joe in the Baltimore PD at the beginning of the novels because he was more dedicated to the police force and its politics. Sean has a wife: Ali, son Ryan aka "Lefty," and daughter Emily. He and his family were endangered in the events of *Dogs of War*.

# FREETECH

An organization formed to repurpose technologies originally created by terrorist organizations such as Majestic Three, the Seven Kings, the Jakoby Family, the Red Order and others. Funded by Alexander "Toys" Chismer and run by Junie Flynn, FreeTech brings these technologies to the people who need them.

## JUNIE FLYNN

Rank: Director of FreeTech
Call Sign: Bookworm (honorary)
First Appearance: *Extinction Machine*
Bio: Junie has a complex past as the subject of a breeding program initiated by the Majestic Project in the years following the Roswell Crash. She is the former host of a conspiracy theory podcast

Each member of DMS field teams has official identification and licenses to operate as agents of the FBI, CIA, DHS, ICE, DEA, or the NSA, to name a few. Out of all these organizational aliases, several personnel from the Hangar, Warehouse, and the Pier are officially assigned to the Coast Guard, TSA, Interpol, MI6, and oddly enough the US Marshals and Royal Canadian Mounted Police.
—Birddog

and an author, and currently heads up a foundation dedicated to repurposing technologies illegally developed by the Majestic Three. She and Joe Ledger became romantically involved during the Majestic Black Book affair.

**IMPORTANT CONNECTIONS:** Junie is in a committed relationship with Joe Ledger, and they live together in Del Mar, California.

## ALEXANDER CHISMER

Alias: Toys

Rank: Chief Financial Officer for FreeTech

Call Sign: n/a

First Appearance: *Patient Zero*

Bio: Toys, a slim young man with cat-green eyes and dark hair, is a former criminal who worked with Sebastian Gault and Hugo Vox. When he helped bring down the Seven Kings, Mr. Church offered him a chance at redemption by entrusting him with billions of the Kings' ill-gotten gains and challenging him to do as much good for humanity as possible with it. He is the private financier behind Junie Flynn's FreeTech. Whether Toys will earn redemption or slip back into his corrupt ways remains to be seen.

**IMPORTANT CONNECTIONS:** Toys struggles with the burden of personal redemption imposed on him by Mr. Church. He lives like a monk and although he is doing a tremendous amount of good in the world, he does not feel that any of it earns him a shred of forgiveness for the bad things he's done.

## HELMUT DEACON

Rank: Junior Executive, FreeTech

Call Sign: The Kid (honorary)

First Appearance: *The Dragon Factory*

Bio: Formerly known as SAM Eighty-Two, Helmut is a teenager whose parentage is both complicated and horrific. He is an identical clone of Cyrus Jakoby. SAM stood for Same as Me, and Eighty-two because the SAMs were numbered. In a move to separate himself from his father, and prove to the world that beyond nature and nurture there's a third option: choice, Helmut has used his genius and specialized knowledge to help humanity. After his liberation from the Hive, he chose to work with the Red Cross and the World Health Organization in order to work in caring for the New Men created and abused by his father. He is currently on the science team for Junie Flynn's FreeTech.

---

## JONATHAN'S COMMENTARY

*The character of SAM—who later takes on the name of Helmut Deacon—is an important one for me. SAM (literally 'Same as me') is more than just a clone, he is a kind of twisted 'son' of Josef Mengele, one of the greatest monsters of all time. Mengele is the vile gold standard for 'mad scientists'. SAM/Helmut, on the other hand, is proof that there are not two but three essential aspects to personal destiny: nature, nurture, and choice. SAM chose to be a good person and since being adopted by Mr. Church he has applied this staggering intellect to helping Junie Flynn repurpose the perverted technologies taken from terrorists and instead using them to benefit mankind.*

# TRANSCRIPT OF INTERVIEW WITH JEROME LEROY 'BUG' WILLIAMS

## (PARTIAL)
## CONDUCTED AT THE HANGAR
## DMS HEADQUARTERS
## FLOYD BENNETT FIELD, BROOKLYN, NY

PROFESSOR JAYDEN SUMMERSTONE: First, I'm a little confused. In various after action reports you are referred to as 'Leroy' and 'Jerome,' and as 'Williams' and 'Taylor.' Which is it?

BUG: All of it. My birth name is Jerome Leroy Williams. My dad called me Leroy and they called me Jerome in school. I pretty much answered to anything. My dad died when I was little and my mom remarried, so when she changed her name, I did, too, though I was never actually adopted by her second husband. It's complicated, so I let people call me whatever.

SUMMERSTONE: But you prefer…?

BUG: I'm Bug. That's what my friends call me.

SUMMERSTONE: Bug it is, then. It's my understanding that you were given the opportunity of joining the DMS rather than going to prison for cybercrimes.

BUG: Yeah, I guess. I was kind of drifting toward being a gray hat…one of those hackers who mess with systems just to show that they can be messed with.

SUMMERSTONE: That's not what the report said. You were arrested for hacking into military intelligence networks.

BUG: Well, okay, sure, but I was trying to find Osama Bin Laden. I wasn't spying, I was helping.

SUMMERSTONE: They managed to find him without your help, though.

BUG: Did they?

SUMMERSTONE: Wait, are you saying—?

BUG: We all do what we can.

SUMMERSTONE: Okay, MindReader is an amazing computer system. It's the most powerful computer on earth, as I understand it. And yet you seem to understand it.

BUG: Is that a question? I guess it is. Sure, MindReader and I get each other. She's smart. She's elegant. And she wants to help.

SUMMERSTONE: 'She'…?

BUG: Well, people think of boats as 'she,' right? I sail around the Internet on MindReader.

SUMMERSTONE: What can you tell me about the new version? Mind-Reader QC. That version is more sophisticated? More powerful?

BUG: (laughs) She's more of a beast than the old version was when I first met her. Before she got hacked and infected and messed with by the Seven Kings and all. QC isn't going to fall for that crap. No one's going to hack her because they can't. You can't hack a quantum computer. Not possible. And as far as powerful? Damn, man, if the old MindReader was, say, a T-Rex, then the QC is the aster-oid that wiped out all the dinosaurs.

SUMMERSTONE: You exaggerate…

BUG: (laughs)

# PART FOUR
## THE BAD GUYS

*"Ludo, for Christ's sake stop saying okey-dokey. We're master criminals."*
—Mother Night, *Code Zero*

### AMIRAH

First appearance: *Patient Zero*

Bio: Creator of *Seif al Din* and wife of El Mujahid. Amirah created new generations of the *Seif al Din* pathogen in the secret bunker Gault had built for her, going beyond what she and Gault agreed upon. The new incarnation spreads much faster, both the initial infection rate and the time for reanimation. Gault is concerned, but tries to hide it even as he realizes Amirah's agenda may not match his own.

**IMPORTANT CONNECTIONS:** Amirah became the target of an Echo Team hunt in the Afghan hills in the short story, "Zero Tolerance."

### ZEPHYR BAIN

First Appearance: *Dogs of War*

Bio: Zephyr Bain is a monster, and she knows it. She's also a technological genius, her specialty being robots with artificial intelligence. Nurtured by John the Revelator and Hugo Vox, she wants to cleanse the world by taking out most of its population, leaving a chosen few in charge of rejuvenating and curating the earth's resources. She's been raised to hate and fear the DMS, Mr. Church and Joe Ledger.

**IMPORTANT CONNECTIONS:** Zephyr Bain was mentored by a variety of unofficial aunts and uncles, including Hugo Vox, the Jakoby Twins, and Father Nicodemus.

## OSCAR BELL

First appearance: *Kill Switch*

Bio: Oscar Bell is a military industrialist and father to super-genius Prospero Bell. Bell's companies have been at the forefront of defense contracting, however Bell is a better administrator than inventor. When he realizes the potential in the devices his son is building, Bell shifts the focus of his work to full support of the 'God Machine' and its 'side effects' (such as the Kill Switch effect). In doing so he trades his son's life and sanity for pure profit.

**IMPORTANT CONNECTIONS:** Oscar Bell is the ex-brother-in-law of one of the scientists running the Gateway Project, which is a covert R&D group spun off from Majestic Three.

## PROSPERO BELL

First appearance: *Kill Switch*

Bio: Prospero is a rich kid in psychiatric care. Prospero insists that he is not human and wishes to find his way to his real home. He draws artwork from his dreams. His psychiatrist, Dr. Greene, has been seeing him for quite a few years. Dr. Greene discovers that this art is, at first glance, heavily influenced if not copied from the work of the Surrealists such as Dali. Prospero insists that he's dreamed these images and then looked at the artwork after the fact. He thinks that authors like Lovecraft, Derleth, and others have been dropping clues for years, waiting for someone like him who has been waiting, watching, and putting the pieces together. He needs to find the books these authors spoke of (a series of books known as "The Unlearnable Truths") and with them he will be able to make his God Machine function properly, and finally be able to go home. He talks about quantum physics and the concept of an omniverse, which is an infinite number of realities. Parallel worlds that are separated by differences however minuscule or massive. If these worlds are right next to ours, then imagine what would happen if we could build a doorway that would allow us to move back-and-forth. Prospero also has dreams about siblings that are all dead, except for a sister whom he thinks

### BELL AH-1Z VIPER HELICOPTER (*CODE ZERO*)

The Bell AH-1Z is an American medium, twin-engine attack helicopter that features a four-blade, bearing-free composite main rotor system (which has 75% fewer parts than a four-bladed articulated system), a semi-automatic folding system for storage aboard amphibious assault ships, uprated transmission, upgraded military avionics, weapons system, electro-optical sensors in an integrated weapons platform, and a target sighting system. It has improved survivability equipment including the Hover Infrared Suppression System (HIRSS) to cover engine exhausts from enemy radar, countermeasure dispensers, radar warning, incoming missile warning, and on-fuselage laser spot warning systems. It is one of the latest members of the Huey family and is also known as a "Zulu Cobra" due to it being based on the AH-1W SuperCobra and the reference to the military phonetic alphabet (Zulu for Z). The AH-1Z has two, redesigned, longer wing stubs that host a wingtip station for launching missiles like the AIM-9 Sidewinder. The wings also have two other stations for 2.7-inch Hydra 70 rocket pods, or AGM-114 Hellfire quad missile launchers, or an AN/APG-78 Longbow fire control radar. The Z-Model's Integrated Avionics System (IAS) includes two mission computers and an automatic flight control system. The navigation suite includes a: digital map system, embedded GPS, and Meggitt's low-airspeed air data subsystem which allows weapons delivery when hovering. The Lockheed Martin Target Sight System (TSS) provides target sighting in day, night, or adverse weather conditions.

Knives are one of the most basic weapons a fighter can use after their own hands. A knife simply consists of a sharpened piece of metal that usually has a handle to help the grip. A double-bladed knife is technically a dagger. Knives come in all shapes and sizes, although after twenty-four inches of blade, it starts pushing the boundaries of becoming a sword.

There are two basic kinds of knives: fixed blade and folding blade. A fixed bladed knife consists of a single piece of metal that is sharpened on one end and has a handle on the other. Additional materials can be bolted through the metal handle to give a better grip. It usually measures between three to twelve inches and weighs in anywhere from a few ounces for a three-inch blade up to a pound for the largest blades. Folding bladed knives fold into the handle or can spring forth from the handle (switchblades). The overall knife surface for a folding blade is shorter, usually around three inches (the longest being a whopping six-inch blade) and weighing about three and a half ounces.

Micro thin Kevlar is a "Friends-in-the-Industry" invention that compresses the Kevlar fibers into smaller areas and reduces the weight accordingly. Allowing for more protection with equal or less weight than standard Kevlar. It is originally worn by the Closers in *Extinction Machine*.

is still alive. She is older in his dreams, and sad because she's been hurt—shot—and cannot have babies. She looks exactly like him, but isn't a clone. She's something else.

**IMPORTANT CONNECTIONS:** Prospero Bell is a genetically-engineered twin of Junie Flynn.

## BERSERKERS

First Appearance: *The Dragon Factory*

Background: These super soldiers are the result of transgenics and gene therapy undertaken by the Jakoby Twins. Given DNA from silverback gorillas, the Berserkers are enormously powerful and highly dangerous (abnormally strong men with anger management issues) for sale as soldiers and mercenaries.

**IMPORTANT CONNECTIONS:** The Berserker program was briefly restarted by Artemisia Bliss during the *Code Zero* case. Some of those Berserkers were infected with the *Seif al Din* pathogen.

## ARTEMISIA BLISS

Alias: Mother Night

First Appearance: *Code Zero*

Bio: Her IQ is off the charts. She helped create VaultBreaker, a program that becomes the leading edge of cyber security technology. VaultBreaker is designed to predict and respond to cyber-attacks and also has some intrusion capabilities that allow it to fight back in creative ways. During her time at the DMS, Artemisia grows increasingly addicted to power and entranced by men with power and what they can accomplish. On hand for cleanup after the outbreaks of the *Seif al Din* virus in the Liberty Bell Center, she surreptitiously collects two complete sets of all the samples from the corpses, secreting one away for herself. She also secretly copies the schematics for Pangaea—the Jakoby Twins computer system—and creates her own upgraded version, Haruspex.

**IMPORTANT CONNECTIONS:** Artemisia Bliss sold a great deal of equipment, science and pathogen samples to Zephyr Bain.

## HARCOURT BOLTON, SENIOR

Call sign: Mr. Voodoo

First appearance: *Kill Switch*

Bio: The CIA's answer to James Bond. Bolton was a field

agent for years until he finally started losing speed and made some mistakes that saw him pulled from the field and put behind a desk. He handled the transition with class and over the last four years has worked his old network of contacts to get mission Intel for other field agents in the CIA and for the DMS. His nickname is Mr. Voodoo because of his seeming ability to get information when no one else can. He harbors a deep hatred for Joe because Harcourt feels Joe's glory has dimmed his own star. Not only did he destroy most of the DMS, but almost launched a pandemic that would have killed tens of thousands of people, most of them children.

**IMPORTANT CONNECTIONS:** Harcourt Bolton, Sr. was the 'spy's spy', and for many years was the hero and role model to Joe Ledger and many of the operators in the DMS.

## THE CLOSERS

First appearance: *Extinction Machine*

Background: The real version of Men in Black. These special agents use advanced technologies including special body armor that protects against most weapons and augments physical strength; microwave pulse pistols; and an assortment of equipment reverse-engineered from crashed T-Craft.

**IMPORTANT CONNECTIONS**: After the fall of M3 many of the Closers went to work for Blackwater, Blue Diamond Security, Oscar Bell, the Gateway Project, and other groups needing specialized killers.

## VICE PRESIDENT WILLIAM "BILL" COLLINS

First appearance: *Patient Zero*

Bio: A long-time non-fan of Mr. Church and the DMS. He wants control of MindReader, for a profit, and once rescinded the DMS's executive charter toward this end. He has close ties with more than one of the DMS's enemies.

**IMPORTANT CONNECTIONS:** Because of the covert betrayal of the DMS by Vice President Collins, the DMS was substantially weakened for several years.

## EVANGELINE REGINA ISADORA SANDERSON

Alias: Eris (a.k.a. the Dragon Lady, the Goddess)

First Appearance: *The King of Plagues*

Bio: To some, she was Eris, the goddess of discord; to Hugo Vox, she was mother; to the Seven Kings, she was Goddess. Eris was tall and green-eyed and was an on-again/off-again lover of Sebastion Gault. In fact, she and Gault were aboard her boat, Delta of Venus, to watch the grand finale of the Ten Plagues Initiative. Unfortunately, Hugo had cleverly planted C4 throughout the ship's hull; the explosion vaporized the boat. Hugo, in *Assassin's Code,* mentions his mother in the present tense, leaving one to assume that Eris lived through the explosion.

**IMPORTANT CONNECTIONS:** Eris was the lover of Sebastian Gault and conspired with him against her own son, Hugo Vox.

## THE FRENCHMAN

Alias: The Concierge

First appearance: *Dogs of War*

Bio: The Frenchman is a former hotelier who was seriously injured during the 2015 Paris Attacks. He was gifted with extensive cybernetic enhancements by Zephyr Bain's organization, and grew into his role as the 'concierge,' able to provide any service for Zephyr and her consort, John the Revelator. The Concierge formed an unusually close relationship with the AI system, Calpurnia.

## SEBASTIAN GAULT

Alias: King of Plagues, the Burned Man, the Gentleman

First Appearance: *Patient Zero*

Bio: The former pharmaceutical developer has used both his genius and his vast fortune to fund terrorist groups and to provide them with dangerous bioweapons, including the fearsome *Seif al Din* pathogen. By the end of *Patient Zero*, Sebastian Gault was listed third on eighteen separate international most wanted lists. Gault was a self-made billionaire by the age of twenty-six, and he wasn't shy about pouring his money into pharmaceutical research endeavors. In time, he launched Gen2000, his own pharma company. Now, this company excelled at finding cures for pathogens created by his own labs, and his money hid the source of the creations from the media even while they praised the cures. Gen2000 and his other companies helped eradicate eighteen disease pathogens. After the covert underground lab in the desert exploded, the words "mass murderer" and "terrorist" also became associated with his name. Gault struggled with the pain of multiple surgeries and of graphic memories, pain that might remain for the rest of his life. However, once he was healed, he had a course set that would give him new fingerprints and tissue grafts and a new eye. Hecate Jakoby, a former lover, grew them as a perfect match to his own, specifically just for him.

**IMPORTANT CONNECTIONS:** Sebastian Gault attacked the DMS three times: first in *Patient Zero*, then as part of the Seven Kings in *The King of Plagues;* and finally through the much-reduced Kings organization in *Predator One*. His onetime ally, Toys, survived Gault and has since become an ally of the DMS and a partner in FreeTech.

## CYRUS JAKOBY

Real name: Josef Mengele

First Appearance: *The Dragon Factory*

Bio: Born in 1911 as Josef Mengele and later became the Chief Medical Officer of the infirmary at Auschwitz-Birkenau. Shortly after he was taken into British custody in 1945, he hung himself. Interestingly enough, he was "reborn" in 1946 as Cyrus Jakoby. By harnessing gene therapy, he was able to change his hair and eye color, and managed to keep himself alive over the years through the use of genetic engineering. One of the worst monsters to come out of the last century, Jakoby wants to systematically destroy those he calls "mud people"—anyone who isn't white. Cyrus stresses the necessity to The Twins for a secret base to protect him from the mud people and from the government. Paris and Hekate turned the design responsibilities over to him, and he created a building shaped like a dodecahedron known as "The Deck." To Cyrus, Tuesday is the most dismal and least worthwhile day of the week.

**IMPORTANT CONNECTIONS:** Jakoby/Mengele is the clone parent of SAM, aka Helmut Deacon, who became the legal adopted son of Mr. Church.

"Maberry has managed to take evil to a whole new level with *The Dragon Factory*."
—Blogcritics

## PARIS AND HECATE JAKOBY

First Appearance: *The Dragon Factory*

Bio: The genetically engineered twins created by Cyrus Jakoby were born at the stroke of midnight on Christmas Eve. Conjoined at the chest in the womb, they came apart at their birth and were each left with a starburst-shaped scar; they consider the birthmark their personal mark. They're both beautifully made, six-foot tall, albino, slim, dark blue eyes, and have white hair.

**IMPORTANT CONNECTIONS:** The Jakoby Twins were allied with Hugo Vox and helped mentor Zephyr Bain. Much of their technology was scavenged and used by Artemisia Bliss.

## KNIGHTS OF THE RED ORDER

First Appearance: *Assassin's Code*

Bio: The Upierczi are a genetic offshoot of humanity that live in the shadows and hunger for human blood. Although they're not supernatural—just products of genetic aberration—they are the basis for the myths of vampires. The Red Knights are incredibly strong and fast and utterly ruthless. Grigori and his fellow Upierczi live in tunnels below the sands of Iran. Grigori and the rest of his kind are albino, have reddish eyes, and unusually sharp teeth. They are remarkably fast and strong, are very well trained in many forms of combat, have great pain tolerance, and are generally considered to be apex predators.

**IMPORTANT CONNECTIONS:** The Red Knights have appeared in other stories, including *V-Wars: All of Us Monsters*, *V-Wars: Shockwaves*, "Mad Science," and "Borrowed Power."

## CHARLES LA ROQUES

Alias: The Scriptor

First Appearance: *Assassin's Code*

Bio: Charles presided over the Ordu Ruber, The Sacred Red Order, a militant and covert offshoot of the Knights Hospitaller. The Red Order conspired with a Muslim splinter group during the Crusades to guarantee that there would never be an end to the strife between Islam and Christendom, because it had been determined that during times of religious strife more people went to church. The deal was struck as a way of insuring the preservation of both groups. Each Sciptor of the Red Order managed this delicate arrangement. When the Muslims created the Hashashin to be their specialized assassins, the Red Order formed the Red Knights, using genetic freaks called the *Upierczi* as their soldiers. Charles La Roques is the last known Scriptor and the Red Order is believed to have collapsed.

**IMPORTANT CONNECTIONS:** The Knights of the Red Ordo were given their charter through the influence and guidance of Father Nicodemus.

## MAJESTIC THREE

First Appearance: *Extinction Machine*

Bio: The Majestic Three was a team of brilliant scientists whose project was originally chartered by President Truman following the Roswell crash. They were tasked with reverse engineering technologies from wrecked UFOs. Eventually they broke away from the government, formed a secret cabal, and developed a rogue plan to use new experimental 'T-Craft' to start—and win—a war with China

**IMPORTANT CONNECTIONS:** M3 is an offshoot of the larger and more bureaucratic Majestic Twelve group formed by President Harry Truman.

## LUDO MONK

First appearance: *Code Zero*

Bio: Has happily killed for Mother Night over thirteen times. During his final mission Ludo was assigned to murder Junie Flynn. Although he did not succeed, his bullet caused grave internal damage to Junie, preventing her from having children.

**IMPORTANT CONNECTIONS:** Ludo Monk very nearly assassinated Zephyr Bain on the orders of Artemisia Bliss during a delicate exchange of cash for stolen technologies.

## EL MUJAHID

Aliases: Also known as O'Brien and The Fighter

First appearance: *Patient Zero*

Bio: Yemen national. A general for Allah (El Mujahid means "fighter in the way of Allah") before he was thirty, he was on wanted lists of over forty nations. He has ties to Al Qaeda and a dozen other extremist groups. On Homeland Security's "must-have" list. Single-minded, relentless, smart. Feared in the way a missile is feared.

**IMPORTANT CONNECTIONS:** El Mujahid's wife, Amirah, was the developer of the *Seif al Din* pathogen. She dosed herself and her husband with advanced generations of the bioweapon, which allowed them to retain their memories and personalities even after transformation.

## JAVAD MUSTAPHA

Bio: Iraqi national and first carrier of *Seif al Din*

First appearance: *Patient Zero*

Bio: Javad Mustapha was the first person with the *Seif al Din* pathogen. His infected body was delivered to a warehouse in Maryland with the intention of using it as a kind of self-directed suicide WMD. Joe Ledger killed Javad during a joint Baltimore P.D./Homeland task force raid. Later, as the *Seif al Din* became more active in Javad's system, he reanimated.

**IMPORTANT CONNECTIONS:** Mr. Church put an unsuspecting Joe Ledger in a locked room with the now zombified Javad. That was part of Joe's 'test' for readiness to join the DMS.

## FATHER NICODEMUS

Alias: Also known as John the Revelator

First Appearance: *The King of Plagues*

Bio: No one really knows who Father Nicodemus is. Some evidence, such as paintings and church records, points to Nicodemus—or at least his name—dating back centuries. One thing for certain, though, is that, depending on the face he chose to show, those he came into contact with had negative physiological and psychological reactions. For example, a prison system psychiatrist

> Ludo Monk's sniper rifle hails from the Soviet Union. It has been around since 1963 and is a magazine fed sniper rifle. It is used by several countries to this day and is a deadly weapon in the hands of a trained sniper. Monk uses a 5-round magazine, but it can be fitted with a 10 or 20-round magazine as well as a 50-round drum! It uses the 7.62x54mm round. Monk mentions a Beretta .50 that he used in the past but, considering the number of drugs he needed to remain level-headed, he was probably thinking of the Barret M82 which fires a .50 cal ammo and was made in the U.S. as an anti-sniper and anti-material (it kills engines in vehicles) rifle. The PSG1 rifle mentioned is made by Heckler and Koch (H&K) and was first manufactured in 1985. It is still used to this day and fires the 7.62 NATO round common for sniper rifles.

was sure he was nothing more than pure evil. Nicodemus had a chilling laugh and spooky, mesmerizing eyes the color of toad skin. Whenever he spoke, he seemed to give vague and evasive answers. His smile gave him a goblin-like appearance. In prison, the man—if that's what he could be called, in truth—makes conversational references to the London Hospital bombing and the Seven Kings. He's supposed to be in strict isolation, without any kind of media privileges. Also, oddly enough, his prison records keep going missing, and he has no medical records that anyone has ever been able to discover. He stood accused of the murder of another prisoner, Jesus Santiago, although he denied ever having any contact with the other man. A guard, the one witness to their alleged conversation committed suicide. Though Santiago had no history of heart disease, the official cause of his death was listed as a heart attack. As well, the numbers 1217 were found carved into his body—the date of the London Hospital bombing.

**IMPORTANT CONNECTIONS:** Father Nicodemus claims to be kin to Mr. Church and also claims to know Church's darker secrets.

## ORDO FRATRUM CLAUSTRORUM AKA 'BROTHERHOOD OF THE LOCK'

First Appearance: *Kill Switch*

Bio: The Brotherhood is an ancient cult of warrior priests created by a Papal Bull but whose existence is generally kept secret. Only a few cardinals knew of them, as well as select people within the global intelligence communities. The mission of this brotherhood is to seek out ancient books, relics and objects that are believed to possess dark powers or contain dangerous information, and then to either destroy or safeguard those items. The books are collectively known as the "Unlearnable Truths" and the objects are The Unspeakables. The Brotherhood believes that these items are so dangerous to humanity that no action is too extreme to keep these secrets hidden. To that end, the Brotherhood is brutal, efficient, and thorough.

**IMPORTANT CONNECTIONS:** The Brotherhood targeted Violin and Harry Bolt in Europe during the events of "The Unlearnable Truths."

Another Italian gun manufacturer is Tanfoglio, a .9mm used by the leader of the Brotherhood of the Lock is a clone of the CZ 75.

## DR. MICHAEL PHAROS

First appearance: *Predator One*

Bio: Michael Pharos had a talent for management. When the Seven Kings fell he gathered up the shards of that organization and kept it running despite the lack of clear leadership. As a result he helped put into play the most devastating series of domestic terror attacks on the United States.

**IMPORTANT CONNECTIONS:** Pharos is currently interred at the same DMS black site where Rafael Santoro is incarcerated.

## ESTEBAN SANTORO

Alias: Mr. Priest

First appearance: *Kill Switch*

Bio: Esteban, working under the false name of Mr. Priest, spent a considerable amount of time searching for ancient books of dark magic known collectively as the "Unlearnable Truths." Prior to becoming a freelance operative, he was one of the warrior monks of the Brotherhood of the Lock.

**IMPORTANT CONNECTIONS:** Following the firing of the God Machine near the end of the *Kill Switch* matter, Esteban Santoro's whereabouts are unknown.

## RAFAEL SANTORO

Alias: The Spaniard

First appearance: *The King of Plagues*

Bio: A killer who has an affinity for knives and has left a trail of tortured and slaughtered 'angels' behind him – mostly women and children. He keeps photos of his victims and uses them to coerce people who love their families into doing horrible things…such as plant bombs in the London Hospital or release an airborne super-Ebola virus into the general population. Santoro is widely regarded as one of the most dangerous men alive. He is currently in a DMS black site prison where he receives regular visits from Dr. Sanchez. Joe Ledger, however, is unaware of Santoro's whereabouts.

**IMPORTANT CONNECTIONS:** Santoro's brother, Esteban (known as Mr. Priest) worked for Oscar Bell and was instrumental in obtaining many of the Unlearnable Truths. His efforts to obtain those evil books is recounted in the novella, "The Unlearnable Truths."

Other knives used by Joe's companions are the KA-BAR, which comes in at almost twelve inches of steel and weighs just over eleven ounces, used by Skip in room 12 of *Patient Zero*, a switchblade used by Top in *The Dragon Factory*, Violin's silver blades and the Katana and Tanto set used by Ash in *Joe Ledger: Unstoppable: Crash Course*.

## MAJOR CARLY SCHELLINGER

First appearance: *Dogs of War*

Bio: US Army, on the payroll of the CIA, and known for being humorless, unapproachable, unkind, and inflexible. She also has an extraordinary amount of political weight. She has overseen most of the practical applications of advanced technology in the past ten years, getting the geek squads and the think tanks to perform at max output and drives development through prototype variations to field-ready rollouts in record time. She's also old-money and went to school with Zephyr Bain.

**IMPORTANT CONNECTIONS:** Carly Schellinger was briefly Zephyr Bain's lover while they were both in high school.

## THE SEVEN KINGS

First Appearance: *The King of Plagues*

Bio: A secret society made up of some of the most powerful and dangerous men in the world who "exist to cause chaos." To build their mystique, the Kings hijacked much of the conspiracy theories built around other groups—such as the Illuminati. The Kings include: Plagues, Lies, Fear, Gold, Thieves, Famine and War, all overseen by The Goddess—Eris, a very wealthy woman in her sixties who looks to be in her thirties, with no plastic surgery involved. She's also the mother of the King of Fear, referred to as the American (aka Hugo Vox). The American organized The Seven Kings. The Seven Kings are in a continual struggle for power with the Inner Circle of the Skull and Bones Society. Gault's predecessor wanted to use the Death of the Firstborn plague to cripple the Inner Circle, but the science behind his plan was faulty.

**IMPORTANT CONNECTIONS:** The Chosen (ground troops) and The Kingsmen (elite group who can hold their own against SEALS or the SAS). Many of these foot soldiers were absorbed into the global market for trained private 'security'.

## HOWARD SHELTON

First appearance: *Extinction Machine*

Bio: One of three Governors of an organization called the Majestic Three, tasked by an old secret executive order by President Harry Truman to repair or re-create a T-craft based on technologies recovered from crashed alien vehicles. Head of Shelton Aeronautics. Vain and rich enough to have his home, VanMeer Castle, moved from Europe stone by stone. Howard is a psychopath and borderline sociopath who enjoys blowing things up.

**IMPORTANT CONNECTIONS:** Howard Shelton oversaw much of the alien-human hybridization program into which Erasmus Tull, Prospero Bell and Junie Flynn were all born.

## J.P. SUNDERLAND

First appearance: *The Dragon Factory*

Bio: Billionaire. Both V.P. Collins and Sunderland want four biotech bills moving through Congress to pass and while there's nothing obvious to connect those bills with Collins' personal interest or Sunderland's private holdings, MindReader, if aimed in that direction, could change that. This could ruin Collins politically as well as making him a pariah in the business world. This is the lever Sunderland uses to convince Collins into taking the action against the DMS.

**IMPORTANT CONNECTIONS:** V.P. Collins, and Harold Sunderland (JP's brother, who is not only a huge proponent of biotech legislature, but a good friend of Vice President Collins).

## ERASMUS TULL

First Appearance: *Extinction Machine*

Bio: Erasmus Tull was part of the same alien-human hybridization program into which Junie Flynn was born. Tull was a remarkably gifted field operative, known for his lack of hesitation, decisiveness of action, independence, thoroughness, and attention to detail. He was responsible for destroying *The Warehouse* and killing two hundred DMS agents and staff. Tull worked as a Closer for Majestic Three and was generally believed to be the single toughest special operator alive.

**IMPORTANT CONNECTIONS:** Tull believes himself to be without a soul, and therefore can bear no guilt for any of the many murders he's committed.

## SAMUEL 'SKIP' TYLER

Combat Call Sign: Joker

Rank: Chief Petty Officer, USN

First appearance: *Patient Zero*

Bio: A founding member of Echo Team who betrayed the DMS and nearly caused a worldwide pandemic.

**IMPORTANT CONNECTIONS:** Skip Tyler was the first known person from within the DMS to betray that organization. Sadly, he wasn't the last.

## CONRAD VEDER

Alias: Also known as Hans Brueker, Hans Ulrich Rudel, and Gunnar Haekel

First appearance: *The Dragon Factory*

Bio: When Conrad Veder was just in the tenth grade, he murdered his social studies teacher's wife for $500—his very first contract killing. During the events of *The Dragon Factory*, at twenty-six years old, he was worth around eleven million euros. Rumor has it he charges around a million dollars per hit. He's very good at what he does, given his efficient and unemotional mind.

**IMPORTANT CONNECTIONS:** Veder escaped the fighting at the end of *The Dragon Factory* and became the target of a very determined hunt by Joe Ledger and his new combat dog, Ghost. That story is recounted in "Dog Days."

## HUGO VOX

Alias: The American and King of Fear

First Appearance: *The King of Plagues*

Bio: The cold-hearted genius who built the Seven Kings was also one of the leading experts in anti- and counter-terrorism. He used his high security clearance to obtain insider knowledge that allowed the Kings to do untold harm. The top security expert in the world. Before he was outed as a villain, Vox ran Terror Town, the most effective counter-terrorism training facility in the world. To have been "vetted by Vox" was to get the gold standard of above top secret clearance and approval. Vox and the Kings funded Al Qaeda and set the 9/11 timetable with the aim of earning billions of dollars from the inevitable shifts in the stock market.

**IMPORTANT CONNECTIONS:** Vox had a lot of irons in the fire and when the Seven Kings organization began to crumble he fled, taking much of their operating capital with him; and set up various business deals with the Red Order and the Red Knights, playing one against the other. He was also an unofficial 'uncle' and mentor to Zephyr Bain.

---

## JONATHAN'S COMMENTARY

Dogs of War *was a long time coming. It's a project I'd been thinking about, in one way or another, since before I wrote* Patient Zero. *Back then it wasn't a Joe Ledger thriller but was destined to be some kind of weird science thriller focusing on artificial intelligence, nanotechnology and robotics. I'd been part of a panel discussion at Balticon (a science fiction conference held every year in Baltimore) and we were talking about* The Singularity *and the Eschaton. I played Devil's advocate on the question as to whether a technological singularity could be curated. Rather disturbingly, I sold the argument pretty well. Maybe too well. When I sat down to plot out* Dogs of War *I remembered my faux arguments, expanded upon them and gave them to John the Revelator. They do make sense, from a certain point of view. And that's a bit scary.*

## OTTO WIRTH

Alias: Dr. Eduard Wirths

First Appearance: *The Dragon Factory*

Bio: A highly trained physician specializing in communicable diseases, Dr. Eduard Wirths was also a fiercely dedicated Nazi. As the chief SS doctor at Auschwitz-Birkenau, his main goal was to stop the typhus epidemic affecting SS personnel. Like Cyrus Jakoby, he reinvented himself, also using genetic engineering to keep himself alive.

**IMPORTANT CONNECTIONS:** Like his partner, Cyrus Jakoby, Otto was a former Nazi scientist working in the death camps.

### FRIENDS IN THE INDUSTRY: WESTON OCHSE

Weston Ochse is a former intelligence officer and special operations soldier who has engaged enemy combatants, terrorists, narco smugglers, and human traffickers. His personal war stories include performing humanitarian operations over Bangladesh, being deployed to Afghanistan, and a near miss being cannibalized in Papua New Guinea. His fiction and non-fiction has been praised by *USA Today*, *The Atlantic*, *The New York Post*, *The Financial Times of London*, and *Publishers Weekly*. The American Library Association labeled him one of the Major Horror Authors of the 21st Century. His work has also won the Bram Stoker Award, been nominated for the Pushcart Prize, and won multiple New Mexico-Arizona Book Awards. A writer of more than 26 books in multiple genres, his military supernatural series *SEAL Team 666* has been optioned to be a movie starring Dwayne Johnson. His military sci fi series, which starts with *Grunt Life*, has been praised for its PTSD-positive depiction of soldiers at peace and at war. His story "Black Water" appears in *Joe Ledger: Unstoppable*.

# TRANSCRIPT OF INTERVIEW WITH MASTER SERGEANT HARVEY 'BUNNY' RABBIT

## (PARTIAL)
## CONDUCTED AT THE PIER
## DMS SPECIAL PROJECTS OFFICE
## PACIFIC BEACH, SAN DIEGO, CALIFORNIA

SUMMERSTONE: Okay, sort of cheating because I'm also asking Top this question…but have you or would you ever question an order from Captain Ledger?

MASTER SERGEANT HARVEY 'BUNNY' RABBIT: Do I look like I've had my head torn off and sewn back on?

SUMMERSTONE: Well, no…

BUNNY: Then stop asking stupid questions. They warned me about you.

SUMMERSTONE: Ah. Let's try another tack. Volleyball. How did you go from volleyball to the Marines? How does someone make that decision?

BUNNY: I started playing volleyball to meet girls.

SUMMERSTONE: Did you?

BUNNY: Another stupid question. Yes. But then 9/11 happened. I was a kid, but I joined as soon as I could. Felt it was important, even though by the time I was a Marine we'd already found out that the whole Iraqi WMD thing was bullshit. But al-Qaeda and the Taliban were real. ISIL's real. The world's going to shit and someone needs to shovel up the manure. And…it turns out I was good at it.

SUMMERSTONE: You were world-class with volleyball.

BUNNY: Sure. Might have had a shot at the Olympics. But tell me, man, how many volleyball players you know ever helped save the world? Give me names. Give me one name. No. Do I regret it? Not most of the time.

SUMMERSTONE: But some of the time?

BUNNY: Sure. Every time I wake up in an ER or ICU or in a mobile surgical field station I tend to question a lot of my life choices. I'm not stupid. Think about it, man. You're lying there with bandages and stitches and drains and you start thinking about cute blonds on a SoCal beach. String bikinis, cold beers, hot sun, no pain, no worries. I'd have to be a complete moron not to play 'what if' now and again. But…then the bandages come off and the stitches come out and some new asshole is out there with a gas can trying to burn it all down. So I take up my sword and shield, so to speak, and go back to the war.

SUMMERSTONE: Will you ever lay down that sword and shield?

BUNNY: When's the last time you saw an old man with a walker going into battle? I'll stop fighting when I'm no longer at my best. Pretty sure the volleyball nets and the beach bunnies will still be there.

SUMMERSTONE: So you've got this relationship with Lydia Ruiz and—

Assault rifles are self-explanatory; they assault you by shooting large numbers of rounds in your general direction, they assault your senses with lots of noise, and your body with lots of pain if you get hit. While an assault rifle can be a deadly and precision weapon in well trained hands, most are used for the "Spray-and-Pray" method of putting as much potential death around the target as possible.

BUNNY: I was just joking about the sun bunnies.

SUMMERSTONE: Understood. But you are in a relationship with Lydia Ruiz. She's no longer with the DMS, but while she was that was technically a violation of policy.

BUNNY: Read the rules, dude. It was discouraged but there wasn't anything specific prohibiting it. They advised against it because they were afraid that emotional connections of soldiers serving together might cause distractions and like that.

SUMMERSTONE: Did it?

BUNNY: No. What it did was convince us to keep our shit wired tight. We talked about it a lot off the job, and we acted at all times like professionals. I can even make a case that our feelings for each other reminded us of what we were fighting for.

SUMMERSTONE: What would it take to make you walk away from your job and the DMS?

---

The most common assault rifle used by "terrorists" is the AK-47 and the AR-15, which can be purchased brand new at most gun stores in America. The Tech 9 and Uzi are more classic examples of "terrorist" weapons. I use the term "terrorist" lightly, because anyone using an assault rifle is going to be causing terror.

For American Police forces, the most common are the M-16, M4, and MP-5. The U.S. Military adds in the CQBR (Close Quarters Battle Receiver, which lowers the length of the barrel by 4" on average), M60, SAW (Squad Assault Weapon), and the SCAR (Special operations Combined Assault Rifle). All of which are made in America except for the SCAR (which is manufactured by a Belgian company).

The common parts to assault rifles are the long barrel for more gas pressure (more killing power), a shoulder stock of some kind (many will be detachable or folding), firing sights that allow one to fire for longer distance with greater accuracy, magazines that hold 30 rounds when in a combat set up, but can be extended if the situation warrants it, a selector switch that allows the shooter to change from single shot to semi-auto and fully auto (when someone is trying to kill instead of "cover fire," most shooters will use the semi-auto setting and fire in short, controlled bursts to stop an enemy and conserve their ammo). ALL assault weapons have a safety to avoid accidental firing.

### STANDARD NATO ROUNDS

Assault Rifles use three standard types of ammunition: .9mm (H&K MP5, TEK 9, UZI), 5.56 (otherwise known as the NATO round) and the 7.62 (the ammo for the AK-47 and the larger belt fed guns like the M-60). The only weird ones are the QBZ-95 which uses a 5.8x42mm round (which is manufactured in China and not found in the U.S.), the Skorpion VZ 61 with its 7.65mm (from Czechoslovakia) and the Gustloff Volkssturmgewehr semiautomatic rifle which uses a 7.92x33mm round (made during the end of Nazi Germany and no longer found except for in collections).

BUNNY: Like I said…if I wasn't playing major league ball, I'd quit. I don't want to play in the minors, and I don't want to get sloppy enough to get myself or someone else killed. For now, though, I'm doing fine and I'm not looking to hang it up.

SUMMERSTONE: Killing is generally not a moral choice, but sometimes it's necessary. How do you feel about the people you've had to kill over the years?

BUNNY: Only crazy people want to kill. But I'm a soldier and that means I'm a realist. If people stop acting like fucktards, if they stop trying to tear the world down then I'll be happy to turn into a monk. But, sad as it is to say, praying for peace so far hasn't worked worth a damn.

SUMMERSTONE: Is there guilt involved? Or is it an unavoidable part of the job?

BUNNY: There can be guilt. I've done some pretty extreme stuff over the years. And during the *Kill Switch* gig I did some stuff that was totally messed up. Does it matter to me that I was being controlled by someone else? No. That fucked me up and I still have to deal with it. Almost knocked me off the job. Guilt? Yeah, there's a lot of guilt. But not because I pulled a trigger on a bad guy. No guilt at all there. It's only when there's collateral damage to civilians that I feel it tearing chunks out of me.

# PART FIVE
## THE WORLD OF JOE LEDGER

### DMS ALLIED ORGANIZATIONS

*"I have friends in the industry."*
—Mr. Church, *Patient Zero*

## ARKLIGHT
First Appearance: *Assassin's Code*
The covert and militant arm of a secret organization of female assassins, Arklight operates according to its own agenda. They are the principle enemies of the Red Knights (aka the Upierczi) and the Red Order. Arklight is run by Lilith, a former breeding slave of the Knights; her daughter, Violin, is their senior field agent. It's rumored that Mr. Church and Lilith have some significant history, and they've shared a number of adventures in the years prior to the establishment of the DMS.

## LILITH
Rank: Head of Arklight
First Appearance: *Assassin's Code*
Bio: Much of Lilith's history is clouded in mystery, misinformation and disinformation. She is a former special operator, though it is not clear for which government she performed her duties. Israel is a leading possibility. She was captured while on a mission and sent to the breeding pits maintained by the Red Order to supply viable offspring for the Upierczi. While there Lilith had at least one child, who is currently known by the combat Call Sign of 'Violin'. Lilith helped train the other women captives of the

breeding pits and led a bloody revolt, doing a great deal of damage to both the Red Order and the Red Knights. At some point she became allied with Mr. Church and it is suspected that they have an older and deeper connection than that of mere colleagues. Following her escape from the pits, Lilith formed a covert black ops group called Arklight, and she directs their actions around the world. Although Arklight is not affiliated with any government or political movement, Lilith guides them in the direction of protecting women from violent men. In that she is uncompromising, ruthless and very efficient.

## VIOLIN

Real name: Classified
Rank: Arklight, Senior Team Leader
First Appearance: *Assassin's Code*

### MOTHERS OF THE FALLEN

Joe has had strong female allies in the past, including the late and lamented Grace Courtland, Lydia Ruiz, and others. However it is in the organization of Arklight that Joe has discovered a large group of women who have overcome terrible adversity to become a powerful force for good in the world. The Upierczi, the genetic freaks who operate under the name the Red Knights, initiated a breeding program with the help of their corrupt masters, the Red Order. The Upierczi were unable to breed easily and rarely produced male offspring possessing the correct genetic markers. Female children where either killed outright or raised to be breeders, like their mothers.

This program went on for many centuries. However, in the 20th century one woman rose up as a leader among the captives. She took the Biblical name of Lilith and formed a group called the Mothers of the Fallen. Lilith, who had been a skilled fighter before being captured and enslaved as a breeder, taught the other women how to fight. Then she led a bloody revolt against the Upierczi, killing many of them and destroying much of their network.

### ARKLIGHT AND THE MOTHERS OF THE FALLEN

Since the dawn of so-called civilization women have been the target for hatred, violence, bad legislation, brutality, harassment, comprehensive belittlement, and degradation. Patriarchal societies and ideologies have long fought to subjugate women and deny them any measure of true equality. Maybe that mattered back when position in the tribe was based on who was big enough to go out of the cave and strangle dinner, but we've moved on since then. Or at least we damn well should have.

Joe Ledger is a manly man, but he is not a chauvinistic jerk. He likes strong women, is not challenged or threatened by them, and they aren't there simply to be rescued.

**LILITH BY JOHN COLLIER**

Lilith and the Mothers of the Fallen escaped and went into hiding, fearing reprisals from the rich and powerful Red Order. They hired specialized tutors to train a select group of survivors how to be world-class special operators. These chosen women became Arklight, the militant arm of the Mothers of the Fallen. The senior field agent for Arklight is Lilith's only surviving child, who fights under the code name of Violin. Like her mother, Violin has abandoned any identity tied to her life as a slave in the Upierczi breeding pens.

Violin is a close ally of Joe Ledger's and often accompanies him on missions.

There is a deep and long-established connection between Lilith and Mr. Church, but the details of that relationship have never been fully disclosed. Although there is occasional animosity between the two leaders, they often work to support each other in critical field missions.

Bio: Violin was born into horror, as the child of one of the breeding slaves kept by the horrific Red Knights. When her mother, Lilith, escaped the Knights and formed the covert counterterrorism hit-squad Arklight, Violin quickly rose to prominence as their top field agent. Beautiful, deadly, and not entirely human. She is Joe Ledger's former lover and sometimes ally. Violin is one of the world's most dangerous and efficient assassins, equally lethal at long range with her sniper rifle or up close and personal with matched fighting knives.

**IMPORTANT CONNECTIONS:** Violin was briefly romantically entangled with Joe Ledger. Later, when Joe fell in love with Junie Flynn, Violin was hostile, but after Ludo Monk nearly killed Junie, Violin and Junie became close friends. Violin is currently traveling the world with Harry Bolt.

Violin's McMillan Tactical .50 is a truly devastating rifle. Firing a .50 caliber bullet, it is designed to stop vehicles and hunt down her enemies even when they are behind brick walls or bullet proof glass. It is a bolt action rifle with a 5-round box magazine.

## BARRIER

First Appearance: *Patient Zero*
Background: Barrier was the first of the modern wave of counterterrorism organizations designed to respond to enemies with the highest level of technology. Based in London, Barrier's teams are made up largely of the best-of-the-best agents from the SAS, MI5 and MI6. The senior consultant on the design and protocols for Barrier was Mr. Church. Predates the DMS by several years. The head of Barrier is Benson Childes.

## HARRY BOLT

Real name: Harcourt Bolton, Junior
Rank: C.I.A. field operative, retired
Call Sign: Jester
First Appearance: *Kill Switch*
Bio: The world's worst spy and the son of one of the country's greatest intelligence agents—who became one of this country's greatest traitors—Harcourt Bolton, Senior. Harry sees himself as the next Indiana Jones, but

looks more like a shorter, dumpier Matt Damon but without the talent or the charm. Harry and Violin bonded during the *Kill Switch* matter and have since been keeping company. Currently Harry and Violin are using his vast inheritance to finance small, covert actions around the world, often in support of unusual but earnest little causes. Harry is a notable ally of the DMS.

**IMPORTANT CONNECTIONS:** Although Harry is the son of the turncoat Harcourt Bolton, Sr., the son proved his patriotism and loyalty by helping Joe Ledger shut down Bolton Senior's Remote Viewing and Kill Switch programs. Currently Harry is traveling the world with Violin—a relationship no one else wants to believe is real.

## DR. CIRCE O'TREE

Full Name: Circe Diana Ekklesta Magdelina O'Tree-Sanchez
Rank: Director of Strategic Intelligence, DMS
Call Sign: Greek Fire (honorary)
First Appearance: *The King of Plagues*
Bio: Circe is a bestselling author and terrorist expert. Her books explore the ways in which religion and political ideologies are used as the basis for war and terrorism. Dr. O'Tree joined the DMS to help stop the terrorist organization known as the Seven Kings. She has since become a valuable member of the team and, most recently, the wife of Rudy Sanchez. Only a handful of people know that she is the only known surviving member of Mr. Church's family. She leaves the DMS after the events of *Kill Switch* and barely speaks to her father, blaming his "lifestyle choices" for putting her family in harm's way.

**IMPORTANT CONNECTIONS:** Circe tried very hard to balance her private and personal lives, but after the events of *Kill Switch* she decided to retire from the DMS and now focuses on writing books and raising her son.

## TERROR TOWN

Location: White Trails Resort, Washington State
Background: Hugo Vox created his first strategic think tank, comprised of select friends of his father, including thriller writers who worked to imagine the worst possible kinds of human carnage. Armed with a report compiled of all the information from the authors, Vox took a proposal to Washington D.C. The report outlined a new training camp for counterterrorism teams for the Allied Powers. The teams in this camp would train again and again until they devised or perfected an adequate response to a given scenario. Hugo was given the go-ahead and bought the old White Trails Resort in Washington State. Over time, Terror town became the world's most effective counterterrorism training resource.

**IMPORTANT CONNECTIONS:** Prior to coming to work for Mr. Church, Circe was an analyst under Hugo Vox and worked at Terror Town.

# AN INTERVIEW WITH MICHAEL HOMLER

## JOE LEDGER SERIES EDITOR

Michael Homler is a Senior Editor at St. Martin's Press and has worked with all kinds of book projects with a variety of authors including Clive Barker, Olivia Munn, Ron Darling, Bob Bowman, Lev Grossman, Tom Hart, Daniel Bryan (WWE Superstar), Ric Flair and his daughter Charlotte (WWE Superstars), Mark Divine, Mike Mignola, Christopher Golden, Tom Sniegoski, and Jonathan Maberry.

Q: How many of the Ledger series have you edited?

MH: I believe nine books.

Q: Have you ever started reading one of the Ledger books and wondered how the hell Jonathan was going to a: wrap up all the plot threads and b: how he could possibly pull Joe's ass—and the respective asses of Echo Team and assorted Friends of Ledger—out of the fire?

MH: Absolutely but that's all in the fun of it. It's interesting and challenging to see where he goes, to

**JONATHAN MABERRY AND MICHAEL HOMLER**
Author-editor relationships are generally grounded in business but sometimes there is a deep friendship and respect that lifts it to a higher level.

see if it all makes sense. You always want to keep reading.

Q: What would be the most challenging part(s) of editing the series?

MH: Making sure that all the pieces add [up] and maybe keeping track of everything that has gone on before, but I trust Jonathan knows where everyone's journey has taken them.

Q: Do you have a favorite in the series and if so, why?

MH: Probably *Patient Zero* because that's where it all started.

Q: Do you have a favorite character(s)?

MH: Easy. Ledger. He's the type of guy you imagine you want to be if you ever existed in this world.

Q: Have you ever been inordinately bummed out by any of the many deaths in the books?

MH: Afraid not. I think it's what helps add to the fun and keeps the series from getting stale.

Author Jonathan Maberry draws on over fifty years as a practitioner, teacher and later master instructor of the Japanese art of Jujutsu.

## ON WRITING FIGHT AND ACTION SCENES

The Joe Ledger novels are known for their visceral fight sequences, including armed and unarmed combat. Author Jonathan Maberry draws on his own experiences as a martial arts instructor and former bodyguard for much of this.

Maberry began studying Japanese jujutsu in 1966. He earned his first degree black belt in 1974 and currently holds an 8th degree black belt in jujutsu and a 5th dan in kenjutsu (Japanese swordplay). He has also studied Indian Varrmannie, Chinese Northern White Crane Kung-fu, Korean Hapkido and other arts. He taught martial arts history at Temple University, where he also taught women's self-defense, jujutsu, and other programs; as well as wrote textbooks for his courses and the judo program.

Jonathan was an Expert Witness for the Philadelphia District Attorney's office for murder cases involving martial arts; and did some private-sector consulting work on misuses of martial arts. His extensive writings for martial arts magazines, police and military training manuals, dodjo handbooks, and mass market nonfiction books, Maberry was inducted into the Action Karate International Martial Arts Hall of Fame in 2004, and was also inducted into the World Sokeship Head of Family Hall of Fame.

Q: Do you ever lose sleep at night from any of the tech/science that the villains use in the Ledger books?

MH: Never. Only real life does that to me.

Q: What do you find the most rewarding when you're working on books like the Ledger series?

MH: I think when I see a fan approach Jonathan or I read a fan letter and I can see how much pleasure they got out of the book. It makes you feel warm and fuzzy inside to know other people are enjoying what you enjoy.

Q: Anything else you'd like to add?

MH: Can someone please turn this into a TV show already!

Jonathan worked as a bodyguard in the entertainment industry, a bouncer in nightclubs, and chief instructor for the Shinowara-ryu Jujutsu Dojo of Philadelphia. Through the early 2000s he co-created and taught COPSafe, an arrest-and-control program for all levels of law enforcement. Jonathan was featured in the 1994 video, *Fighting Jujutsu.*

"The fighting skills I give to Joe Ledger," said Maberry, "are based on what real fighters can do. There are no jump-spinning double ninja death kicks. No absurd fighting skills. Everything in those scenes is possible, and much of it is based on direct experience from my own tussles or encounters involving police and military friends of mine."

# PART SIX
## THE MISSION FILES

*"Jesus, I need to get into a safer line of work. Lion taming, maybe."*
—Joe Ledger, *Assassin's Code*

## SYNOPSES OF NOVELS & SHORT STORIES IN READING ORDER

Title: **COUNTDOWN**

Format: This is a teaser released prior to the publication of *Patient Zero*. It includes some material from the first Ledger novel but also some scenes not included anywhere else.

Published: 2009

After-Action Report: Short story teaser: "I didn't plan to kill anyone. I wasn't totally against the idea, either. Sometimes things just fall that way, and either you roll with it or it rolls over you. Letting the bad guys win isn't how I roll." Meet Joe Ledger, Baltimore PD, attached to a Homeland task force…who's about to get a serious promotion.

The scariest handgun on any list has to be the "Plastic Handgun." While there is debate of such things being in existence, anyone with a 3D printer can construct one. This also means that the concept of one making it onto a plane or into a government facility is truly scary. The concept of ceramic bullets for one makes it doubly dangerous since they would not be caught by a metal detector. Top Sims uses one that he finds on a terrorist in *Patient Zero*.

## Title: **PATIENT ZERO**

Format: 1st Joe Ledger novel

Published: March 3, 2009

After-Action Report: Joe Ledger, former Army Ranger, is a detective with the Baltimore Police Department, about to transition to the FBI. As a teenager, Joe and his then girlfriend were attacked. Joe was beaten badly and his girlfriend raped. The experience and subsequent psychological counseling resulted in a semi-fractured personality, with three dominant personalities taking turns at the wheel, depending on Joe's moods and needs: the Modern Man (the civilized part); the Warrior (the killer); and the Cop (the thinker).

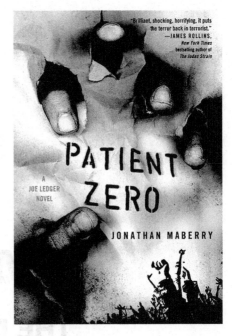

Part of an interjurisdictional task force for the past eighteen months, Joe takes part in a Special Forces raid on a warehouse where terrorist activity is suspected, a wiretap revealing the possible involvement of El Mujahid (the Fighter), a big fish in the terrorist pond. The raid turns into what Joe refers to as an 'OK Corral' shootout, with eleven terrorists dropped, six of them killed. One of them, Javad Mustapha (whom Joe assumes is a drug addict) tries to bite Joe, but Kevlar pads save the day and his gun arm. Joe puts two bullets in the man's back. Two trucks manage to escape the raid, one of them tracked and the other going off the grid.

Later, Joe is enjoying an afternoon at the beach (on administrative leave pending the result of a routine investigation into the shootings) when he's picked up by three FBI agents. He's taken to an interrogation room at an undisclosed location where he's introduced to Mr. Church, the head of the Department of Military Sciences (DMS), a secret anti-terrorist organization. Church is a mysterious man with an equally mysterious taste for vanilla wafers. He has friends in high places and numerous fields and organizations. Church might want to offer Joe a job in the DMS if he can pass an 'audition' (Joe's angry word for it), which consists of cuffing and restraining a prisoner in an adjoining room.

Joe accepts the challenge, goes into the room and discovers the prisoner is Javad Mustapha, the man he thought he killed at the warehouse. Javad attacks Joe, again trying to bite him. The difference this time is there's nothing in the the man's eyes and he smells like dead meat. Instead of freaking out, Joe fights back and snaps Javad's neck, killing him for the second—and final—time.

Church tells Joe this is the new face of terrorism, a prion disease that brings the dead back to life. The DMS believe Javad is the "patient zero" in an intended plague directed at the United States. The surviving cell members of the warehouse raid committed suicide before being questioned about possible additional teams carrying the plague, and one of two trucks that left the warehouse that night is still missing. If the threat is over, Joe will probably never hear from Church again, but if it's not, he'll likely be in touch.

Joe is taken back to the beach. He's not a happy camper.

Meanwhile, a few days earlier in Afghanistan, Sebastian Gault, multi-billionaire molecular biologist and bio-terrorist meets with El Mujahid. He's made billions by curing diseases in third world countries, although the fact that he's engineered at least half of the pathogens he's cured has never even been a rumor in the wind. Gault has funded the research facility and the research behind the creation of the

There is no cure for anyone unfortunate enough to be infected by *Seif al Din*

*Seif al Din* (Sword of God) pathogen, which has essentially created zombies. He is also sleeping with Amirah, El Mujahid's wife…and the creator of *Seif al Din*. Gault's plan is to scare America into putting billions of dollars into a cure. As he tells Amirah, he wants to buy the world, not bury it.

Amirah, on the other hand, has been creating new generations of the *Seif al Din* pathogen in the secret bunker Gault had built for her, going beyond what she and Gault agreed upon. The new incarnation spreads much faster, both the initial infection rate and the time for reanimation. Gault is concerned, but tries to hide it even as he realizes Amirah's agenda may not match his own.

Meanwhile, a small village is attacked by four infected subjects, observed by El Mujahid. Gault, now in Bagdad with his assistant Toys, gets a coded message letting him know the operation was successful. Toys reflects that Amirah—whom he hates—may have spent so much time in the bunker with the monsters that she may be halfway to becoming a monster herself. He asks Gault if he's sure Amirah shares his goals. Gault doesn't answer. He takes a call from the American, someone with major connections in Homeland Security, etc., who is concerned about the development of what he calls The Geek Squad (meaning the DMS). Gault asks whether he's gotten someone inside the organization. The American says he has.

Church discusses Joe with Grace Courtland. Grace is now with the DMS, formerly with Barrier (a U.K. organization), and helping Church evaluate potential recruits. Grace is not sold on Joe, despite video from the warehouse raid where he shows no hesitation doing what's necessary to stop the enemy. Grace points out his psyche evaluation reads like a horror show. Church points out hers aren't much better. They agree to observe Joe a little longer.

Joe spends some time trying to research the

DMS and Church but comes up empty. He calls his friend and psychiatrist Dr. Rudy Sanchez. Rudy's a genuinely good guy and Joe trusts him. The two meet up, Joe tells Rudy what happened. Rudy believes him, even though he wishes he didn't. Rudy advises Joe to stop trying to look into the matter any further. Joe spends that evening trying to see what he can find on the DMS and Church and comes up blank. He also checks his apartment for bugs and comes up equally blank, as did Rudy when he searched for surveillance equipment in his office.

The equipment is there, however, but so high tech that neither man finds it. Grace keeps tabs on both of them and finds herself unwillingly drawn to Joe. She, in turn, is observed by Church, who finds her response very interesting indeed.

The next day, Joe goes to meet Rudy for an appointment, only to find out Rudy didn't come back from lunch. When Joe goes back out to his car, he finds Rudy's business card in an opened package of Oreo cookies. The card has an address on the back: the dockside warehouse where Joe had killed Javad... the first time.

Joe goes to the address, murder in his heart. The warehouse now has a bunch of new security measures—a heavy duty gate, fence, and guards who all have a military trained look despite innocuous civilian uniforms. Joe decides against his initial going in quick and dirty and gives his info to the guard at the gate instead. Once inside, he meets Grace Courtland, who takes him to meet with Church. Joe demands to know where Rudy is. Church shows him a video of Rudy, cuffed and blindfolded, a gun held to his head.

Church tells Joe he put the gun to Rudy's head by telling him about the DMS and patient zero. The DMS is a secret organization and nothing, not even the Bill of Rights, is as important as what the DMS is

## ASSORTED GEAR

An Anorak jacket (worn by Joe in *The King of Plagues*) is basically a waterproof jacket with a hood originally designed for use in cold-weather environments. They are standard issue for military units in Germany, Alaska and similar military bases.

A Balaclava is a hood that covers the wearer's face and nose. It is usually black for military purposes, but can be found in several colors and designs in motorcycle and sporting goods stores.

Ballistic Shields are used by police forces to repel low caliber bullets and thrown projectiles. If you have ever seen riot police in a line getting ready to break up a crowd, you have seen a ballistic shield.

BDUs: Battle Dress Uniforms are standard issue military clothes (worn by both enemies and friends in the Ledger Universe). They come in multiple colors and designs depending on the conflict and the task being performed. For Joe and Echo, they are almost always black and unmarked. Today's BDU's can be fitted with Kevlar body and limb pads to help better protect soldiers.

Combat S.I. boots are the Standard Issue combat boots that all personnel receive in basic training. They were originally black, made of leather and a pain in the backside to shine. Today's are varied colors due to the conflict being fought and the task being performed.

"Terrifyingly terrific! *Patient Zero* has you holding to the edge of your seat and begging for more!"
—Sherrilyn Kenyon, #1 *New York Times* bestselling author of the *Dark-Hunter* series

trying to do. Bottom line, Church wants Joe to join the DMS. He has five other candidates, waiting in an adjacent room, and no time to sort out who the leader will be. It's up to Joe to figure that out. When Joe asks how he's supposed to do that, Church advises him to 'think outside the box.'

Inside the room, Joe meets the five other candidates. One of them, who Joe nicknames Scarface, tells Joe to make himself comfortable and that they've been there for three hours trying to sort out who should lead the team. Joe responds by basically kicking the shit out of all of them in four point six seconds. Church and Grace come in, Church introducing Joe as the new DMS team leader. Joe asks where his team is. Grace indicates the five men he just trashed. All give him stink-eye, and one threatens him. Joe punches the man in the throat, ending the argument.

Grace fills Joe in on the fact that three temperature controlled containers were smuggled in the country. One with Javad, the other two still missing and most likely in the trucks that slipped away from the raid. One has been tracked to a crab-processing plant in Maryland. The other has been 'lost' in traffic. Grace and Joe declare a truce after Grace apologizes for initially blaming him for the loss of the truck. She then tells him about MindReader, a 'cascading analysis package' (computer) that can find patterns through covert links in multiple databases, go into any computer system, extract data and leave no trace. Long story short, MindReader found indications of bioweapons research.

Joe asks what happened to the initial DMS teams. Grace and Church tell Joe about the slaughter at St. Michael's Hospital, which burned to the ground the same night as the raid. Javad was taken there after Joe shot him, where he reanimated and infected staff and patients. Two out of three teams died that night, and Church had the hospital burned to prevent any further spread of the infection. He tells Joe he would 'burn down heaven itself' to stop it. They know there are two remaining strike cells and that three small isolated villages in Afghanistan were destroyed by the *Seif al Din* pathogen, indicating someone has been taking it out for a test drive.

Church wants a quiet infiltration of the crab plant. He wants a thinking weapon to use against the people who'd send a monster like Javad against the American people. The only three people to face a 'walker' and live are in that room. He wants to know if Joe is in. Joe is pissed as hell, but yeah, he's in.

Joe meets his team again, which consists of Bradley "Top" Sims (Sergeant Rock); Harvey "Bunny" Rabbit; Oliver "Ollie" Brown, and Skip Tyler. He also is reunited with a somewhat bemused Rudy, who thinks Church might be trying to recruit him as well. Things are cut short when the third truck is found at a meat packing plant in Delaware. Joe's newly formed Echo Team is officially done with training.

Inside the meat packing plant, Echo Team finds a number of guards and people in lab coats, a cage full of children, and a bunch of walkers. The guards are herding the walkers towards the children. Echo Team attacks, showing no mercy after one of the lab techs shoots a child in the chest. During the ensuing battle, some of the children turn into walkers, and the team has to kill them…again. When all is said and done, seventeen children are rescued, and one wounded lab tech is taken prisoner.

Back at the warehouse, Church and Joe discuss the next steps. It's agreed Echo Team will rest for three hours, then hit the crab plant before whoever the enemy is expects them to do so. They'll be

Bell 206 JetRanger/LongRanger Helicopter (*Patient Zero*)
The Bell has been through multiple upgrades since its debut and subsequent failure in 1961. It now hosts more powerful engines that are designed to be an advantage in hot-day and high altitude operations. In 2007, the aircraft was modified to include a strengthened airframe, new tailboom, improved transmission, and an upgraded engine. It was said to be decommissioned in 2008 once the last of the orders were fulfilled but Bells have still been produced up to 2015.

backed up by Alpha Team—which includes Grace—and Gus Dietrich, one of Church's top agents.

In the meantime, Joe meets with Doctor Hu, the DMS 'mad scientist,' who is brilliant but pretty much at the far end of the spectrum, with no social skills to speak of. Hu is disturbingly enthusiastic about the idea of a super villain with enough money and intellect to create the zombie disease, even while admitting that the current infection rate means disaster if any of the infected get out into the general populace.

Joe also talks with Rudy, who has agreed to join the DMS because now that he knows the truth about the situation, he needs to be a part of the solution or 'go mad.' They're about to go to their respective quarters for an hour of rest when Dr. Hu yells "Room Twelve!" and gunfire is heard.

Room Twelve is where the prisoner from the meat packing plant was secured, along with four walkers. The prisoner is dead, and the guards and lab techs are dead or turned. Joe, Top, and Bunny take out the walkers and secure the room. There's no damage to the door, so it's obvious someone let the walkers out. Joe tells Church his security sucks. Church responds with a full lockdown on the facility. The irony that the DMS finally had a prisoner to interrogate and then this happens is not lost on either of them. Subsequent investigation shows sabotage and infiltration are the cause of the breach. Someone on the inside is a traitor, and someone close to the President supplied the person.

Joe decides they should hit the crab plant immediately before the spy has a chance to message out, even though they have to consider the possibility that word got out before the lockdown. Their intel shows that the plant has been closed for a few months, with a lone security guard on duty four times a week. There's also an assortment of nine vehicles, including the missing truck, parked there. Thermal scans are inconclusive because of ice machines and freezers…which shouldn't be in operation.

The teams are outfitted with special suits (Church has a friend in the industry), which provide extra protection along with the Kevlar and padding.

Creating a diversion with explosives on a boat hitting the dock outside the plant, Echo Team gains access to the plant. Once inside, they split up. Joe finds a bunch of human detritus: clothes, personal items. Stuff that's been taken away from ordinary people. A lot of them. It's outside of a door sealed with a heavy padlock. What Joe first takes as rusty water laps against the door. It's not rust, though. It's blood.

Joe meets up with Bunny and Top. Ollie's gone missing and Skip is positioned by the entrance. The three men find a lab tech and cuff him. The man is terrified, doesn't want to talk because 'they' have his wife and children. Joe knocks him out and has Bunny take him to the exit for questioning.

Helmet cams have been around since 1965, when they were little more than a small camera taped to a helmet. Since then, they have become smaller, more powerful and more cost effective. Today, anyone with a desire to capture what they do on video can spend as little as fifty dollars to get a camera. The helmet cams used by SWAT and the military are more rugged, have better optics and more options than the standard versions available to the public. First used in *Patient Zero*.

Bunny comes running back to let them know he left the prisoner at the door and called it in because Skip is MIA as well. The refrigeration units suddenly all switch off, and dozens of aggressive walkers are released, all former civilians.

Joe, Top, and Bunny shoot and retreat, making it to a room where they find three hostiles and Ollie, the latter tied to a chair. They release him; he was blindsided with a liquid Taser. One of the terrorists presses a detonator, setting off a series of explosions in the building. Alpha Team, headed by Grace, storm the building to help Echo Team. They find a mound of corpses and Skip, still alive and also apparently blindsided with a Taser. Most of Alpha Team is decimated when one of them triggers an explosive booby trap. The explosion also releases hundreds more walkers. Grace, Skip, and the three remaining Alpha Team members find Joe and the rest of Echo Team. A firefight against the walkers ensues, and only the timely arrival of 'the cavalry' in the form of Dietrich and his team prevent the wholesale slaughter of Joe et al.

Once again the plague is stopped from spreading.

The assessment after the fact is that the crab plant was a trap and they walked into it. They have one prisoner, Aldin, the lab tech Echo Team captured. Church interrogates him with Joe present. Church gets Aldin to talk via psychological manipulation and ultimately by promising to protect his family. They find out that that people were abducted, infected and studied, and eventually stored. Aldin didn't know of any plans to release them. Aldin eventually succumbs to the control disease but not before telling Joe to find a Lester Bellmaker…and to save everyone.

Hu thinks he might be able to come up with a possible inoculation that will prevent the infected from becoming aggressive and biting. They'll need the help of Big Pharma, it will cost billions, and will prevent America from funding big ticket war efforts overseas. It's a new kind of battlefield. Joe hopes that Church has some friends in this industry.

Joe is convinced that either Ollie or Skip is the traitor and interviews them separately, with disparate results. Ollie is pissed off and Skip remorseful. Neither admit guilt. In the meantime, a forensics team (including Jerry Spencer, injured in the original raid that turned up Javad) have gone over the crab plant and concluded that whoever is in charge wanted to stage a big event that would scare the hell out of the good guys. Why? Joe asks who would benefit. Rudy answers that question: the pharmaceutical companies and indeed, the entire medical profession. Which leads them to the conclusion that there's one pharmaceutical company with deep pockets funding terrorists while working toward their own agenda. Joe also points out that the terrorists will probably not pack up and go home, and that if El Mujahid is involved, he'll have his own needs to satisfy. Religious needs.

Meanwhile, El Mujahid has been 'smuggled' to America by ripping open a gash in his face and pretending to be a British soldier injured by insurgents. He's flown out by a

British med team. In Afghanistan, his lieutenant Abdul has arranged for raids with pre-recorded messages from El Mujahid so no one knows he's out of the country. Abdul meets with Amirah, who gives him information she's stolen from Gault and given to her husband, including schematics for a device to release the plague via a pre-set clock instead of an active trigger as per their original agreement. This will enable El Mujahid to rewire it. Amirah has also disabled a program Gault installed that would allow him to blow up the research bunker he built for her.

A subsequent conversation Gault has with Amirah causes him to realize that he has not fooled El Mujahid or hidden his affair. El Mujahid and Amirah have had their own agenda and played him for a fool. Their ultimate goal is jihad, not money. Gault realizes he may have signed the death warrant for the world. He tells his right-hand man, Toys, who is disgusted but not surprised. Toys also points out that while Amirah is crazy, he thinks she's come up with a cure to save those who are true believers.

Toys and Gault decide to go to the Bunker in Afghanistan, find the cure, and kill Amirah. In the meantime, they arrange to have El Mujahid killed and retrieve the trigger device. They receive a call from the American, who tells them that the assassination attempt fails, and a woman has picked up the trigger device. El Mujahid meets with Ahmed, Amirah's brother. The woman who picked up the device is Ahmed's girlfriend, Andrea, who secretly converted to Islam three years prior. Ahmed reveals that his sister has sent something else for him and El Mujahid—Generation 12 of *Seif al Din*, which is, in effect, an antidote.

Joe has a hunch that if the terrorists are going to try to release the *Seif al Din* plague, they'll do it at a big ticket event. The next day is Fourth of July, and the biggest event Joe can think of is the rededication of the Liberty Bell, taking place in the Liberty Bell Center in Philadelphia, with the First Lady and the vice president's wife in attendance. Joe was supposed to be part of that detail before joining the DMS, and he wants to not only follow through but make it a 'field trip' and take Echo Team, Grace, and Gus. Church agrees and promises to reinforce his warning to all commands to be on high alert.

That night Grace shows up at Joe's door with a six-pack of beer. She's emotionally fragile, drinks two beers in rapid

Night Vision Goggles (NVG) have been in use by the military since WWII. They fit over the user's head and, when activated, turn the darkness into greens and black (light and shadows). Older versions were very bulky and uncomfortable, but newer versions for both military and personal use are lighter and fit better on the wearer for long periods of time. NVG used by Echo Team and the DMS have more than just night vision capabilities and can cycle through the different spectrums of light to help see heat and even act as x-ray if needed. First used in *Patient Zero*.

Another version that Echo Team uses are "Full Spectrum Visibility" glasses. Originally made for ghost hunting, they are regular sized glasses with a built-in camera and attachable infrared light. They will be used by Echo Team in *Joe Ledger: Unstoppable*. Another version is the "Spy glasses" used by Echo Team in *The King of Plagues*. These glasses are designed to record what the wearer is seeing and relay it to a command post for use in facial recognition and threat assessment.

"Wow! *Patient Zero* made me pleasantly nervous for one long afternoon, when I consumed it. It's a fast-paced, creepy thriller that's as prickly as a hospital needle and sounds a little too convincing. This guy is good."
—**Joe R. Lansdale, author of the *Hap and Leonard* series, *Bubba Hotep*, and *Cold in July***

Fan art by Tony Jones of Amirah after dosing herself with *Seif al Din*.

succession, and tells Joe about losing her baby years earlier, ending up in a psychiatric med center for three months. That was the worst time of her life, and she hasn't cried in years. The events at St. Michael's Hospital and the crab plant, however, are even worse and she breaks down and cries. They spend the night together—platonically as Joe refuses to take advantage of Grace while she's so vulnerable.

The next morning Echo Team, Rudy, Grace, and Dietrich head to Philadelphia, dressed and badged as a special detachment of the Secret Service. They also plan to question agency directors in attendance who sent staff to the DMS in an effort to figure out where the traitor came from—and if there's one higher up the food chain.

Two directors interest them the most: Linden Brierly, the regional director of the Secret Service, and Robert Howell Lee, the director of special operations for an FBI/Homeland joint command. Brierly confirms there's much more to Ollie than meets the eye, but he'd stake his reputation that Ollie is a 'true American.' Joe calls Lee on the phone and asks to meet with him in the bell chamber. Lee is harried, but agrees to meet with Joe and Grace after Joe reveals they're with the DMS. A Special Agent O'Brien joins the security team. Something about him doesn't sit right with Joe, who keeps a close eye on him while they wait for Lee.

Toys and Gault arrive at the Bunker to find all of the men secretly on Gault's payroll dead. So much for the element of surprise. Gault also receives a call from the American, panicked because the DMS is onto him. Gault tells him to do what he has to in order to nullify the threat of the plague. They separate and go inside the Bunker, Gault to find Amirah, who knows that he's there. Amirah has injected herself with Generation 12, turning her into a sentient zombie who has died without any loss of personality, brain death or motor function. She plans on sending out thousands of doses to the Faithful and infecting the rest of the world with Generation 10, which causes immediate reanimation after death. She sends walkers after Gault, telling him she knows all of his secrets. Gault escapes the walkers and heads deep in the earth to close vents that will result in the destruction of the Bunker. He succeeds.

Joe asks to have O'Brien removed. Agents start moving in on O'Brien while the First Lady gives the dedication speech,

In the event of a nuclear catastrophe, 1000 rads is the max tolerance for humans, but insects like the H. hebetor wasp can withstand up to 158,080 rads. So, it's the wasp—not the ubiquitous cockroach—that can survive the apocalypse!

mentioning the original metalsmith Thomas Lester. His descendent Andrea Lester has made the new bell. Joe realizes Aldin was trying to warn them about Andrea all along—Lester, the Bellmaker. Just as he figures this out, he sees O'Brien pull out a detonator. Andrea tries to kill the First Lady, but is stopped by Joe.

The room erupts in panic and gunfire, and O'Brien moves towards the bell. Joe realizes the danger and orders the room sealed, knocking the vice president's wife off the podium just as O'Brien hits the detonator. The Freedom Bell explodes, releasing thousands of tiny glass darts infused with Generation 10 of the pathogen. The doors have been sealed, so no one can leave the building. Joe advises Brierly they need troops and a Class A biohazard team waiting outside. He then goes to track down O'Brien, finding out from Skip that O'Brien and Ollie were part of the contingent of agents who escorted the First Lady to a safe room in the building. Joe tells Skip to guard the door and goes after O'Brien and Ollie.

The disease starts breaking out in the bell chamber as Grace and Echo Team take out the hostiles in the crowd. Grace has the sick people isolated against the wall on one side of the room. The vice president's wife tries to order her to stand down, but Grace refuses. Just as they come to an agreement, people start to turn, and Echo Team is forced to open fire.

Meanwhile, Joe is attacked by agents turned into walkers. He kills them, finding more walkers as he searches for the First Lady. He finds her surrounded by dead bodies and walkers, being defended by one remaining agent. Top and Skip join Joe, and the three shoot the walkers. The agent dies of his wounds. Joe makes sure he won't come back. Ollie and O'Brien show up, guns drawn. Joe is about to shoot Ollie when someone beats him to it. Ollie goes down. Joe orders O'Brien to stand down, then notices he looks ill. The heavy sweat running down his face also washes away what looks like make-up, revealing a scar. O'Brien goes for his gun and Joe shoots him.

Skip reveals O'Brien is actually El Mujahid, surprised Joe hasn't figure it out. Skip also reveals he's the traitor, putting a gun to the First Lady's head. When asked why, Skip says he's in it for the money. He also wants payback for getting his ass kicked by Joe. He, however, doesn't want to fight. He wants to see Joe go up against someone he can't beat. Which happens to be El Mujahid, who has now reanimated into a Generation 12 zombie.

Joe and El Mujahid fight, Joe getting his ass kicked for much of the battle. He ultimately defeats El Mujahid, and Top puts Skip out of commission with a bunch of lead to his kidney. Joe apologizes to Ollie for doubting him just before Ollie dies. The rest of Echo Team, Grace and Rudy, however, are still alive.

The *Seif al Din* plague has been stopped.

### Title: **"ZERO TOLERANCE"**

Format: Short story
Published: 2009
After-Action Report: This sequel to *Patient Zero* brings Joe Ledger back into action, hunting for zombies

Sikorsky SH-60 Seahawk (*Patient Zero*) Is a multi-mission maritime helicopter that was designed after the Blackhawk but the main differences are that the Seahawk has: corrosion protection (to protect it from the corrosive, salty sea air), more powerful engines, single-stage landing gear, two additional weapon pylons, and a shifting tail landing gear that moves thirteen feet forward to reduce the space it takes up on board a ship. Their primary missions are surface warfare and anti-submarine warfare. Still in use world-wide today.

in the deadly mountains of Afghanistan. This story was the first Joe Ledger short ever written, and it stands as one of the author's favorites. It almost became the opening scene of *The Dragon Factory*, but the author felt that it should stand on its own.

## Title: "DEEP, DARK"

Format: Short story

Published: 2010

After-Action Report: In an underground bioweapons lab a team of scientists working to develop super soldiers instead create something that is far deadlier and infinitely stranger. Joe Ledger and Echo Team must hunt—and be hunted—deep down in the dark. Although this is a short story it's indicative of the deep amount of research that goes into every Ledger weird science tale. And the germ of the story began with the author wondering if the urban legend of cockroaches being able to survive a nuclear war is true (hint: it's not).

## Title: "MATERIAL WITNESS"

Format: Short story

Published: 2011

After-Action Report: A stand-alone short story that takes place in the early days of Joe Ledger's service in the Department of Military Sciences, a top secret division of Homeland Security. Joe Ledger and the DMS must protect a Pine Deep resident spook and author who is in over his head with the wrong people and may know more than he is letting on. This was the first Joe Ledger crossover story, and brings Joe into the town featured in Maberry's Pine Deep Trilogy: *Ghost Road Blues, Dead Man's Song*, and *Bad Moon Rising*. Joe returns to the town in "Three Guys Walk into a Bar," but as a supporting character in what is otherwise a 'Sam Hunter' story.

## Title: THE DRAGON FACTORY

Format: 2nd Joe Ledger novel

Published: March 2, 2010

After-Action Report: When the President of the United States goes in for bypass surgery, Vice-President Collins (longtime non-fan of Mr. Church and the DMS) sics the NSA (National Security Agency) on the DMS with the

### The Pine Deep Trilogy
By Jonathan Maberry

Original Mass Market Paperbacks from Pinnacle Books

10th Anniversary Special Trade Paperback Editions
From Pinnacle Books

Special Hardcover Editions from JournalStone Publishing

Audio Editions from Blackstone Audio
Read by Tom Weiner

Pine Deep is a troubled little town in Eastern Pennsylvania with a reputation as the 'most haunted town in America'. They build their tourism industry around all things spooky. Unfortunately Pine Deep is the most haunted town in America, and that doesn't prove to be a good thing for the residents or the tourists.

end goal of taking MindReader (the DMS computer system that can defeat any software protection and cover all traces of its presence) out of the equation once and for all. Collins is talked into this by J.P. Sunderland, a billionaire with his own agenda, to gain control of MindReader for profit.

Both Collins and Sunderland want four biotech bills moving through Congress to pass and while at the moment there was nothing to connect those bills with Collins' personal interest or Sunderland's private holdings, MindReader, if aimed in that direction, could change that. This could ruin Collins politically as well as making him a pariah in the business world. This is the lever Sunderland uses to convince Collins into taking the action against the DMS.

NSA agents make the mistake of approaching Joe Ledger when he's visiting his ex-girlfriend's grave. They refuse to tell him why he's being detained. Joe contacts Church, who tells him not to let himself be taken or he'll 'disappear into the system.' Church also advises Joe that pulling the trigger could lead to the dismantling of the DMS. Joe says he may have to dent a few of 'em. Church can live with that. Joe proceeds to do some 'denting' and makes his escape. More NSA agents join the chase, so Joe ditches his vehicle and vanishes into downtown Baltimore. He calls Grace, finding out there's a bunch of agents outside the Warehouse, and she has to sort them out. Then he calls Rudy, who is also hiding out per Church's instructions.

Meanwhile, other DMS agents go to ground, including Top and Bunny. They were on a routine pickup to arrest a Burt Gilpin, who'd used a computer system similar to MindReader to hack into University mainframes, the schools involved with virology and genetics. They're greeted by a hail of bullets. Big Bob Faraday, another member of Echo Team, is critically wounded, and Gilpin, a computer nerd who used to work for the Jakoby twins, is already dead, having been tortured by the same Russian mercenaries that shot Faraday. Top and Bunny talk to Church, who advises them to get off the radar and stay there until they make contact with Grace, Joe, or himself. They're given a list of locations and told to go to each one in order, wait ten minutes, and then proceed to the next one if Ledger doesn't arrive.

Sunderland's motives are also connected to infamous jetsetters, Paris and Hecate Jakoby, who are identical twins. The twins are corrupt geniuses involved in the field of bio-

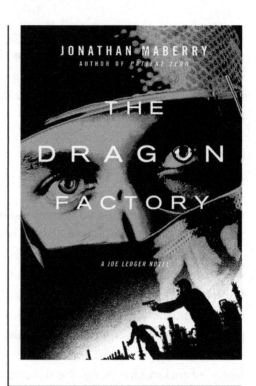

Popular misconception has it that cockroaches will be able to survive the radiation and extreme conditions after a nuclear exchange. That's actually not true, and the cockroach would die shortly after humans. However the wood-borer has an astounding capacity for resisting radiation.

tech with access to Pangaea—a computer system that's an earlier version of MindReader—that has helped them gain access to research in the field of transgenics and biogenetics, putting them far ahead of the game. The twins have made millions bioengineering 'mythical' creatures and selling them to the highest bidder to be hunted (Sunderland's brother is involved in these hunts); Berserkers (abnormally strong men with anger management issues) for sale as soldiers and mercenaries; and more. However, Pangaea can only get them so far in terms of the research they can steal, so they want MindReader.

Paris and Hecate are on the way to visit their father, billionaire Cyrus Jakoby (who is admittedly and happily insane) at his hidden base in Arizona, known as the Deck. They've just finished one in a long line of many shared sexual encounters on their private jet, some of which have ended with the deaths of their playthings, the ashes scattered over the ocean. They're also interested in finding out what lies in Deep Iron, a records storage facility near Denver. Rumor has it that there's a legendary trove of data based on covert mass human testing; the Holy Grail of black market genetics. They also suspect their father had ties to groups that pioneered this genetic research and that he doesn't want them to find it first.

Ostensibly the twins and their father work towards the same goals, but in reality they all have their own agenda. The twins have their own secret laboratory—the Dragon Factory—the location hidden from their father and his longtime aide and companion, Otto. The twins' main goal is money. Cyrus and Otto, on the other hand, while they practice reclamation genetics (mammoths, dire wolves, and the like populate their zoo at the Deck), have a larger goal in mind; wipe out the 'Mud People' (non-whites) with their Extinction Wave.

Cyrus and Otto have taken diseases that are genetic, such as sickle-cell and Tay-Sachs, and made them communicable. They've done test runs in small, isolated locations and are now ready to bring their plan to full fruition. They don't, however, trust the twins, whose psychological evaluations show that they'd oppose the Wave. This is a great disappointment to Cyrus.

Cyrus and Otto wait for the twins to arrive at the Deck, eating breast of dodo and discussing the twins and the SAMS. According to Otto, several are coming along nicely, including Ninety-five, who is showing an aptitude and taste for surgery. Cyrus asks about Eighty-two—currently sequestered at The Hive, another of Cyrus's labs—telling Otto he feels more kinship with this one than the others. Otto points out Eighty-Two's psych evaluations are not favorable. Cyrus has had six doctors executed over the last three years for delivering this news and still wants more tests run. Otto also tells Cyrus that 'the Russians' have gotten information from the man Gilpin—a computer nerd who used to work for the twins.

Joe is sent to Denver by Church, who tells him that Jigsaw (the Denver DMS team) has gone 'dark' during a mission. Church adds that what's happening in Denver looks to be a DMS project and is also likely connected to the deaths of some of Church's colleagues in Europe. These colleagues, unbeknownst to Church, are being taken out by Conrad Veder, a hitman. Veder also has a contract out on Church.

Joe then talks to Grace Courtland, who confirms that the colleagues in question were mostly from the U.K. and Germany and that they worked with Church on projects in the early eighties. After they

"*The Dragon Factory* is like a video game on steroids mixed with *The Island of Dr. Moreau*. Maberry has done an excellent job of ratcheting up the action. Expect this straight-ahead thriller to hook action-crazed readers and inspire them both to seek out the first Ledger book and eagerly anticipate the next installment."
—**Booklist**

hang up, Joe tells himself that warriors should never fall in love.

Meanwhile, Church talks to Linden Brierly with the Secret Service, and convinces him to try and wake the President up from his post surgery earlier than planned. Collins and Sunderland find this out and figure they have at most about seven hours left to try to dismantle the DMS and snag MindReader. If they fail, they plan on pretending they were duped and going to the Attorney General.

On the way to Denver, Joe watches a video sent to an old email account of Church's via an anonymous Yahoo account. This video is what caused Jigsaw team to hit Deep Iron; the faces of one of the men has been identified as Gunner Haekel, who was associated with a heavily subversive organization back during the Cold War. Haeckel's only living relative was an uncle who died in 1978, and who had all his belongings stored in Deep Iron.

Joe watches the video, which shows a group of men hunting and killing what appears to be a genuine living unicorn. One of them also mentions the Extinction Wave. Joe tells Church he thinks the unicorn is bullshit, either CGI or a 'horse with a strap-on.' That unfortunate image aside, bottom line is the video is real, and the unicorn most probably the result of transgenics, which is the transfer of genes from one species to another. Church reveals that they've run facial and voice recognition on the five men in the video and have identified several. One of them is Harold Sunderland, brother to JP Sunderland, who is not only a huge proponent of biotech legislature, but a good friend of Vice President Collins. The attack on the DMS is suddenly making sense.

The man leading the hunt is Gunnar Haeckel. The only problem, according to Church, is that Haeckel is dead. Joe asks how good Church's intel is on this. Church says he

Sikorsky UH-60 Black Hawk (first appearance in *The Dragon Factory*) is a medium, four-bladed, twin engine, utility helicopter that was first introduced in 1976 then brought into military service in 1979 to replace the Bell UH-1 Iroquois. It was named after the Native American Warrior Black Hawk. Since its invention, the Black Hawk has undergone numerous upgrades and variations including: improvements to lift from one-thousand pounds to nine-thousand pounds in 1987. Improved rotor blades, electronic instrumentations, flight controls, and navigation in 2006. A "low-observable" model was released in 2011 that allowed the helicopter to evade Pakistani radar. A zero-vibration system, adaptive flight controls, advanced fire management, and a damage tolerant airframe were added in 2012. And in 2014, and Enhanced Speed Bag System (ESBS) was introduced as a way to protect supplies during a supply drop intact. Currently, Black Hawk helicopters are widely used in several areas of the world.

Fiber optic cameras are small, flexible cameras used by spies, plumbers, doctors, etc., to see things in hard to reach places. Ever needed to find out what clogged your pipes at home? Your plumber probably used a camera to look down the drain. The first fiber optic camera was invented in 1964 for the medical community. Used by Echo Team in *Patient Zero* and *The Dragon Factory*.

Joe's favorite knife is the Wilson Rapid Response Folding Knife. Weighing only four ounces and having just over a three and one-quarter inch blade. It is light and fast in the hands of a master and able to retain a sharp edge. Joe also uses a Ranger combat knife (that can have a blade from four to nine-and-one-half inches and weighs anywhere from four ounces up to a pound), a machete, and a utility knife with a three-inch blade.

has personal knowledge. Haeckel was part of a group of assassins called the Brotherhood of the Scythe, each with a code name: East, West, North and South. The Brotherhood were the muscle for a group called the Cabal, made up of ex-patriate Germans, mostly Nazis who'd escaped the postwar trials. The Cabal wanted ethnic cleansing, serving the Nazi extermination ideal. These men and women do not represent Germany. They didn't want to remake the country. They wanted to remake the world. The video is possible proof that the Cabal still exists and now has access to cutting-edge genetics.

Bottom line: they only have two links to Haeckel, which are the video and the stuff stored in Deep Iron. Haeckel, in turn, is the only possible connection they have to the Cabal. So Joe's priorities at Deep Iron are 1. to recover the files Haeckel's uncle stored there, and 2. find Jigsaw Team. Finding Jigsaw is definitely the secondary priority, a fact neither Joe nor Church find easy to stomach.

The team for this mission consists of Joe, Top, Bunny, and Gunnery Sergeant Brick Anderson, head of the DMS field office in Denver. Because of the situation with the Vice President and NSA, they don't have any additional backup. Brick's pretended to be a potential customer who wants to look around Deep Iron. According to their intel, the facility is built into a series of limestone caverns, the lowest levels being nearly a mile underground. Haeckel's items are stored on the lowest level, and consist of mixed paper records and a box of microfiche.

When the four arrive at Deep Iron, the guard shack is empty, the electrified fences are turned off, and the man Brick is supposed to meet doesn't answer his phone. Brick stays up top with a well-armed vehicle while Joe, Top, and Bunny go inside. They find the guards, dead and brutally disfigured. They discover more corpses, also torn apart, as if someone had messed with the bodies after their deaths. Whoever did it would have to be incredibly strong. They also find Russian shell casings, same type used by the ones who killed Gilpin.

Meanwhile, Church talks to the First Lady in an attempt to get her to allow her husband to take

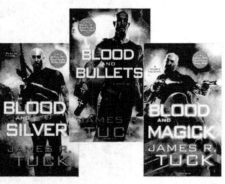

**FRIENDS IN THE INDUSTRY: JAMES R. TUCK, JR.**

James R. Tuck is the author of the Deacon Chalk series, co-author (with Debbie Viguie) of the *Robin Hood: Demon's Bane* series, and the author (as Levi Black) of the *RED RIGHT HAND* trilogy. He tattoos people for his day job and used to throw folks out of bars for money. His story "White Flame on a Sunday" appears in *Joe Ledger: Unstoppable*.

back office earlier than planned. She agrees and the Vice President's plans are derailed.

In Cyrus's other laboratory, the Hive on a small island in Costa Rica, SAM Eighty-Two is hiding. Most of his days are spent being tested by doctors who don't talk to him, forced by Otto to watch films showing war, torture, and sex. He has sympathy for the New People; a passive slave race kept in the Hive and abused routinely by the guards. Eighty-two was also made to go on occasional hunts, such as the one with the unicorn… and during the celebration after the hunt, managed to send a video of the occasion to the Americans in the hopes they will come and stop what's going on in the Hive.

Down on J Level, Echo Team find more dead bodies and live Russians, walking into an ambush. They kill a few Russians and move on, finding blood but no bodies. They hear a roar, like a really pissed off animal, followed by someone calling for help in Russian. They find the entire Spetsnaz team, dead. Torn to pieces. Then Joe, Top, and Bunny are attacked by a couple of brutes with abnormal strength. The ambushers vanish after Echo team puts some hurt on them. Joe says it's clear that two teams are down there searching for the same thing. Three, if they count Jigsaw Team.

They find Haeckel's files: detailed info regarding tests on humans in (extreme conditions). One of the letters in the files is from Josef Mengele, from Birkenau, the town where the Nazis built Auschwitz.

Meanwhile, Paris is going through a crisis of conscience, wondering if what he and Hecate are going through is just bullshit rationalization. If instead of being young gods, they're just a couple of psychotic mass murderers with no right to live. Hecate tells him they are gods because she says so, and yes, they're evil, because evil is delicious, strong,

The British Harriers introduced in *The Dragon Factory* are amazing aircraft because they were one of the first to achieve Short Take-Off and Vertical Landings (STOVL). Harriers are designed to land on Carriers at sea by hovering down to the deck. This also allows them to land in areas only helicopters can get to. Developed in the mid-1960's and in service since 1969, the last Harrier was manufactured in 2003 for use by the U.S. Marine Corps. The Harrier is very distinctive due to its large air intakes just behind the cockpit, under the fixed and slanting wings. It only has a max speed of 662 MPH, but with the ability to land in hard to reach places for refueling and reloading, it is a sneaky and dangerous aircraft.

In the Ledger Universe, as in our own, it is almost impossible to get anywhere without wheels of some kind. For the DMS, they can call upon almost any military vehicle while having access to a wide range of civilian vehicles as well. For civilian vehicles, besides the numerous SUV's that Joe and Echo Team have gone through, there are two planes and two speedboats that they have used, Joe's personal Gulfstream G650 ("Shirley"), the Pilatus PC-6 Porter single engine plane, the Cigarette Boat and the XSR high velocity speedboat.

The Gulfstream G650 (manufactured by General Dynamics here in the U.S.) has been in production since 2005 but was not offered to the public until 2008. It is a twin-engine jet airplane that can hold up to eighteen passengers and has a top speed of almost Mach 1 (.0925). It has a price tag of sixty-six million dollars. The G650 is sleek in design with swept back wings (the tips pointed up), jet engines mounted on each side of the rear of the plane and a swept back tail fin. Sleek inside as well, it can be fitted with a full bar, kitchen and satellite communications. It is very sad that the previous owner had a dispute with Joe about who should own it.

The unicorn of legend and pop culture is a thing of innocence and beauty. So it's only fitting that the corrupt Jakoby Twins would create one just so some entitled rich guys could hunt and kill it.

Known as "the Angel of Death" during his 21 months at the death camp Auschwitz, Dr. Josef Mengele enjoys a new lease of life as Cyrus Jakoby.

The "New Men" created by Cyrus Jakoby

and beautiful. Paris notices that her eyes are not quite normal and asks what she is. She says she's a monster, just like he is.

Cyrus and Otto, in the meantime, succeed in tracking the twins' plane to the Dragon Factory. Cyrus orders a team sent in with the directive to kill one of the twins. If done right, he thinks it will drive the surviving twin closer to him. The two-person team fails, one of them killed and the other captured. Hecate extracts information from the surviving team member, uncovering Cyrus's plan to have one of them killed. She and Paris decide to invite their father to the Dragon Factory under the pretext of being scared and wanting his advice. They will then lock Cyrus in a dungeon, kill Otto, and have the Deck 'sterilized.'

Later, Church tells Joe, Grace, and Dr. Hu about the List, a group of operatives from various countries dedicated to taking down the Cabal. This included a raid on the Pangaea lab (Pangaea was developed by an Italian scientist, who was subsequently murdered and the system stolen). Pangaea was recovered by a member of the List (Church) and the system used to search down and destroy the information the Cabal had amassed. Church then reveals that in the last few weeks, five of the surviving seven members of the List have been murdered. The last two? Church and Aunt Sallie.

Church goes on to talk about the info pulled from Deep Iron. A lot concerns experiments by Josef Mengele, his obsession with twins, and the fact that everything he did was fueled by his insanity and driven by his need to participate in the eugenics program, and the master race concept. Life unworthy of life.

The talk is interrupted by a call letting them know that Jigsaw Team was found, the entire team taken out by RPGs before ever reaching Deep Iron. Then Church receives another video from SAM Eighty-Two, a young teenage boy, telling him that they need to

"*The Dragon Factory* is a fast-paced novel with even more intrigue, a more epic scope, and a deeper sense of emotion than *Patient Zero*. It is a tale that throws around fantastic ideas from the world of science and genetics, a book that plumbs the depths of that same science to show you just how vile a person can be, and the novel turns Joe Ledger into a hero yet again."

—Factoidz

destroy the Dragon Factory, the Deck, and then find the Hive. The kid gives a frequency that they can broadcast to him and tries to show the location on a map. The video is cut off abruptly. Church prepares an attack on multiple targets.

Joe and Echo Team are sent to the Hive, where Joe contacts SAM Eighty-Two (who he calls the Kid), who tells him he contacted Mr. Deacon (Church) because he discovered an old file that made it clear Otto and his father (Cyrus) hate Church. So SAM figured Joe would be a good person to contact. The Kid plans on sneaking into the communications room so he can see Echo Team on camera and help them infiltrate the Hive. He tells them not to hurt any of the New Men, and to watch out for the dogs.

Joe, Top, and Bunny run into a bunch of guards and technicians. Joe takes things up close and personal rather than let the guards use the non-combatants as shields. He and his team take out the guards.

Cyrus and Otto receive word that the Hive is under attack. Cyrus is sure the twins have turned against him; Otto convinces a heart-broken Cyrus that he must sacrifice Eighty-Two for the sake of the Extinction Wave. He plans on destroying the Dragon Factory, taking the twins alive and at the very least, harvesting sperm and eggs from them to create more of them.

Back at the Hive, the lights go out, and Echo Team is attacked by the 'dogs,' a hybrid of feline and canine. Joe manages to kill two of them. They then receive more info on the unicorn hunt video. Church has had a lip-reading expert look it. The conversation references the Extinction Wave and makes it clear that someone plans on launching a major plague in Africa that targets non-whites. MindReader also has shown a hit on Cyrus Jakoby and the twins.

Joe and Echo Team find the Kid with the New Men, rescuing him from Carteret, one of the guards who has brutalized the Kid and the New Men. The New Men are Neanderthals, programmed not to fight back and to accept any abuse as normal. The Kid tells Joe that the New Men have been bred for sale as the perfect slaves. Joe takes him back to Church, who finds out that Cyrus and Otto have a trigger device that will set the Extinction Wave into motion. It's most likely a flash drive. They plan on going in quietly, with an EMP that will hopefully prevent the trigger from being pulled.

Joe and Grace get a brief respite and some time alone, during which they each tell the other that they love them.

Hecate and Paris, in the meantime, invite their father to the Dragon Factory, in hope of convincing him they need his help. Paris is sure Cyrus doesn't know their plans; otherwise he wouldn't have agreed to come. Hecate is sure that Cyrus knows everything. Cyrus does know what his children plan and has schemes of his own. He's called Veder off the assignment to kill Church and Aunt Sallie to accompany a team to the Dragon Factory and protect Cyrus from his children.

The DMS has found the Deck. Joe and Echo Team go to raid the Deck. Joe sees a young teenager that looks like the Kid's twin just before the Jakoby twins arrive to pick up Cyrus and Otto and take them to the Dragon Factory. Meanwhile Joe finds laboratories with huge vats and realizes these were used to mass produce the pathogens for the Extinction Wave. In the meantime, Grace and Alpha team

"Genetic manipulation, clones, transgenics, reconstructed DNA from extinct animals, cool gadgets and high-tech computer systems—all ingredients that you may expect to see in a sci-fi novel, but here blended seamlessly into an explosive thriller that pushes the boundaries of science."

**—The Science of Fiction**

have found the Dragon Factory. They go in first, with Joe and Echo Team about ninety minutes behind.

Cyrus, Otto, and Veder are at the Dragon Factory, getting a tour from the twins. Hecate and Paris show their father the Chamber of Myth, where they've bio-engineered dragons, centaurs, and even a mini-Loch Ness monster. At first Cyrus is seemingly entranced by his children's creations but points out that their clients will be dead in less than two days and 'the dead don't need fucking toys.' He snaps the neck of Nessie, then tells the Twins his plans to wipe out the 'mud people.' He also reveals his real identity—Josef Mengele. Antiaging gene therapy has kept him and Otto alive all these years. He also reveals that the SAMs are his clones. Paris is horrified and Hecate entranced.

Meanwhile, Grace and Alpha Team have reached the Dragon Factory. Grace kills two of the Berserker guards and infiltrates the Chamber of Myth just as the place goes into lockdown. Hecate smashes her brother in the face, knocking him out, and tells her father they should burn the world down right now instead of waiting. Grace interrupts the family moment and demands the trigger device. The lights go out. Both Hecate and Cyrus assume Grace is on the other's side; when they find out she's

### FRIENDS IN THE INDUSTRY: AARON ROSENBERG

Aaron Rosenberg is the author of the best-selling *DuckBob SF* comedy series, the *Dread Remora* space-opera series, and, with David Niall Wilson, the *O.C.L.T.* occult thriller series. His tie-in work contains novels for *Star Trek*, *Warhammer*, *World of WarCraft*, *Stargate: Atlantis*, and *Eureka*. He has written children's books (including the award-winning *Bandslam: The Junior Novel* and the #1 best-selling *42: The Jackie Robinson Story*), educational books, and roleplaying games (including the Origins Award-winning *Gamemastering Secrets*). He is a founding member of Crazy 8 Press. You can follow him online at gryphonrose.com, on Facebook at facebook.com/gryphonrose, and on Twitter @gryphonrose. Read his short story "No Guns at the Bar" in *Joe Ledger: Unstoppable*.

not, Hecate sends her pet Berserker TonTon after her, and Cyrus sends Veder. The EMP is deployed to stop Cyrus from triggering the Extinction Wave. Cyrus, Hecate, and Otto head to an office where Hecate has a ruggedized laptop they can use to trigger the device. Grace kills TonTon in the dark, then follows Cyrus, Hecate, and Otto. She and Hecate fight, and Grace is knocked out during an explosion.

Meanwhile, Joe, Top, and Bunny head in to help, encountering scorpion dogs (a combination of mastiffs and scorpions). They kill all the dogs, but Top is wounded, so Joe and Bunny continue on their own, running into and killing a squad of Russian mercs, and then into Alpha Team. They try to blow an entrance into the Chamber of Myth, but the hole is only large enough for Joe to hear Hecate and Cyrus and the possibility that Hecate has killed Grace. Joe heads after them because he realizes they may be headed for a ruggedized computer even though it means leaving Grace on her own, possibly dead.

Grace comes to and follows the Jakobys and Otto to Hecate's office. She shoots Otto, killing him, and is about to kill Cyrus when Veder appears and shoots her.

Joe defeats a group of Berserkers and reaches Hecate's office in time to kill Hecate. Grace, however, is dying. She tells him there's a code to stop the Extinction Wave, that Cyrus knows it. Grace dies. Joe gets the code from Cyrus. He gives it willingly but not easily.

Joe, badly injured, quits the DMS. He goes to pack up his room at the Warehouse and finds a file there with his passport, plane tickets, a credit card, and a picture of Conrad Veder in the Italian Riviera.

Title: **"DOG DAYS"**

Format: Short story

Published: 2011

After-Action Report: Joe Ledger returns in this tale that follows the tragic conclusion of *The Dragon Factory*. In the wake of a devastating personal loss, Joe Ledger and his new canine partner, Ghost, go hunting for the world's deadliest assassin. This is the first story featuring 'Ghost' and it includes a cameo by Zan Rozin, who won a contest to name Joe's dog and pick the breed. Henceforth Zan is the official dog trainer for the DMS.

Westland Sea King (first introduced in *The Dragon Factory*)—Unveiled in 1969, the Sea King is the British version of the American Sikorsky S-61, and it was built by Westland Helicopters in Great Britain. After utilizing the design, Westland Helicopters redesigned the Sea King to be primarily used for anti-submarine warfare. It was given a Rolls-Royce Gnome engine, British-made anti-submarine warfare systems, and a fully computerized flight control system. In addition to being a submarine killer, the Sea King provides a wide range of services to both the Royal Navy and the Royal Air Force in search and rescue operations as well as ship-based early warning. When it is used for the Royal Navy Search and rescue, the Sea King is painted red and grey. When used for Royal Air Force Search and Rescue, it is painted yellow. One variant of the Sea King, called Westland Commando, was designed and modified to meet Egyptian Air Force requirement. Since anti-sub technology is not necessary for desert tundra, the Commando was designed for troop relocation and extended flight so that it could reach six-hundred nautical miles between refueling. It is still in use today but the Sea King is slowly being phased out by more modern helicopters. A Sea King is also used as Marine One, the Presidential Helicopter.

"Much of Maberry's writing and his construction of the narrative is reminiscent of a David Morrell thriller, and that is a damn fine thing. Maberry is rapidly ascending to a deserved place amongst the greats in his field—with *The Dragon Factory* you will see why."
—Horrorscope

"Powered by a cast of over-the-top characters, breakneck pacing, nonstop action, and a subtle sense of humor, (*The King of Plagues*) is an utterly readable blend of adventure fiction, suspense thriller, and horror."
—*Publishers Weekly*

Title: **"CHANGELING"**

Format: Short story

Published: 2013

After-Action Report: Joe Ledger teams with a mysterious British agent named Felicity Hope to investigate a dangerous bioweapons factory. This story touches on the Celtic legend of the 'selkie,' a kind of were-seal who sheds its sealskin when it comes on land in human form.

Title: **THE KING OF PLAGUES**

Format: 3rd novel in the Joe Ledger series

Published: March 29, 2011

After-Action Report: Joe Ledger is on extended leave from the DMS, traveling with his German Shepherd, Ghost, to Europe in order to find and kill Conrad Veder, the man who killed Grace Courtland at the Dragon Factory.

Church pulls Joe back on duty when someone blows up the Royal London Hospital, killing over four thousand people. Thick black smoke covers the sky 'turning a horrible morning into the dead of night,' and the entire structure is destroyed. Church asks Joe to help investigate the explosion, putting him contact with Barrier, the United Kingdom version of the DMS (it predates the DMS by a few years and

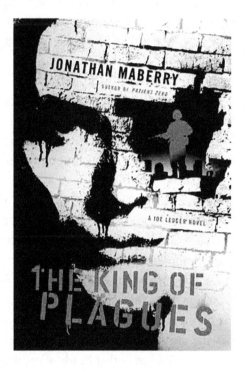

### FRIENDS IN THE INDUSTRY: CHRISTOPHER GOLDEN

Chistopher Golden is the New York Times #1 bestselling, Bram Stoker Award-winning author of such novels as *Snowblind, Ararat, Of Saints and Shadows,* and *Tin Men*. With Mike Mignola, he is the co-creator of two cult favorite comic book series, *Baltimore* and *Joe Golem: Occult Detective*. As an editor, his anthologies include *Seize the Night, Dark Cities,* and *The New Dead,* among others, and has also written and co-written comic books, video games, screenplays, radio plays, and a network television pilot. A frequent lecturer and speaker at libraries, schools, and conferences, Golden is one-half of River City Writers (with James A. Moore), providing writing workshops, seminars, and editorial services, and one-third of the pop culture podcast Three Guys with Beards (with Moore and Jonathan Maberry). Please visit him at www.christophergolden. com. His story "Target Acquired," co-written with Tim Lebbon, appears in *Joe Ledger: Unstoppable*.

Church served as a consultant to the U.K. during its creation). Church and Rudy Sanchez will fly out to meet him.

One of the terrorist groups suspected in the destruction of the hospital is the Seven Kings, a relatively new group of baddies that the DMS first heard about via an anonymous call to Church a few months earlier. According to this 'Deep Throat,' the Seven Kings exists to cause chaos. The caller gives Church the name of a Hamas terrorist cell operating in Washington D.C., along with information that they plan on striking the next day during afternoon rush hour. The DMS act on the tip, with Joe leading Echo Team (then consisting of Bunny, Tops, Khalid, DeeDee, Big Bob Faraday, Joey, and John Smith, the group's sniper). They lose Joey when one of the terrorists with a vest of explosives blows up the building, but ultimately win this particular fight and save a lot of lives.

That was Joe's last encounter with the Seven Kings up until he starts investigating the possibility that they may be involved in the destruction of the Royal London Hospital. This possibility becomes more likely when he sees a video taken before the explosion, showing someone spraying the mark of the Seven Kings on the wall at the hospital. After viewing the video with Benson Childes, the head of Barrier, and several other heads of security and anti-terrorism units and organizations, Joe tells them about the Seven Kings and their suspected involvement. He also tells them about the Chosen—the Seven's ground troops, and the Kingsmen, a more elite group who can hold their own against SEALS or the SAS.

It's discovered that there were fourteen bombs detonated at the hospital and that they all went off at 9:11 that morning. They also discuss possible upcoming events that might be targeted next. One of them is a star-studded fundraiser due to take place on a cruise ship, SS Sea of Hope, in five days. The security for that event has been vetted by Hugo Vox, the top security expert in the world. Vox runs Terror Town, the most effective counter-

Boeing CH-47 Chinook (which appears in *The Dragon Factory*) is a large, twin engine, tandem rotor heavy-lift helicopter which is used primarily with troop movement, artillery placement, and battlefield resupply. It has a wide loading ramp in the rear and three external cargo hooks for loading and unloading. Though reminiscent of the utility and attack helicopters used during the Vietnam War, the CH-47 has been through vast improvements including upgraded engines, composite rotor blades, redesigned cockpits, improved electrical systems, and major upgrades to the flight controls, as well as an installation of two four-thousand, seven-hundred and thirty-three horsepower Honeywell engines. A commercial model of the Chinook is used world-wide for logging, construction, fire and rescue, and petroleum extraction operations.

"*The Dragon Factory* by Jonathan Maberry is an action/horror/sci fi mash-up that grabs you by the scruff of the neck, gives you a good shake, and doesn't let go until the last page."
—San Francisco Book Review

terrorism training facility in the world. To be 'vetted by Vox' is to get the gold standard of above top secret clearance and approval. So while there's some concern over the event, there's not as much as there would be if Vox had not vetted the staff.

Joe tells Church all of this in a subsequent phone call. Church mentions a conversation he had with the warden of Graterford Prison in Pennsylvania, about a dead prisoner with the numbers 12/17 carved into his skin nine times and a current inmate who seems to have unusual personal knowledge of the incident; a strange character named Nicodemus. Joe asks if there are any traces of the number eleven. Church tells him to add the digits.

Nicodemus was convicted of the murder of four people in a bizarre 'locked room' type mystery, by way of strong circumstantial evidence and the fact he offered no defense. People who cross Nicodemus in prison have a habit of dying—including the dead prisoner. Records indicating any possible involvement on his part vanish with no rational explanation. The guards don't like to touch him, and both the warden and the prison psychiatrist are clearly afraid of him. The psychiatrist believes Nicodemus might be the 'face of true evil.'

Church and Joe agree that someone needs to talk to Nicodemus, and that someone is Rudy, who is less than thrilled to be diverted from London back to Pennsylvania.

Joe is almost killed by three police officers, all with good, solid reputations, upon leaving the Barrier offices. One of them says "Happy Christmas from the Seven—," which is enough to clue Joe in time to avoid being shot. He and Ghost disable all three cops and are nearly shot by other policeman who show up at the scene. It's uncertain whether the three officers were actual Chosen or under coercion to kill Joe. Either way, Joe is very aware of the eyes of the Seven Kings on him.

Joe and one of the London constables, Rebekkah Owlstone, find out that one of the janitorial staff

---

### FRIENDS IN THE INDUSTRY: BRYAN THOMAS SCHMIDT

Bryan Thomas Schmidt is an author and Hugo-nominated editor of adult and children's speculative fiction. His debut novel, *The Worker Prince* received Honorable Mention on Barnes & Noble Book Club's Year's Best Science Fiction Releases. His short stories have appeared in magazines, anthologies and online and include entries in *The X-Files, Predator, Joe Ledger, Monster Hunter International,* and *Decipher's WARS,* amongst others. As book editor for Kevin J. Anderson and Rebecca Moesta's WordFire Press he has edited books by such luminaries as Alan Dean Foster, Tracy Hickman, Frank Herbert, Mike Resnick, Jean Rabe and more. He was also the first editor on Andy Weir's bestseller *The Martian.* His anthologies as editor include *Shattered Shields* with co-editor Jennifer Brozek, *Mission: Tomorrow, Galactic Games, Little Green Men—Attack!* with Robin Wayne Bailey, and *The Monster Hunter Tales* with Larry Correia all for Baen Books, *Space Battles: Full Throttle Space Tales #6, Beyond The Sun* and *Raygun Chronicles: Space Opera For a New Age* for various small presses and *Joe Ledger: Unstoppable* with Jonathan Maberry for St. Martin's Press. Find him online via his website at www.bryanthomasschmidt.net and on Facebook and Twitter as BryanThomasS. He co-wrote "Instinct (A Ghost Story)" with G. P. Charles for *Joe Ledger: Unstoppable,* the first story written from Ghost's POV.

at the hospital has a strange note taped to his apartment door, saying: They are with Jesus. May God forgive all sinners. They investigate the apartment and find the sign of the Seven Kings on the door as well. They evacuate the building and then go into the apartment, where they find the dead bodies of Trevor Plympton's wife and daughter, shot in the head. Trevor left a note making it clear he killed his family to save them. Among other things the note says "They are not kings. They are monsters." And "I am only the monster. They made me."

In the meantime, the rest of Echo Team is at Area 51, a military base outside of Las Vegas, doing a 'babysitting' job because the surveillance cameras failed three nights in a row. Area 51 is home to the Locust FB-119, the newest generation of stealth aircraft, and it's vital that no

Selkies are a part of Celtic folklore—either seals who take on human form; or humans that can transform into seals.

photographs of the newly developed aircraft fall into the wrong hands. Echo Team is there with Lucky Team and a team of military investigators. The investigators, Lucky Team and two members of Echo Team—Ricky Gomez and Snake Henderson—go inside the hangar housing the planes while the rest of Echo Team stay outside. They are just about to call it for the day when the hangar explodes, killing everyone inside. It turns out all the buildings at Area 51 have been wiped off the face of the earth.

Rudy meets with Nicodemus, who talks about the Ten Plagues of Egypt and the Goddess, refuses to answer any question with a straight answer, and tells Rudy that his friend is walking in harm's way. The one who has lost the grace of the Goddess. The one who walks with ghosts. He will be swept away by the river of blood.

At the same time Rudy is talking to Nicodemus, Joe is sent to the Shetland Islands and the Fair Island Research Endeavor, a viral research station, where one of the doctors, a Dr. Grey, has taken the rest of the staff hostage, threatening to release a jacked-up version of Ebola into the air. Joe goes inside, and the first person he encounters is Mikey, Dr. Grey's son. It's obvious that Mikey is ill. He tells Joe he's there to take him to his father. They go to a doorway that can only be opened by two people with special cards and codes. Mikey gives Joe one of the cards and manages to use the other himself and type in the code before bleeding out.

Joe goes inside and finds the staff being held at gunpoint by Dr. Grey. The doctor's wife is already dead. Dr. Grey gave them the virus along with morphine so they wouldn't suffer and so they wouldn't fall into the hands of the 'Spaniard.' Dr. Grey has waited until Joe arrives to infect himself with the virus. He doesn't want to destroy the world.

Dr. Grey tells Joe about being threatened by the Spaniard, who shows him photos of women and children he's killed, along with pictures of Dr. Grey's family in their most intimate moments to show that there is nowhere they can hide if the doctor doesn't do what the Spaniard says…which is to release the Ebola into the Hot Room. The doctor thought all they'd want is an incident, with some of the staff dying and exposing America's involvement in secret bioweapons testing. But the vent controls didn't work and fail safes didn't kick in. The virus would have been released if Dr. Grey hadn't taken steps to insure it didn't, including taking the rest of the staff hostage because he's sure one of them is working with 'them.'

Joe gives Dr. Grey a mercifully quick death with a bullet to the head, then talks to the hostages, telling them if any of them have been coerced that they should speak up now, that he can help protect their families. One of the staff steps forward, tells Joe his family was threatened. Before he can say anything else, he's shot and killed by one of the women there, who then tries to kill Joe. Joe shoots her first.

After he is thoroughly decontaminated, Joe and Church talk. One of the common denominators of the hospital bombing and the failed release of the Ebola is that the people targeted to do these things are the sort who will do anything to protect their families. A very specific psychological profile is involved, and they need to figure out how the Seven Kings are identifying people susceptible to this type of coercion. They plan on getting Hugo Vox's help with this since, along with his security screening business, he owns a number of employment agencies who would help find people for jobs like Dr. Grey's.

Joe's canine partner, probably the most beloved character in the Ledger Universe. Most likely to get the author death threats if Ghost is ever killed off.

Church tells Joe that he's received another call from Deep Throat, who tells Church 'They want to break the bones of their enemies and suck out the marrow.' When Church tells him this doesn't seem helpful, Deep Throat insists that it is. Church plans on adding the words 'break,' 'bones,' and 'marrow' to their keyword search in Mind-Reader.

Joe gets on a plane to head back to Philadelphia, where he meets Circe O'Tree, sent by Church to liaise with him. Circe is a bestselling author and terrorist expert. Her books explore the ways in which religion and political ideologies are used as the basis for war and terrorism. Circe has been following tweets, articles, etc., that reference the Goddess, many of them in conjunction with hate crimes, and is positive she's on to something solid.

She works for Hugo Vox at Terror Town, but after discovering Circe gave her report on the Goddess to Grace Courtland a few months prior without Hugo's okay, he has sent her to London to be the liaison for the Sea of Hope event. She'd done this in the hopes that Grace could run things through MindReader and possibly make a connection between all of the random posts. Unfortunately, Grace was

### FRIENDS IN THE INDUSTRY: G.P. CHARLES

After years of working in fantasy game design and Web development, G. P. Charles traded in computer programming for fiction writing and escaped the nightmare of missing semicolons and infinite loops. Now, instead of daydreaming about throwing the computer out the window, G.P. finds every day an exciting adventure. When not writing, downtime is spent at home on the farm, raising horses, chickens, and two boys who are too intelligent for their own good but a constant source of joy. To learn more, check out www.gpcharles.com. G.P. co-wrote "Instinct (A Ghost Story)" with Bryan Thomas Schmidt for *Joe Ledger: Unstoppable.*

killed before she could do anything with the report.

Joe and Circe don't exactly hit it off at first but manage to get past an awkward first encounter. Circe is more inclined to like Joe after she finds out he's the man her friend Grace was in love with, and they agree to wipe the slate clean and work together.

Meanwhile, the reality of the Seven Kings: it's a secret society made up of some of the most powerful and dangerous men in the world. To build their mystique, the Kings hijacked much of the conspiracy theories built around other groups—such as the Illuminati, etc. The Kings include: Plagues, Lies, Fear, Gold, Thieves, Famine and War, all overseen by The Goddess—Eris, a very wealthy woman in her sixties who looks to be in her thirties, with no plastic surgery involved. She's also the mother of the King of Fear, referred to as the American.

Four months earlier, they recruited Sebastian Gault, then recovering from his injuries sustained in *Patient Zero*, to replace the prior King of Plagues (now deceased). Gault had undergone plastic surgery and had his fingerprints replaced/changed, as did his companion Toys, who has stayed with Gault throughout his surgeries and recovery. Gault used to have a relationship ('a fly in her erotic web') with Eris and had often thought of marrying her. Had she been younger and saner, he might have done so. The two are quick to resume their relationship after Gault accepts the invitation to join the Kings.

The Kings all have their Consciences. An increasingly reluctant Toys is Gault's. The American's—the King of Fear—conscience is Rafael Santoro, also known as The Spaniard, who has an affinity for knives and has left a trail of tortured and slaughtered 'angels' behind him—mostly women and children. He keeps photos of his victims and uses them to coerce people who love their families into doing horrible things…such as plant bombs in the London Hospital or release an airborne super-Ebola virus into the general population. Most of these people, like Plympton and Dr. Grey, choose to 'mercy kill' their families to keep them out of Santoro's hands.

Outside of the DMS, there are three additional planes and speedboats mentioned.

The Gulfstream G550 in which Sebastian Gault and Toys are transported to their meeting with the other kings in *The King of Plagues*. Also made by General Dynamics in Savannah, Georgia, it is the older sister to Joe's G650. Still made for luxury with a price tag over sixty million dollars, it is primarily operated by private individuals, companies and executive charters, as well as sixteen Governments and military (including the United States) for use as VIP transport. Crew is two pilots and up to two attendants. Capacity is up to nineteen passengers. Its maximum speed is a tick slower than Joe's at only Mach .85. Unlike jet aircraft in the movies, the pilots have four high definition screens and cursor controls for the instrumentation.

The Seven Kings also make use of a Boeing 747-8 VIP which is the largest 747 ever built, the largest commercial jet built in the U.S. and the longest passenger aircraft built in the world. It has a cost of over 379 million dollars per plane and has been in service since 2008. Able to carry 467 passengers and fly over fifteen-thousand miles at MACH .855, it is also the official aircraft for Air Force One.

Cole McAdams in *Joe Ledger: Unstoppable* "No Business at All" tries to impress Joe by mentioning that he owns and pilots a 747-100. Unfortunately for Cole, Joe has had more than his share of experience with top of the line aircraft and the 747-100 just doesn't stack up with a price tag of only 24 million dollars and having been around since 1968.

The Jakobys have a ZT-280 Checkmate powerboat that was designed by Checkmate Marine from Bucyrus, OH. Not as outlandish in price as something the Seven Kings would own, it still fetches a price of over one-hundred thousand dollars.

We come back to the Seven Kings and their toys with the 350 Sundancer yacht used by Dr. Pharos in *Predator One*. Manufactured by Sea Ray in Knoxville, Tn., like all things with the Kings, this has a price tag close to four-hundred thousand dollars for the base model. It is designed with luxury, comfort and all the latest technology.

In folklore, a trickster can either be a mischievous prankster or a malevolent character intent on destruction. Father Nicodemus brings a hefty dose of malice to his mischief.

Gault is delighted to find out his predecessor planned a terror campaign based on the Ten Biblical Plagues of Egypt and embraces the idea and the whole idea behind the Seven Kings wholeheartedly. Toys is less enthusiastic, cautioning Gault that they are not cut out to be evil geniuses and that joining the society is a mistake. Gault disagrees. He feels that the universe has opened the door to greatness and that they are no longer ordinary men. Toys agrees to stay, but he's deeply unhappy about it.

The Seven Kings are in a continual struggle for power with the Inner Circle of the Skull and Bones Society. Gault's predecessor wanted to use the Death of the Firstborn plague to cripple the Inner Circle, but the science behind his plan was faulty. Gault comes up with an alternative idea. Toys tries to reason with him, but to no avail. Gault falls further and further into the trap of believing his own press and has less and less patience for his best friend.

As his relationship with Gault slowly disintegrates, Toys finds an unexpected ally in the American, who is the only one of the Kings who doesn't buy into the whole Goddess mythos his mother has started. He also has an agenda of his own. The American tells Toys that some people don't think of Judas as a traitor. They think he was trying to stop Jesus from fucking up a good thing and that some people need to be saved from themselves. Even Kings and goddesses.

Circe and Joe discuss the Ten Plagues of Egypt and realize that the hospital bombing was the Plague of Darkness (the unusually dark and persistent smoke creating night during the day), the Ebola attempt was an attempt to metaphorically make the rivers run red with blood, and that the bombing of Area 51 was (again metaphorically) the Plague of Locusts, with the Locust stealth aircraft being destroyed. Joe thinks there will be more attacks and asks Church to make a video that might help them head off another Seven Kings attack at the pass.

The video is of Church (using a different name) under the auspices of Homeland Security, talking about the London Royal Hospital bombing and how the security of the hospital had been compromised by employees due to threats made against their families. Church promises protection to anyone who has received similar threats. There's a toll-free number and an email address at the bottom of the screen. Viewers who have been threatened are urged to contact Church immediately. The video is shown to anyone employed in a critical area of viral research, energy, health sciences, or defense.

One of the people who sees the video is Amber Taylor, who is on the verge of doing something unthinkable—release fleas infected with the plague into the Philadelphia subway system—in order to protect her children from the Spaniard. Instead, she leaves her office, picks her kids up from school and calls the number. Joe and Circe head over to Amber's house, where the frightened woman has barricaded herself and her kids inside. They are joined by Top and DeeDee, who are there to escort Amber and her kids to a safe house. The rest of Echo Team is outside, keeping an eye on the area and they spot four hostiles on foot and two in a white van closing in on the house. Echo Team dispatches four. Two are injured, but taken alive for questioning.

Joe and Circe are sent to a Starbucks in Southampton to meet with Martin Hanler, a writer friend of Church's who says that the idea to blow up the London Royal Hospital was originally his. Joe and Circe are met by Rudy in the Starbucks parking lot. Circe stays out with Rudy (she and Hanler don't get along that well) while Joe goes in to meet with the writer.

Joe wants to know who Hanler has told about this plot idea. Hanler tells him it's not from a published or even written book yet and that he's only talked about it with a group of writers at Thrillerfest,

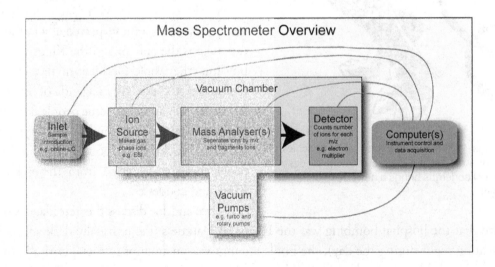

These man-portable bio-aerosol mass spectrometers have been used at select airports, government buildings and event facilities as part of an ongoing campaign of detection and prevention of biological threats.

a crime writer's conference. Some of the writers he mentions have been in think tanks at Terror Town. Hanler tells Joe if he finds out that someone stole his idea and used it to destroy the London Hospital to please put that person down like a rabid dog. Not for stealing his idea but because he now has to live with the fact that he may be inadvertently responsible for the deaths of over four thousand people. At that point, the windows of Starbucks explode.

There's a firefight in which many of the customers and employees in Starbucks are shot and either killed or badly injured. Martin Hanler is one of the casualties and Rudy is injured. The rest of Echo Team arrives and all of the hostile shooters except for one are killed. Sucks to be him.

Toys tries one more time to reach Gault and get him to step back from his plans to launch a program that would not only cause countless deaths but could easily spark conflicts that will tear nations apart. He accuses Gault—and Eris—of trying to outrun their mortality. At playacting at being gods because they can't stand the thought of being human. Gault punches Toys in the face and leaves.

A nearly broken Toys and the American talk. The American confirms that he is not behind the Ten Plagues initiative and indeed tried to stop it with the convenient death of the former King of Plagues. He started the Seven Kings to make money, not to destroy the world, but his mother has taken her role as Goddess very seriously. Santoro, Gault and the other Kings are on her side. The American only pretends to be. It also turns out that Kirov's (former King of Plagues) Conscience was unmasked as the person making calls to Church but died before Santoro could 'question' him. A very convenient turn of events for the American. The American leaves Toys alone in his office, dropping his cell phone as he goes.

Meanwhile several of the Inner Circle's eldest children die of an unknown disease marked by boils, as Eris seeds the internet and social media with posts about the Goddess striking down the firstborn of the wicked.

Toys uses the American's phone and calls Joe. He gives Joe information after extracting a promise that Joe does not kill Sebastian Gault. Joe guesses who the caller is. Toys tells him that if he finds Gault, he'll find Santoro, and that the Kings and their agents are everywhere, and that he should trust no one. He also asks Joe for a favor—to light a candle for his soul.

Joe wonders if he can trust anyone now. The only person he doesn't put on a possible enemy list is Church, who he calls and discloses the details of his call with Toys. He goes to the Hangar for a brainstorming session with Church, Circe, Dr. Hu, and Aunt Sallie (who he meets for the first time—not love at first sight for either of them). Joe tells them about the results of his interrogation of Sarducci, the shooter left alive after the Starbucks incident.

The C-140 "JetStar" created by Lockheed Martin in the U.S. in the 1950's and seeing service today was only produced from 1957-1978 and retired by the U.S. Air Force in the 1990's. Still in use today as a business jet, it is most distinguishable by its four rear mounted engines. It is a transport aircraft that Joe flies back in after the *King of Plagues* attack on the Sea of Hope.

Sarducci told Joe about Santoro, and that 'Santoro had a worse hard-on for the DMS than the Kings have for the Inner C.' Church brings up the quote from Deep Throat about breaking the bones of their enemies and sucking out the marrow, with 'bones' being the operative word. Circe adds that one of the Goddess's posts was 'Woe to the firstborn of the House of Bones.' They all realize that the Kings are after the Skull and Bones Inner Circle. They pull up a list of the Inner Circle and learn that five of their children have died. The death toll rises to twenty-one, all of them from what Circe identifies as mycotoxicosis, a toxic chemical produced by fungi.

The Goddess posts a Tweet that says: The Ten Plagues have been visited on the house of the wicked. Witness the fall of the House of Bones. It is complete.

This demoralizes everyone in the meeting. They've lost. The Seven Kings have accomplished their goal. Church, however, says the war is not over.

Joe has a revelation in the middle of the night and goes to Church, who says he was wondering how long it would take Joe to figure it out. They call another meeting, and Joe says it's about the coercion, the fact that one or two in three hundred thousand would fit the profile of people who would do horrible things in order to protect their families. People like Dr. Grey, Plympton, and Amber Taylor would have been red-flagged and not hired at their jobs. Yet none of their profiles showed their obvious psychological vulnerability. They would have had to have been deliberately placed by whoever did the psych screening. The screeners were all vetted by Vox, otherwise known as the American.

The DMS go after Vox, who has already vanished. He leaves them a parting gift, however: blueprints of the SS Sea of Hope and an apology to Circe.

Echo Team flies out to the Sea of Hope, disguised as security for the many celebrities on board for the fundraiser. Over seven thousand five hundred people are on the ship, and there's no way of knowing how many of them belong to the Seven Kings. Circe figures out that the deaths of the firstborn of the Inner Circle was actually the Plague of Boils and that Gault is planning something huge for the Sea of Hope fundraiser.

In the meantime, Gault discovers Toys has betrayed him with the phone call to Joe Ledger. The two shoot each other, Toys getting hit in the leg and Gault in the heart. Gault, however, is wearing Kevlar and escapes. Vox finds an injured Toys, who asks why Vox is helping him. Vox says he hasn't been able to trust Santoro for years and that he needs someone he can trust.

Back on the Sea of Hope, Joe spots Santoro. He and DeeDee detain him. DeeDee pats him down and finds a small syringe. Santoro says it's for his allergies. Santoro injures DeeDee badly and runs into the crowd. The Chosen and Kingsmen emerge out of the crowd but so do forty or fifty DMS agents via

The Boeing C-17 "Globemaster," referenced in *The King of Plagues*, is one of the largest military transport jets in use today. Produced from 1991 until 2015 it has been in service since 1995 with a cost of over two-hundred million dollars per plane and manufactured here in the U.S. It is still in use by eight nations (including NATO) as well as the U.S. The final C-17 was completed in Long Beach, CA in 2015. It has four large jet engines, two mounted on each side under the fixed wings, and a large tail fin with flaps that form a capital "T" when looking at it from the front. While it has a huge interior capable of carrying 102 troopers, or thirty-six liters with fifty-four walking wounded and caregivers, or up to one-hundred and seventy thousand pounds of cargo; it also has a huge price tag of over two-hundred million dollars per plane. However, even though it is a jet aircraft, it can take off from airfields as small as five-thousand feet long.

hang gliders. There's a pitched battle, finally won by the DMS.

Santoro and Joe fight, with Santoro getting the upper hand and demanding his syringe back. Ghost attacks but is cut badly. Santoro tells Joe he will drown in a river of blood. Joe finally beats him, badly enough that all Santoro can say is "No, please," which infuriates Joe even more considering the torture and murder that the Spaniard has inflicted. Church and Circe appear on the scene in time to stop Joe from killing Santoro. Church takes Santoro into a stateroom for questioning, telling Circe to stay out of sight. Circe tries to stop him, calling him "Dad." Church tells her to do as he says and vanishes into the room.

It turns out that balloons on the ship scheduled to be released in Rio were filled with the Ebola. The balloons are taken out to sea in nets and hit with flamethrowers. Santoro also tells Church everything he knows about the Seven Kings: who they are and the attacks they'd masterminded, including 9/11.

Church tells Joe that Circe is his daughter, but very few people know this because he wants to protect her because his enemies had already killed his ex-wife and other daughter. Only ten people know who Circe is. Hugo Vox is one of them, as is Rudy Sanchez.

Eris and Gault are on Eris's yacht, mourning the death of their plan when Hugo calls, informing his mother he's drained her and Gault's bank accounts. He tells her he left her a nest egg and to call him when they reach port. He's left her a cell phone with his new number plugged in. He hangs up. Eris finds the cell phone and dials Hugo's number, intending on demanding the return of their money. As soon as she presses the 'call' button, the yacht explodes.

Rudy, Circe, and Joe go to visit Nicodemus, but he has disappeared from his prison cell. Manhunts in three states cannot find him. He has vanished without a trace.

## Title: **ASSASSIN'S CODE**

Format: 4th Joe Ledger novel

Published: April 10, 2012

After-Action Report: Joe is on a mission in Iran with Echo Team to rescue three American hikers on a scientific expedition who were arrested while hiking in the Iranian mountains. One of them is the only son of an American senator, so when diplomatic channels fail to secure the hikers' release, more drastic measures are taken. Echo Team successfully rescue the hikers, but Joe is separated from the rest of the team and has to lay low for a while before getting out of the country.

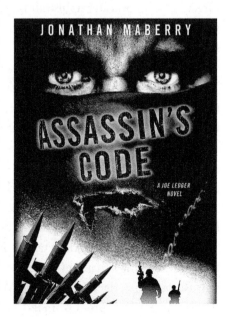

He is outside Starbox (the Iranian equivalent of Starbucks) when he receives a phone call from an unknown woman, who has laser sights on him (specifically his crotch). The woman confirms Joe's identity and tells him that he is to go back to the coffee place after taking the battery out of his cell phone and tossing it down the sewer. A man will meet him there and they will talk. Joe will know who the man is when he shows up.

Joe does as she says and is approached by Rasouli, a well-known Iranian politician. Joe's first instinct is to kill the man, who, because of his position and politics, is responsible for a lot of deaths, but Joe realizes to do so may insure his own death by the unknown female sniper. Rasouli mentions Joe came recommended by Hugo Vox, who sends a message that Grace Courtland was 'clean' and not one of Vox's spies. This shakes Joe up, but he doesn't show it.

Rasouli tells Joe he needs help 'saving the world,' and talks about about seven 'rogue' nuclear devices spread in different countries. The details are cloudy as to where the devices are located, but Rasouli believes that one is either in America, or that America is one of the targets, and that one of the devices is in Iran. He thinks that the plan is to blow up the Iranian oil fields. Rasouli also mentions something called the Book of Shadows and Saladin's Codex. The mention is casual, but Joe knows that there's more to it than meets the eye.

Finally, Rasouli gives Joe a flash drive that was recovered from one of his operatives, who swallowed the device to avoid having it taken by enemies when he was captured. Joe transfers the info on the flash drive to Bug in the States until he can ship the actual drive itself and goes back to his hotel, where Ghost waits for him.

The info on the flash drive is received by Bug. He and Circe (who is now involved with Rudy Sanchez) do their best to pull the non-damaged information off of it. The unusual thing about the drive is that all of the readable information is useful in one way or another. It seems very deliberate. They speculate the liquid damage was actually done deliberately, and that the flash drive was never actually swallowed. This could be either because Rasouli wants their help but doesn't want it known for political reasons…or he's trying to set them up. One of the things they pull from the flash drive is a still of Hugo Vox talking with an unknown man, which tells them that he is part of this whole mess.

Meanwhile, Joe is being spied on by the same female sniper who threatened him in the first place. She watches Joe and Ghost in his hotel room and pulls up his record via a computer system called Oracle. She follows an impulse and calls him, knowing that the call will be logged in her mission record, which will be seen by her mother, Lilith…who will not be happy about it. The sniper and Joe talk, and she identifies herself as Violin.

Shortly after the call, Joe is attacked in his hotel room by a man with his face covered in a baklava. The attacker Tasers Ghost right off the bat, taking the dog out of the equation. The man is strangely reluctant to go anywhere near Ghost during the fight. His eyes are red, with elliptical pupils, and he is freakishly strong. His teeth are sharp, like shark's teeth. They do not look like they've been filed but rather have grown in that way. He wants to know where the flash drive is and if Joe is working for Rasouli or for 'that whore.' He says the word 'Arklight' after that, telling Joe if he doesn't tell him who he is and who he works for, he'll rip out his throat and drink his life.

Joe is nearly killed, but his attacker is taken out by a sniper's bullet to the head. Joe tries to pull out his attacker's teeth in the hopes that they are fake, but no dice. They are real.

Church and the president talk. It is discussed that their only source of information about a potentially catastrophic situation (i.e. the seven nukes) came about because of Vox. Since he was the one that sent Rasouli to Ledger, Church says Vox is a trickster and a manipulator and that if he is helping them that he has a way to profit from it. Or, on the other hand, if one of the bombs is a real threat to Iran's oil fields, Vox could be using the DMS and United States to help Rasouli, who is one of his allies.

A year previously, Hugo Vox met with Grigori, the head of the Knights of the Red Order, known to very few as the Upierczi. Grigori and his fellow Upierczi live in tunnels below the sands of Iran. Grigori and the rest of his kind are albino, have reddish eyes, and unusually sharp teeth.

It takes a lot to scare Hugo Vox, but being in Grigori's lair with his kind is one of the few things that does. The Upierczi are a genetic offshoot of humanity that live in the shadows and hunger for human blood. Although they're not supernatural –just products of genetic aberration—they are the basis for the myths of vampires. They're incredibly strong and creepy as hell.

Women generally do not come with the genes that they do, however, so the Upierczi have basically practiced slavery and rape for eight hundred years in order to procreate. Most of the children born are either female (half Upierczi/half humans known as Dhampirs) or deformed. Only a few women can successfully bear healthy males, so the Upierczi have bred them and their children over and over again, leaving a pretty shallow gene pool.

Vox is there because he's found out that the Red Order's last Scriptor (head of the Order) decided to try something different by way of genetics in order to breed healthy Upierczi and circumnavigate the effects of inbreeding. As Vox tells Grigori, he found out about this because if it's illegal and involves science then he is always involved.

It turns out that the scientists did indeed crack the Upierczi DNA, discovering why they never get sick and why they live for such a long time. It's called Upier 531 and Vox wants it. Vox has terminal cancer and is going to die in about eighteen months. The Upier 531 could be a possible cure. In return, he will help Grigori and his people stage a revolution and break the chains of the Red Order, for whom they've basically been indentured servants for centuries.

Fast-forward to present day: Toys, who Vox basically adopted as a son, has abandoned his mentor.

---

Although Saladin was the enemy of the Crusader's, he was a deeply educated man and a moral one, and often showed more compassion and tolerance to his Christian prisoners than his people were afforded by the Crusaders.

HESA Shahed 285 (*Assassin's Code*) is a light, attack and reconnaissance helicopter that was developed and manufactured in Iran. Unveiled in 2009, the helicopter is produced for attack and recon and is armed with fourteen 2.75 inch rockets, a heavy or light machine gun on a rotatable turret, an under-fuselage gondola, and a EO/IR camera on top. When it is used for maritime use, it is armed with a search and track radar on the chin for tracking enemy ships, anti-ship missiles, and a multi-function display in the cockpit. Still in use by the Iranian government today.

Toys hacked into Vox's computer files and discovered the extent that Vox would go to get what he wanted, including the Upier 531. Toys told him that he could forgive him any risk he would take for the cure for his cancer, but the price he was willing to pay was not acceptable. Toys also tells him that he basically adopted him by way of gaining immortality, so he would have a son to pass on his legacy to. A legacy of murder, millions of deaths. He asks Vox how he could hate anyone enough to want them to be like him? Toys adds that it's not about the money and that Vox is a monster. Toys, on the other hands, is just damned.

Joe calls Church from the hotel basement. Church tells him he'll call back. Joe receives a call but instead of Church it's the female sniper. He mentions Arklight to her and she hangs up. Joe goes to a nearby safe house, which has been compromised. One man is dead and the other dying. The dying man draws a symbol. Church calls Joe back at that point, and Joe fills him in on what's happened including: Violin (the sniper), the super strong attacker, and the mention of Arklight. He describes the symbol the dying man drew. At that point Church tells him he was attacked by a Red Knight and to get out of that house. He's to go to a CIA safe house, immediately.

Church tells Aunt Sallie that Joe is being hunted by the Red Knights. She wants to know if he's going to call the Mothers, because who knows the Red Knights better than Lilith and her secret society of psycho bitches? It's obvious there's past history all the way around. Church plans on talking to Lilith and also going to Iran to see her face-to-face.

Church talks to Lilith, who is Violin's mother and the head of Arklight. It is obvious she and Church have some sort of history, but it is unspoken between them. Lilith tells him that each Scriptor in the Red Order has had a priest advising them and that the priest has always gone by the name Father Nicodemus. The bizarre thing is that photos and paintings of the priests throughout the centuries all look like the same man, who also looks like the prisoner Nicodemus from *The King of Plagues*.

Meanwhile Grigori is reamed out by the Order's current Scriptor (head of the organization) Charles LaRoque for the Knight's failure to kill Ledger. Grigori hangs up to find Vox, a wasted shell of his former self, standing next to his throne listening. Vox tells Grigori he will not get the codes until he gets his last set of Upier 531 shots. Grigori says that the doctor does not think Vox will survive the last set. Vox doesn't care, adding that the doctor better be wrong, because if he dies, then Grigori's dreams of freedom for his people from the Red Order will die with him.

Joe makes his way to a CIA safe house next. Along the way he sees Violin in a car and calls Bug to have him track the make, model, and license plate. Bug tells him any inquiries on that particular plate number are to go through

A button camera is literally a camera designed to look like a button. It can also look like a lapel pin or even a pin-on button like a smiley face. Button cameras have been around in the espionage world for longer than anyone is willing to admit. Today, anyone can buy one for as little as twenty dollars online and get HD quality. First seen in *Assassin's Code* with Top Simms.

Church, who is currently busy. Joe sees a Red Knight as well and continues to the safe house. There he is ambushed by Sabbatarians (people who are born on Saturdays who've formed a crazy religious cult), who think Joe's a Red Knight and a vampire. Joe kills all but one of them, Krystos, whom he questions. The man calls Ghost a 'fetch dog,' saying he would never hurt him. Krystos is a member of the Holy Inquisition, with permission to torture and kill for the good of God. They fight to save the world from the Upierczi, who have 'great weapons' and now fight in the open instead of in the shadows. Joe realizes this means the Red Knights most likely have nukes and asks his prisoner if they were sent by Hugo Vox or Rasouli. The answer is neither. They were sent by Father Nicodemus, who, according to Krystos, will 'lay waste to Joe's world.'

Joe kills Krystos, takes his locked briefcase, and heads for the next safe house, which he reaches without incident. He talks to Church; one of the nukes has been located on an oil rig in the Gulf of Mexico. Steps are being taken to disarm it. Joe, Church, and Hu discuss, amongst other things, vampires and their possible physiology, and Hu says there may be something to the myth of using garlic as an effective weapon against them, possibly because of congenital allergies.

Joe opens Krystos's briefcase and discovers eight by ten photos of him and his team, including handwritten notes about their training. He recognizes the handwriting as Hugo Vox's. Even worse, there's a list of all DMS personnel and their family members, including all contact info. Circe is on that list and it states that she's Church's daughter. Joe calls Church immediately to give him the bad news.

As soon as Joe hangs up, he discovers a tracking device in the briefcase. An explosion rocks the house as more Sabbatarians show up. Joe kills them just as Violin arrives to warn him that two more teams, at least twenty people, are coming. There's a firefight, with Echo Team coming in to turn the tide in Joe's and Violin's favor. Violin vanishes after the fight is won, and Echo Team bails to a new location and discusses the situation and the plan. The plan is to search and locate each nuke and disarm them. Echo Team is assigned to the Aghajari oil refinery in Iran. Joe has his team pair up and buddy-test each other on the schematics of the nukes. In the meantime, he retrieves the Sabbatarian's equipment, which includes bags of garlic powder and jars of garlic oil, and comes up with another plan to give them an edge over the Upierczi.

Violin arranges for Joe to meet with her mother Lilith and the rest of the 'Mothers of the Fallen' at a warehouse. The Mothers are all armed to the teeth and none of them are impressed with Joe. The meeting doesn't start out well, with Joe in no mood to put up with "bullshit and runaround." Echo Team arrives with laser sights on Lilith to insure things don't go south on Joe again. He tells Lilith that if she screws with him one second longer, his team will kill the women, including her daughter. Lilith says he wouldn't do that.

A voice from the shadows belonging to Church disagrees.

Alamut Castle, "eagle's nest," was the mountain stronghold of Hassan-I Sabbah, founder of a group of deadly group of fedayeen whose members are often referred to as the Hashshashin, or "Assassins."

No one saw Church enter the warehouse, including Echo Team. And no one expects Church and Lilith to greet each other with the sort of hug that speaks of serious familiarity and intimacy. Regardless, they do. Echo Team stands down and Lilith fills them in on the history of the Red Order and the Red Knights.

Eight hundred years ago, Sir Guy LaRoque, a member of the Knights Hospitaller, a noble order dedicated to good works, created a second and secret group within the Hospitallers—the Ordo Ruber, or Red Order. The group was illegally sanctioned by a Father Nicodemus, the senior Hospitaller priest in the Holy Lands during the Third Crusade. Sir Guy's Islamic counterpart, the head of the Islamic Tariqa and also a religious zealot, shared Sir Guy's observation that both Islams and Christians flocked to church and showed the greatest fealty to God during the times of the worst strife. The two men dedicated themselves to a course of action that would ensure the preservation of their respective churches; an agreement that there should always be tension and conflict between Christendom and Islam.

Long story short, they started a succession of hate crimes, always regulated and agreed upon. Essentially the start of terrorism as we know it today. At first the Holy Agreement between them dictated that each side would only carry out acts against their own people but plant evidence to implicate the other side. Both Muslims and Christians, however, became sickened carrying out atrocities against their own so the Agreement was amended to allow each side to carry out the acts against the other, although still strictly regulated. This became known as the Shadow War, which endured through the centuries.

The War took on an even darker turn when the Red Order decided they needed a group of assassins to match the Tariqa's Hashashin, who were so effective that they'd tipped the balance of the Shadow War in Islam's favor. Nicodemus sent Sir Guy to find Upierczi where they hid in the shadows, the basis for the vampire legends. The Upierczi, though more than a match for most assassins, were few in

Entry of the Crusaders into Constantinople by Gustav Dore

Hughes OH-6 Cayuse (*Assassin's Code*)—Nicknamed "Loach" after the acronym LOH which stands for Light Observation Helicopter. First entered service in 1966 during the Vietnam War and quickly won world records for speed, endurance, and climbing speed. Some records are still unbroken. In 1972, a modified pair of Loachs were used by the CIA for a covert wire-tapping mission near Vinh, Vietnam which provided useful information that was utilized during the peace talks. The Loach is still in use today, including being used for a special aviation task force trained to rescue hostages called Operation Honey Badger.

Grigori and his fellow Upierczi are albino, have reddish eyes... and unusually sharp teeth.

The tension and violence that troubles the sands of the Middle East are nothing new. There have been conflicts in that region of the world since the first seeds were sown in the Fertile Crescent. And there does not appear to be an end in sight.

number so the Red Order began the process of the forced breeding programs: capturing women, chaining them in pens, and encouraging the Upierczi to rape them.

Lilith and the other Mothers of the Fallen are the ones who finally escaped and took their daughters, the dhamphyrs, with them to save them from a lifetime of enslavement and rape. Arklight is the militant arm of the Mothers, and most of the field agents are their daughters.

In the meantime, Vox, who it turns out is related to Nicodemus, has received the last shots of Upier 531, and his strength is returning. He is behind the whole thing. He's played the Red Knights against the Red Order, the Tariqa against the Sabbatarians, playing all sides of the field to create as much confusion and chaos as possible. He calls Grigori and gives him the password to activate the scrambler with the codes for all the missing nukes. The Upierczi have a resistance to radiation and with the new genetic tweaks to their breeding, can become the dominant species on the planet if they set off the nukes. Even if they don't, they can hold the rest of the world hostage. He tells Grigori that Arklight is now working with Ledger, insuring that Grigori will go to the oil refinery to attack his enemies. Vox hangs up on Grigori in mid-tirade about drowning his enemies in lakes of blood, satisfied he's set everything in motion to his satisfaction.

Joe and Echo Team are smuggled into the oil refinery. Once there, they blend in as security guards. A picture of the nuke shows poured concrete floors and rock walls, which, while it rules out certain parts of the refinery, still leaves miles to search. They ingest garlic powder, Ghost getting it rubbed into his fur, and split up into three teams. Joe goes with Lydia and Ghost to do a sweep of part of the lower level, where they run into soldiers and the ranking major of the refinery, a buck-toothed man who knows Joe and Lydia are fakes.

Joe sics Ghost on the major before he can do more than clear his holster. Joe and Lydia take out the rest of the soldiers and handcuff them in a small bathroom, along with a very pissed off and injured major. They can't kill them because Church and the president very specifically told them not to use lethal force against Iranian nationals. Joe and Lydia then find themselves at a dead-end and go back to question the major further. They find the soldiers, throats ripped out. The major is gone, however, his handcuffs bent out of shape and a hidden door now ajar at the back of the toilet. The stench of decayed flesh wafts out from behind the door.

Joe sends Lydia to gather the team and meet him back down there as the device may be hidden there. He and Ghost find themselves in a vast cavern filled with wooden crates and the corpses of two dozen men, all of them male

Religious extremism comes in all shapes, faiths and denominations. Violent intolerance is not owned by any one religion but, sadly, is a common infection in many.

and most likely Iranian. The bodies are at least two days old and have been savaged, throats torn out, limbs ripped off, skulls crushed.

Joe finds a set of buck-toothed false teeth, the kind meant to fit over regular teeth, and realizes the major he'd disarmed was an Upier. He'd gone down as easily as he had because he'd been attacked by Ghost, a white dog—a fetch dog as far as the Upierczi were concerned. Ghost had garlic in his fur and had eaten some as well and bitten the Upier. Joe figures there was enough garlic to weaken but not kill him.

Joe also finds the nuclear device. He starts to disarm it but realizes it hasn't been armed yet and if he takes out the triggering system, it'll defang it. Which is a good thing. What's not so good is two Red Knights show up behind him.

Meanwhile, Church and his team are still trying to find the locations of the rest of the nukes. He receives a call that shows ID not available on the screen. As there are only two systems that can block MindReader's phone trace technology, and one of them is Lilith's (who is there with him), he assumes it's Hugo Vox. It's not. It's Toys, calling to make 'a confession.' He tells Church about Vox's cancer and the Upier 531, which gives Church the insight needed to figure out Vox's motivations. When Vox thought he was dying, he wanted to destroy the world. When he found out he was cured, he supplied the DMS with enough info via Rasouli's flash drive to hunt for the nukes. Why? Vox no longer wanted to burn the world because he intended to live in it.

Joe and Ghost take out the two Red Knights with the help of garlic oil in the ammo. Joe knows he can't leave without taking out the triggering system, but more Red Knights flood the chamber, and he doesn't have enough bullets to take them all out. Grigori leads them, and although Joe manages to kill a few with his garlic infused ammo, Grigori overpowers him. Ghost cowers to the side, too scared to attack. The Upier laughs. As soon as he drinks Joe's life he's going to activate three nukes hidden under the Vatican, Mecca, and Jerusalem to bring the faithful to their knees.

Joe grabs Grigori by the balls and squeezes hard, punching him in the face and spitting into his mouth. The garlic in Joe's saliva is enough to set off an allergic reaction but not enough to kill Grigori. Ghost, however, attacks the Upier. Whether it's because he sensed his master's desperation, the vulnerability of Grigori, or had just had enough, he's back to his bad-ass attack dog self. He rips off several of Grigori's fingers as the Upier flails at Ghost in terror, calling for his fellow Upierczi to help. They converge on Ghost, but before they reach him, a hail of bullets tears into them. Echo Team has arrived, and Joe has the code scrambler.

Violin shows up to the fight, taking out Upierczi with silver blade, the embodiment of vengeance for the Mothers and the rest of the women abused by the Upierczi over the

A helmet visor is a face shield that attaches to the helmet and uses holographic technology to project onto the shield information to the wearer. They can also be used to filter through the different light spectrums. Where the camera is used to record what is happening, the visor is used to protect the wearer and impart valuable data during an operation. First used by Echo Team in *Assassin's Code*.

Geiger counters are designed for one thing: detect radiation. In the old days they were analog only, meaning that there were louder and louder clicks as the radiation became stronger. Today's Geiger counters are digital, a lot smaller and a lot easier to use. Used by Echo Team in *Assassin's Code* to search for the Teller-Ulam nuclear warheads.

centuries. But there are at least a hundred of the monsters in the room, and Joe realizes they're going to lose the fight. John Smith, the Echo Team sharpshooter, is killed by Grigori, who runs out of the chamber. He's pursued by Khalid, who vanishes with several Upierczi on his trail. The Mothers of the Fallen and Arklight show up at the battle at that point, slaughtering their enemies and leaving Joe free to go after Grigori.

He finds the Upier surrounded by several of his Knights, Khalid on the ground with his gun on them but bleeding badly. Joe takes out the Knights and tells Grigori if he wants the scrambler device, he can take it from him. Grigori attacks, but makes the mistake of underestimating Joe, who manages to kill him nastily and brutally before collapsing. He wakes up in a truck with a possible skull fracture. Top and the rest of the team are there, except for John Smith and Khalid, who both died at the refinery. The refinery was blown up by charges the Red Knights had set, their plan to bury the nuke after it was armed so no one could stop it. Violin and the Arklight team had tried to stop the Knights from setting off the charges…and she'd never made it out.

Joe wakes up again in a hospital. Church is there and tells him Ghost has gotten titanium dental implants for the teeth he lost in the attack. All eight nukes have been secured, and the rest of Joe's team made it out okay. Circe and Bug managed to decode the Book of Shadows, with the help of Saladin's Codex and MindReader, and discovered it's a 'confession' of all the deeds done under the Holy Agreement over the centuries. It's nothing that can be made public, but as weeks pass Joe notices the strife in the Middle East has calmed down.

A satisfied Vox is in Verona, content with how things played out and already planning to restart the Seven Kings and possibly hunt for more Upierczi. He has over a hundred billion dollars hidden in accounts worldwide…but discovers his access codes no longer work. A voice from the darkness tells him he's wasting his time. Church, with a coded cell phone received by a 'mutual friend' reverse engineered to be used as a tracking device. Vox recognizes the cell as one he gave Toys and asks Church to spare his 'son.' He tries to convince Church that he's giving all his money to Toys because he, Vox, is going to be dead in a few months anyway.

Church reveals he knows about the Upier 531. Tells Vox that Circe's name was on the list provided to the Sabbatarians and the Upierczi. Vox says he'd never hurt a

H.P. Lovecraft created the character of the great god 'Cthulhu,' the Elder Gods, the Ancient Ones, and many of the other staples of what has been variously labeled 'cosmic horror,' 'the Cthulhu Mythos,' or 'Lovecraftian horror.'

"Maberry delivers on every promise he makes in this book. The various plots unfold at a breakneck pace, drawing readers in from the very first page."
—California Literary Review

hair on Circe's head. Church shoots him.

Joe receives a call on his way home. It's Violin.

Not exactly a happy ending, but a happier one than he expected.

### Title: "A FOOTNOTE IN THE BLACK BUDGET"

Format: Short story

Published: 2015

After-Action Report: Joe Ledger, Top and Bunny go to the bottom of the world all the way to the Mountains of Madness in this crossover with H. P. Lovecraft's Cthulhu Mythos. This story is one of the few that is no longer in true continuity with the Ledger series. It was expanded and substantially revised into the novel *Kill Switch*.

### Title: "MAD SCIENCE"

Format: Short story

Published: April 2012

After-Action Report: Joe Ledger and Violin go after a kill-squad of Red Knights in this sequel to *Assassin's Code*. This story was written for a fundraiser audiobook, *Liar Liar*, written and published by the members of the Liars Club. Proceeds from the book benefitted the Mighty Writers literacy program. Keith R.A. DeCandido edited the book, and "Mad Science" appeared in the Blackstone Audio edition.

The Liars Club is a group of professional writers who host the Writers Coffeehouses (coast to coast), give classes and workshops, run the Liars Club Oddcast podcast, and stage events in support of literacy foundations, brick-and-mortar bookstores, and libraries.

Title: **"BORROWED POWER"**
Format: Short story
Published: 2013
After-Action Report: A story told in two parts: A young Mr. Church teams with Lilith to hunt monsters in the sewers beneath Paris; and when that ancient evil rises again, Joe Ledger and Violin close in for the kill. This story is the first-ever adventure of a younger Mr. Church.

Title: **EXTINCTION MACHINE**
Format: 5th Joe Ledger novel
Published: March 26, 2013
After-Action Report: Over the last few months there have been attacks on the computer systems of several of the most important defense contractors. Access to their records is supposed to be impossible (unless the Department of Military Sciences used MindReader to gain it), but these attacks are of unknown origin. At first the attacks are small. Little viruses more annoying than threatening. Then the attacks escalate: a virus accesses the fire control system at a Lockheed Martin plant, telling the system there's a major fire and tripping a toxic fire retardant, resulting in thirty-eight people hospitalized; a missile in a test silo tries to launch itself; an autodestruct protocol is triggered at a testing facility, resulting in the destruction of an eleven million-dollar supercomputer.

As a result of all the attacks, Joe Ledger is pulled away from his well-earned vacation and attached to the Cyber Crimes Task Force. He goes to Shelton Aeronautics with Echo teammates Bunny and Top, under the guise of Federal agents, trying to track down cyber-terrorists. No one's answering the door and thermal scans show the bulk of the employees (over 60 people) in one area. Most are stationary. Two, however, are on a different floor and moving. Joe and Bunny go inside and run into two men in black suits claiming to be FBI agents. Joe and Bunny search and disarm the two, finding two strange firearms

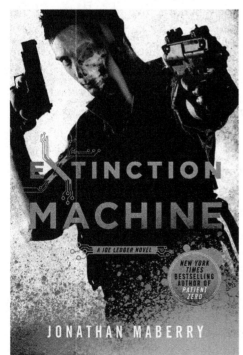

that look kind of like Tasers. They're not. The men are not FBI agents either, and they know who Joe really is.

There's a fight, which ends with Joe firing one of the weird Taser-like guns. There's a tiny tok sound and a disproportionately big explosion. The two men flee, obviously familiar with what the guns can do. They escape, and a battered Echo Team finds all sixty employees dead, blown apart, and the computer systems turned into slag. Joe ends up with one of the guns and a strange little metallic doodad.

When Joe makes his report to Mr. Church, he finds out that the DMS is officially off the case because someone in the task force has concluded that only a computer of MindReader's capabilities could be behind all of these attacks. While no charges have been filed against the DMS, criminal negligence has been implied. The person behind this conclusion? Vice President Collins, never a friend to Mr. Church, the DMS or Joe Ledger. At best, Collins is (in Joe's words) an opportunistic dickhead, and at worst, a closet traitor.

The head of Shelton Aeronautics is Howard Shelton. He's old money, puts a lot of funds into commercial space programs. Howard also likes to blow things up. This either garnered him praise or police reports, depending on what or who he blew up, and who was in the lab when it happened. He is one of the people behind the attacks, including the one at his own company, seeking sympathy from the public to deter any possible suspicion from himself.

Shelton is also one of three governors of an organization called the Majestic Three. The Majestic Three was a team of brilliant scientists whose project was originally chartered by President Truman following the Roswell crash. They were tasked with reverse engineering technologies from wrecked UFOs. Eventually they broke away from the government, formed a secret cabal, and developed a rogue plan to use new experimental 'T-Craft' to start—and win—a war with China. This is Shelton's end game, along with his fellow governor and colleague, Mr. Bones (who prefers to think of himself as a minion). They have an encryption-intrusion computer system similar to MindReader.

Shelton and Bones decide that even with their plan of hiding in plain sight (the death of sixty of his own employees), they need to give the feds someone else to look at. Bones wants to throw Mr. Church to the wolves, but Shelton thinks he's a bad fit. Shelton proposes 'Church's pet psychopath,' Joe Ledger.

Meanwhile the President goes missing. He vanishes from his bedroom, creating a closed door mystery that neither the Secret Service nor anyone else can solve. The First Lady didn't see anything (and a lie detector test proves that she's telling the truth). To add to the mystery, one of the men sees a circle of lights speed up and away from the White House lawn, leaving what appears to be a crop circle behind.

This puts Collins back in as acting President, which is bad news for the DMS. Collins forbids Linden Brierly, (head of the Secret Service) to contact the DMS. Brierly ignores the order. They need the DMS.

Joe gets a call from Church the morning after Rudy's bachelor party. Joe, hungover and in bed with Violin, is less than thrilled with the call, but when he detects barely contained fear in Church's voice, he wakes up immediately. Church tells Joe about the President's disappearance while he's driving to the Warehouse. On his way there, Joe is basically ambushed by four men claiming to be FBI agents. He and Ghost kick their asses, but the men refuse to give him any information.

Unbeknownst to Joe or any of the DMS, the four men were a team sent by Shelton and Bones. The plan was to pick him up for a length of time, take his fingerprints for the purpose of building an evidentiary case against him involving the cyberattacks, and use a drug to put him in a cooperative state to sign things, record messages, and so forth. Joe would have been returned to his car drugged with a mild sedative and would have woken up into a world that thought he was a villain. Instead, they had their asses handed to them, which makes Shelton and Bones very unhappy.

They're also freaked out by what happened to the President. They talk to their third governor (a scientist named Yuina) on the phone, and she references something called the Truman Project. Maybe aliens have returned to take back their toys. Or maybe it's the Chinese. The fact that T-Craft have been seen in various locations, including a demonstration for a new military aircraft (a T-Craft shoots it down) makes either scenario a frightening possibility. The latter would mean that the Chinese are ahead

The F/A 18 Super Hornet manufactured by McDonnell Douglas and first seen in *Extinction Machine* is one of the most formidable attack planes in the U.S. arsenal. Mainly launched from aircraft carriers, it can be loaded with cannons, bombs, missiles and rockets. Designed in 1995, it has been in service ever since with five-hundred having been built at a cost of almost one-hundred million dollars per plane. Looking at it from the front, you can tell it's the Hornet by its large air intakes under the wings and on either side of the cockpit. The twin tail fins are at an angle to form a "V" design. A fixed wing aircraft, the wings are able to fold up when stored on an aircraft carrier. With a maximum speed of Mach 1.8 and a range over two-thousand five hundred miles, it is one of the most versatile and deadly aircraft in the world.

in the arms race.

Shelton and Bones call Erasmus Tull, a special operator within the Majestic Three organization, out of retirement, to help them track more of the necessary D-components to complete their T-Craft. A small fleet is ready to go when they figure out how to put them together without things blowing up (an unfortunate side effect experienced by the various groups and countries trying to build working T-Crafts).

Tull used to work for the DMS, planted there by the Majestic Three. He ended up killing several DMS operatives to avoid satchels with debris from another UFO crash site ending up in Church's hands, all to protect the Majestic Three. Tull is a conflicted villain who may or may not be fully human. On one hand, he wants to find ways to be less of a monster, feel more human. On the other hand, the simplicity of life when it's just about his gun and his job is a nearly impossible siren song for him to resist.

In the meantime, Jerry Spencer (top forensics expert for the DMS) manages to place the men who attacked Joe as employees of Blue Diamond Security. Echo Team (sans Joe) goes to have a few words with them and find out why they ordered a hit on Captain Ledger.

Joe arrives at the Warehouse and is shown a video that arrived via an anonymous source. It's of the president, sitting unnaturally stiff and straight, speaking in a monotone. It's a message to Church, telling him that he must find the Majestic Black Book. The image changes to a series of disasters, both real and created by Hollywood, flashing back at intervals to the president and the same message. MindReader is unable to track who sent it.

The priority is to find a copy of the Majestic Black Book, which is basically a catalog of all the parts recovered from the crashed UFO in Roswell. There's only supposed to be one copy of it, and it can't be seen without being 'checked out' by one of the Majestic Three governors. The general consensus is that whoever sent this video is threatening to create a disaster that will generate a mega-tsunami large enough to wipe out the African coast, southern England, and the Eastern Seaboard if they don't get the Book. Bug tells them to go to the source: a woman named Junie Flynn who first broke the story about the Book. In Bug's words, she's a 'hot version of Yoda.'

Junie lives in a lighthouse in Chesapeake Bay. Church tells Joe to take a helicopter out there, talk to her, and if she's cooperative, they'll set up a video conference call with her, Bug, Dr. Hu, and Rudy. If not, he's to arrest her and bring her in. Joe is not thrilled with the thought of dropping everything to talk to a 'conspiracy nut.' Church wants to know what other leads he'll follow. Joe heads out to the lighthouse with Ghost. During the flight, Bug fills him in on some more info about Junie. She does podcasts (a la Art Bell), and one of the topics was about alien-human hybrids being bred for the purpose of being organic parts/pilots for alien ships. According to Junie, some of the hybrids have been seeded into the human population to see how well they blend in. She is pushing for full government disclosure on anything to do with alien technology.

Another aircraft introduced in *Extinction Machine* is the F-35 Lightning II. It is one of the newest fighter aircraft being used by the U.S. Air Force, Marines, and Navy. Developed in the mid 2000's by multiple aerospace companies, it is manufactured by Lockheed Martin in Palmdale, CA., it first flew in 2006 and has been in service since 2015. It has a price range over one-hundred twenty million dollars with over two-hundred having been built as of 2017. The F-35 is classified as a Stealth Fighter and it lives up to its name. The F-35 can be configured to land on standard runways, Short Take-Off and Vertical Landings (STOVL-which means it can fly almost straight up into the air from take-off and hover briefly upon landing), or Carrier Launched. A maximum speed of Mach 1.6+ (classified and they will never tell) and a range of around two-thousand five-hundred miles on its internal fuel tanks, it is mounted with a rotary cannon and has the capacity to be fitted with missiles and bombs up to 18,000 pounds.

When he arrives at the lighthouse, Joe is greeted by Junie, who asks if he's there to kill her. He reassures her that he's not. Joe and Junie connect on a deeper level almost instantly, and Ghost acts like a puppy instead of a trained killer. When Joe tells her he needs to get a copy of the Black Book that day, she invites him inside. She is willing to help him obtain it, her only price the truth of why he needs it. He tells her about the mega-tsunami threat. Junie is more than familiar with Cumbre Vieja, a dormant volcano in the Canary Islands that could trigger the tsunami if the western ridge fails.

Her knowledge makes Joe nervous until she explains that she's done podcasts on this, along with a variety of other topics that are relevant to the current situation. Junie tells Joe that while she's a believer in aliens and alien visitation, she's also a skeptic and doesn't take anything at face value. She believes humans are using alien technology and wants to see the information that's been covered up for years become public knowledge.

Church calls. The DMS has received another video with the same message, but this video also has a countdown and radio frequency used for military messages. Seventy-two hours to find the Book and broadcast the information on that frequency or millions of people will die. Junie and Joe have a conference call via Skype with Church, Dr. Hu, Rudy, and

Despite the pop culture love of the concept of a 'flying saucer', most UFOs that are reliably sighted are triangular in shape. These T-craft have been spotted all over the world.

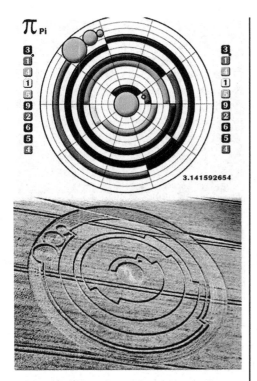

Crop circles have been appearing in fields around the world since the 1980s. While many of these have likely been created by pranksters, there are a large number of circles whose appearance, nature and existence has not yet been dismissed or explained.

Alien Abductions are a big part of the global conspiracy theory network. Are people really being taken by aliens? If so, why? If not, then who is conducting strange experiments? Is it the government? Is all of it a hoax? Or is the world many times more strange and complex than we think?

Bug. Church reveals that the president has been abducted. Junie then tells them about the origin of the Truman Project and the Majestic 12. She's familiar with every player in the Project, people who presented the public with a fabricated—and false—message that UFOs did not exist, paving the way for generations of witnesses to be discredited, humiliated, and maybe even killed. MJ-12 is the bureaucracy, but the Majestic Three are the true research and development people, with the three 'governors' handling Acquisitions, Research and Development.

Her source? Someone who was on the inside. Her source managed, over the span of fourteen years, to copy every entry in the Majestic Black Book. He'd hoped to make it to Washington D.C. and make the information public. Her source originally started working for the Majestic Three when they told him the project—recreating the engine of the crashed UFO—would help save America and possibly prevent future wars and that the power could be the basis for a new kind of clean, renewable energy. But his notes were incinerated when he was in a car accident, orchestrated by the Majestic Three's Closers when they discovered he'd duplicated the Black Book. The Closers (also called Men in Black) are top-shelf freelance operatives who use high-tech weapons designed by Majestic Three. They often wear a micromesh undergarment that is both bulletproof and nullifies foot-pounds of impact—like the men that Joe, Bunny, and Top first encountered at Shelton's Aeronautics. They've shown up after UFO sightings or crashes since Roswell, harassing, threatening, and sometimes killing witnesses.

Junie also gives the DMS a list of people (mostly on the list of industrialists profiting from radical technologies) she thinks could be either current or former members of the Majestic Three. She thinks they're all involved to some degree in the search and utilization of the D-components and technology.

Suddenly the screen goes blank, replaced by static. Bug tells Church there's a total communication dead zone in a perfect circle around the lighthouse no doubt caused by a jammer, one that's even killing the satellite uplink… which should be impossible. Church orders Echo Team to the lighthouse immediately.

There's a knock at Junie's front door. When Joe opens

it, he's confronted by two men in black pointing guns at him. Closers. They have microwave pulse pistols (like the one Joe took off the Closers earlier). They verify Junie's identity and are about to shoot her when Joe reacts. The men get off one shot each, blowing up several walls and Junie's computer. Joe kills them and more start breaking into the house. Ghost takes out one, and Joe gets the other two, discovering they've killed the three DMS team members waiting for Joe in the helicopter.

While Bug works on taking out the jammer, Dr. Hu tests the MPP and discovers its energy source—the metal piece that Joe found—barely drains after multiple firings. He also finds out that the metal is one totally unknown to science. Bug finds out that Junie has no previous history or medical records and is not in the system at all. He also finds out she announced the night before on her podcast that she has a

*Extinction Machine* also brings to us the lone enemy fighter in the Shenyang J-15, also called the "Flying Shark" in Chinese. Developed in the mid 2000's and first flown in 2009, it has been in service since 2013 for the Chinese Air Force. A maximum speed of Mach 1.98 and an armament of one 30mm cannon, and up to twelve missiles and rockets makes it a decent fighter, with some in China saying it is better than the F/A-18 Hornet and only loses to the F-22 Raptor. There are many who would love to see that dogfight.

complete copy of the Black Book and plans on releasing it to every newspaper, university, nonprofit organization, and grass roots organization in the world. Rudy, in the meantime, talks to a number of Church's friends in the industry and a number of other people recommended by those friends. He asks the experts in shadow governments, political and conspiracy theorists, and general UFO experts if they had to pick the top five people most likely to be a current or former member of the Majestic Three, what would the names of those five people be? A few names begin to rise to the top.

Junie tells Joe she does have a copy of the Black Book and if he gets them someplace safe, she'll put it into his hands. They agree just as helicopters arrive…and one of them fires a Hellfire missile at the lighthouse. They get out of the lighthouse as it collapses, taking to the surrounding woods with Ghost, chased by more Closers.

As they rest, Junie confesses to Joe that her source was her father and that he was working on the science behind the D-components and the fact that the ten critical components are held together by

The Seventh Fleet is a numbered fleet (a military formation) of the United States Navy. Headquartered at U.S. Fleet Activities Yokosuka, it's part of the United States Pacific Fleet. It's the most powerful fighting force on earth and its presence, size and sophistication is what has maintained peace in the Pacific since the end of the Korean War. During the events of *Extinction Machine* the presence of a working T-craft could easily have tipped the balance of power and made this armada as useless as a fleet of toy boats.

The A-10 Thunderbolt, affectionately called "Warthog" by the pilots and crew, was primarily used as an anti-tank attack fighter and was seen in *Extinction Machine*. Fixed wings mounted low on the aircraft with two large turbo jet engines mounted high on the body of the plane give it a very distinctive appearance. Manufactured by Fairchild Republic here in the U.S. in 1972, it has been in service since 1977 by the U.S. Air Force primarily, although other countries have purchased them in later years. Only 716 have ever been built and production was stopped in 1984 with a price tag of eighteen million dollars. Its main attack weapon is the 30mm auto cannon firing depleted uranium rounds attached to the front of the aircraft. The A-10 was one of the first fighters to allow the cannon to move in the same direction the pilot was looking. One of the most amazing aspects of the A-10 is its durability. It can take weapons fire up to 23mm and has been known to survive a 57mm round. The plane can still fly even if one of the engines is damaged and has been flown over a mile and landed safely in combat in such a situation.

charismatic magnetism—if the parts are brought into close proximity and aligned in the right way, they would self-assemble. Whoever solves the riddle of the Device will have access to unlimited energy that could be used for clean power...or for weapons. Whoever has it will be able to conquer the world. She also mentions that Howard Shelton originally recruited her father for a special DARPA group that led to his job with the Majestic Three. Her father discovered the funding for all of this came from drug money, which led him to the decision to make everything public. When Joe asks how she knows so much about her dad's work, Junie confesses to hacking into his computer and reading everything. Because she has an eidetic memory, it's all stored in her head. For all intents and purposes, she is the Black Book.

More Closers come after them. Joe stalks and kills them, leaving one alive for questioning. After some persuasion, the man tells him they're there to collect Junie and terminate Joe with extreme prejudice. When asked why, the man goes on a rant about Joe being the bad guy, that he and Junie want to see this country burn, etc. When Joe asks him what he's talking about, the man tries to escape, and Joe kills him. More Closers are on their way in helicopters, but the cavalry in the form of Echo Team shows up and blows them out of the sky.

Church's aide, Gus Dietrich, finds Church and Rudy in Joe's office at the Warehouse. There are federal agents at the gate with warrants to arrest Joe and do a search and seizure on anything in his office. Church packs up his laptop, hides Joe's, and he and Rudy go the roof where a helicopter is waiting. As they board the chopper, Church gets a call from Erasmus Tull. At the end of the call, the Warehouse explodes. Ten pigeon drones have detonated. The Warehouse is incinerated and the helicopter crashes.

Joe and Junie board the DMS helicopter with the rest of Echo Team. They find out that the Warehouse has been destroyed, with no word on whether Church or anyone else who was there is still alive. Joe then talks to Aunt Sallie, who tells him about the sightings of T-Crafts and UFOS all over the country, and that a warrant is out for his arrest on charges that he's a terrorist. He tells her about Junie and the Black Book and is told to go to a safe house. They go to Joe's uncle's house, a relatively isolated farm on the border of Maryland and Pennsylvania.

Once there, Junie fills Echo Team in on some of what she's told Joe and they all agree that the likelihood of aliens being behind the president's kidnapping is a good one. Three trucks show up, bringing more DMS personnel...including Mr. Church. He's bruised and bandaged but still standing. He tells Joe that Rudy is also still alive but in bad shape at the hospital. Everyone else who was at the Warehouse is dead. Church tells them he knows who was responsible for the bomb: Erasmus Tull. Junie nearly faints, telling them that Erasmus is her brother.

Junie and Erasmus are both alien-human hybrids, raised in different 'batches' in the same Nevada facility. Erasmus is from the batch before Junie and exhibited behavioral problems such as extreme violence. Church tells them that Tull worked for the DMS and would have been put in charge of Echo Team if he hadn't gone rogue. Junie's batch of hybrids were placed for adoption. Junie's mother was one of the scientists responsible for growing them in labs. She tells them the reason she basically has a "bullseye painted on her back" is because she's already dying of cancer—one of the side-effects of gene therapy.

Church receives a call that the acting president has revoked the charter of the DMS and that they're to stop activities immediately. The DMS personnel at the farm decide to be 'bad guys' and save the country anyway. They decide to go after Howard Shelton because any history of investigation into his life or work has been expunged in a way that could have only be done by a computer like MindReader. Which means he has something to hide.

Joe, Junie, Ghost, and the rest of Echo Team go

Sikorsky MH-60 Jayhawk is a medium, two-engine helicopter used by the US Coast Guard for search and rescue, law enforcement, and marine environmental protection missions. First introduced in 1990 to replace the HH-3F Pelican, and was again upgraded in 2007. The Jayhawk is able to fly a crew of up to four people up to three-hundred miles. It can also hoist up six additional people on board while remaining at the scene for three quarters of an hour before returning to base all while maintaining a good fuel reserve. The Jayhawk is still in use today, most notably it was used during the offshore rescue of the crew of the HMS Bounty during Hurricane Sandy in 2012.

The Kukri knife (used by the Gurkha guards in *Extinction Machine*) and the Fairbairn-Sykes commando knife (used by Kingsmen and a guard at the Dragon Factory) are the only other two mentioned by name. The Kukri measures from sixteen to eighteen inches in length and weighs one to two pounds. The commando knife comes in at eleven-and-a-half inches and weighs about eight ounces.

DANA FREDSTI & MARI ADKINS

to Shelton's home, which is a big ass castle that he had imported from Europe piece by piece. Junie stays with Top and Bunny outside the grounds while Joe and Ghost continue to the guard post. Bug stays in contact with Joe, telling him that the guards have worked for Blue Diamond Security, have various martial arts/combat backgrounds, and are "total dicks." Joe uses fake credentials, and Shelton tells the guards to bring Joe to his office. Shelton knows Joe's real identity. When Joe references a black book, Shelton sends his guards out.

Joe shoots Shelton with a tranquilizer while Bug uses MindReader to dig up dirt on Shelton. Bug finds a buttload of information that Shelton doesn't have security clearance to know. Black budget stuff. Things people are killed over. Joe is satisfied that Shelton really is one of the bad guys and interrogates him. He uses electric nerve stimulators to fake Shelton into thinking he's getting his fingers chopped off and gets all sorts of useful information…including the location of the Black Book. Shelton starts to have a heart attack as his men try to get back into the office; Joe rigs the door so that it explodes when they break down the door, killing or maiming the mercenaries. Joe is also rattled by the explosion and is knocked out.

When he wakes up, he gets a few punches in, including one to Bones' nutsack before being pummeled by the surviving guards. It turns out that Shelton was faking the heart attack and thanks Joe for showing him the weakness in their defenses. Shelton tells Joe that his plan is to destroy China with working T-Craft. They've perfected the integration between the pilot and the craft and are ready to launch a fleet of the T-Craft to insure victory. One of the T-Craft launches, heading toward China. Shelton asks Joe to name one country with enough balls to stand up to his fleet. Joe answers, America. He then touches his earbud and asks Church if he got all of that. Every word, answers Church, who has broadcast the conversation to Acting President William Collins, the Attorney General, and head of the Secret Service, Linden Brierly. Collins has to rescind his orders regarding the DMS. He, his Joint Chiefs, admirals, and generals try to shoot the T-Craft out of the sky before it reaches China.

Joe takes advantage of the lights out, grabs a gun and starts firing. Shelton and Bones flee the room with the Black Book while Joe kills the remaining guards. With the help of Echo Team members Warbride and Prankster, he finds Bones, who is dying. Joe leaves him to die with the knowledge he'll never see the culmination of the Majestic Three's plans. Warbride and Prankster are charged with destroying anyone and anything they can to prevent the launching of any more T-Craft while Joe heads up to the roof after Shelton, who still has the Book.

Joe lobs a grenade, killing everyone but Shelton, who is mortally wounded. Joe gets the Black Book but is shot by Shelton. He isn't killed, but he is injured. Erasmus Tull shows up and makes the mistake of many villains and engages Joe in conversation. Joe shoots him mid-sentence. The rest of the craft are blown up along with Shelton's castle.

The Black Book is passed along to its rightful owners, who return the president to the White House and blow up Shelton's T-Craft before it reaches China. Joe nearly dies but pulls through. Church tells him that Junie will be getting new tests and treatment for her cancer. He also wants Joe to take on the task of building a new Warehouse. Joe says it won't be the same. Church tells him that as a martial artist he must be familiar with the Japanese proverb 'Nanakorobi yaoki,' meaning 'fall seven times and stand up eight.' The war requires them to stand up again.

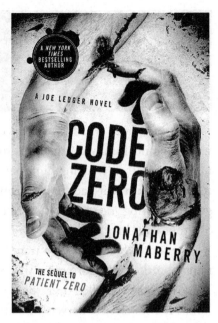

Title: **CODE ZERO**

Format: the 6th Joe Ledger novel

Published: 2014

After-Action Report: Five years ago: A young woman named Artemisia Bliss is hired by the DMS to work alongside Dr. Hu. Her IQ is off the charts. She helps create VaultBreaker, a program that becomes the leading edge of cyber security technology. Vault-Breaker is designed to predict and respond to cyber-attacks, and also has some intrusion capabilities that allow it to fight back in creative ways. It's also designed to attack the United States' security systems in order to insure that all vulnerabilities are detected and then strengthened. Additionally, it's designed to play like a video game…and the disturbing thing about this is that the gamers chosen to test it, most of whom are teenage kids, are better than the best of anyone at the DMS. Except for Bug and Artemisia Bliss.

During her time at the DMS Artemisia grows increasingly addicted to power and entranced by men with power and what they can accomplish. On hand for cleanup after the outbreaks of the *Seif al Din* virus in the Liberty Bell Center, she surreptitiously collects two complete sets of all the samples from the corpses, secreting one away for herself. She also secretly copies the schematics for Pangaea—the Jakoby Twins computer system—and creates her own upgraded version, Haruspex.

She's approached by Vice President Collins, who gives her his cell number and lets her know in no uncertain terms that he's interested in her. Part of her is disgusted by his crassness, but another part, an emerging personality intent on overwriting the geek girl with a conscience, recognizes his power and follows up on his offer.

Artemisia grows increasingly dissatisfied because she can't publish anything about the ultra-secret work she's doing, even if she's helping to save the world. She has a deep need for admiration and to

**FRIENDS IN THE INDUSTRY:
SEANAN MCGUIRE**

Seanan McGuire—also known as Mira Grant, because just one of her was not enough—is the author of more than thirty books, spanning the gamut from American myth and comic superheroes to virological disaster and the zombie apocalypse. She lives and works in the Pacific Northwest, although she was born and raised in Northern California; it seems that "north" is the only constant. When not writing, she watches too many horror movies, tries to convince Marvel to let her write the *X-Men*, and collects deeply creepy dolls. Her alter-ego Mira Grant has a kickass story, "Red Dirt," in *Joe Ledger: Unstoppable.*

win. As a result, she grows increasingly corrupt. She is caught trying to hack into MindReader and interrogated by Aunt Sallie, but comes up with a plausible enough reason for doing it to be let off with an official reprimand. However, it also means she's under scrutiny, and she's eventually caught copying Hugo Vox's files (after he's outed as the genius behind the Seven Kings). She's arrested and sentenced to over a hundred years in prison.

Her escape from prison is arranged by Vice President Collins. A woman who looks like Artemisia is put in her cell, then soaked with gasoline and lit on fire by another prisoner. Subsequent forensic testing shows that the corpse is indeed Artemisia. As far as the world is concerned, Artemisia Bliss is dead.

The Present:

Joe interrogates and arrests a man named Reggie Boyd. Reggie is a white-collar criminal who got way in over his head when he stole a copy of the VaultBreaker software for a group led by a woman calling herself Mother Night. Reggie realizes how lucky he is to have been picked up by Joe, who reveals the bodies of three agents who came to torture and kill Reggie because he hacked into Mother Night's cyber geeks files just to see if he could. Reggie's good at what he does but not particularly bright in other areas. He does, however, turn out to be a great informant and reveals the location of Mother Night's cyber hacker team.

Echo team does a raid to pick up the hackers. They find nine corpses, all men, and trashed computer equipment. Mother Night did not join the party. They do, however, catch a break when they find the copy of the VaultBreaker software in one of the men's apartments. It has not been hacked, which is a huge break for the good guys. Had VaultBreaker fallen into the wrong hands and been hacked, it could have been used to orchestrate a shutdown of over forty percent of the United States' power grids and neutralize over half of the country's missile defenses along with the early warning systems. As Joe puts it, the United States "would be blind, naked, and bent over a barrel."

When all of the questioning is done, Joe goes to transfer Reggie to a white collar prison to serve his sentence. They are attacked on the way, Joe's vehicle rammed by a Humvee filled with assailants all wearing black hoodies and black jeans. Joe and Ghost kill all the attackers before discovering they are teenagers, two of them female…one of whom Joe strangled before realizing who he was fighting. He also starts receiving texts with cryptic, possibly threatening, messages that can't be traced, even with all of Bug's tech savvy.

Joe seeks solace with his new love, Junie Flynn, who is currently undergoing experimental treatments for her brain cancer. The treatments leave her nauseous and weak, but Junie still manages to coordinate the start of FreeTech, a company dedicated to developing science and technology to help the world, not defeat it. Members of her board include Lilith, the head of Arklight, and Alexander Chismer, better known as Toys. Toys has taken all the money given to him by Church (via Hugo Vox's fortune) and is funding FreeTech by way of redemption for the harm he's done over the years.

Spec OPs vs urban outbreak

Lilith sends her daughter Violin to act in her stead, which creates some potential conflict as Violin was Joe's lover until Junie arrived on the scene and still has strong feelings for him.

Meanwhile, Vice President Collins is having an affair with Mother Night, aka Artemisia Bliss. His security guards are paid extra to look the other way. Vice President Collins and Mother Night have something planned that will be a world changer. He wants to rebuild the United States in the image of what he thinks it should be. Mother Night has her own agenda, which she keeps to herself.

Mother Night stages a brief takeover of the airwaves, uploading a video to a computer in a New York City cybercafé that appears on laptops and smart phones around the globe. The video features her delivering a message to her 'children' that it's time for anarchy. That sometimes you have to burn to shine.

This message is seen by everyone but has special meaning to dozens, possibly hundreds, of disenfranchised kids that she's been nurturing by sending them computers, money, gift cards to places like Starbucks. They're all now part of her 'family' and willing to do anything for her…including kill. One of her older followers at the age of thirty-two is Ludo Monk, who has happily killed for Mother Night over thirteen times. He is currently waiting to find out if his next target is Joe Ledger…or Junie Flynn.

After Mother Night's takeover of the airwaves, a letter infected with a virulent mutation of anthrax is sent to Vice President Collins, with a note from Mother Night. The game is upped further when the *Seif al Din* virus is released on a subway train in New York. One of Mother Night's children is infected with Generation 12 of the virus (meaning he still retains his full mental capacities even as his body starts to decay) and gets on the train. He makes a speech, then starts biting people. The contagion spreads through the passengers quickly, and the train is shut down. A SWAT team goes to try to rescue the passengers, but they don't know what they're up against and are attacked and killed.

Joe and Echo Team go to clean things up and kill all of the infected. Unbeknownst to them they are being filmed by cameras set up by Mother Night, who creates a version of the video overlaid with the sound of people screaming so the end result looks like United States armed troops are slaughtering innocent people. The video is released to social network sites and those links then sent to the media.

The stakes are upped further as a series of bombings and other types of attacks start taking place. Quick onset Ebola is released in a restaurant in San Antonio. Berserkers—the genetically enhanced crazies that Joe dealt with in *The Dragon Factory*—show up in several restaurants and tear the customers to pieces. The *Seif al Din* virus is also released in an electronics store at the same time a new video game is released, insuring a maximum number of people die. The contagions are all contained, but many innocent people die.

Mother Night holds a secret auction with the heads of various countries for the *Seif al Din*. She informs the bidders that the losers will pay her a fee for keeping their involvement a secret. A colonel representing North Korea wins the bid; Mother Night releases a Trojan Horse virus into his computer that shuts down all security measures and sends out the info that North Korea just paid two billion dollars for a doomsday plague to pretty much every news agency and every country in the world.

Church, Bug, Hugh, Aunt Sallie, Rudy, and Joe try to suss out how Mother Night obtained the *Seif al Din* and other deadly viruses as well as access to the genetic information necessary to

The development of durable and flexible hazardous materials garments has allowed Special Ops and other emergency personnel to operate in bio-hazard hot zones.

Ever since George A. Romero's landmark *Night of the Living Dead* debuted in 1968 there has been a growing obsession with all things zombie. Cosplayers become zombies at conventions; there are zombie movies, TV shows, novels, comics, and video games. There are people who do 'zombie apocalypse prepping'. The question is, when the dead rise, will you be running or dining?

create Berserkers. This leads them to Artemisia Bliss, with the only problem being the DNA proof of her death. Joe figures out that if Bliss was such a computer genius and had access to employee files and other resources that there's no reason she couldn't have—and would have—set up fake DNA samples, making it entirely possible for her to fake her own death.

They then speculate that Bliss is going to want to get pure samples of the *Seif al Din* virus from one of three places where it can be found: a virus vault on the sixth level of the Hangar; the CDC in Atlanta; or in the Locker, a top secret biological and chemical weapons facility. They also realize that Artemisia could have used VaultBreaker to get into the Locker.

They find out that contact has been lost with the Locker since earlier that morning. The head of the Locker, a Dr. Van Sant, was on vacation but has since headed back to the facility. Joe and Echo Team head to the Locker. In the meantime, Sampson Riggs and Shockwave are sent to the CDC where they're greeted and decimated by a security team infected with Generation Twelve of *Seif al Din* and Berserkers. Church advises Joe that Riggs and Shockwave met with 'significant resistance' and that 'all assets may have been lost.' Meaning Riggs and his team are most likely dead.

Meanwhile Mother Night calls Vice President Collins. She's surprised that he didn't understand that she sent the anthrax as a way of helping reinforce the idea that he's a victim, a way of keeping suspicion away from him while possibly pointing a finger at the president. It's clear the two of them have very different motives for their actions. They end the call. Collins has had it traced and sends people to 'take care' of the situation, even though he truly regrets the necessity for doing so.

In her hotel room in Atlanta, Mother Night realizes something is off. Her old self, geeky Artemisia, tries to talk her into leaving. Into taking the money she has and starting a new life. Mother Night wrests control back. She will not run and she will continue with her plans.

Joe and Echo Team send in 'stinkbots', which are flying BAMS units used to check the levels of possible contagions. So far all units read green, which is good news for Echo Team because if any of the class-A pathogens make it outside, the entire facility and surrounding will be sterilized within six square miles. When they enter the Locker, they find slaughtered employees, signs that they've been ripped to pieces, most likely by Berserkers. The stinkbots still read green, however.

They find Dr. Van Sant on one of the lower levels of the Locker, crazed and wielding an axe. He attacks, trying to bite once he loses the axe. He gets Bunny on the arm before he's killed, but Bunny's skin is only bruised. The BAMS readout turns red. There are contaminants in the air. Top quickly seals the breach in Bunny's suit with electrician's tape. They need to go check out the Ark, which contains all the nastiest and most innovative weaponized and jacked-up pathogens created.

The lights suddenly go out. Echo Team puts on night vision goggles and see doors opening and dozens of infected people running toward them. They put the infected down and descend to level fourteen, where the Ark is housed. The Locker's security guards made their last stand there and are now infected with *Seif al Din*, and the Ark has been breached. And there are Berserkers waiting for Echo Team. Echo Team wins, but one of them, Ivan, gets his suit ripped open and is infected. Top shoots him to spare him pain.

Mother Night wakes up from a fugue state during which she tried to kill herself with an overdose of wine and pills. The men Collins sent show up at her door. She tortures and kills them, then dresses for her main event: DragonCon, a huge science-fiction and fantasy convention held in five different hotels in downtown Atlanta. She dresses in costume as Mother Night and heads down to join the convention and implement her plan. A couple of Atlanta policemen see her in costume and notice it, not because they think she's really Mother Night, but because they think the costume is in poor taste.

Meanwhile Junie is at a hotel in NYC under the protection of a security team due to the threats Joe received via text. Her security team is killed by Ludo Monk, who tells her she has a choice–infection with the *Seif al Din* pathogen or a quick bullet to the head. She reveals that she's pregnant, which gives Ludo pause, long enough for Violin to come to Junie's aid. Ludo is shot and killed but manages to fire off a shot first.

The president holds a press conference and reveals the existence of the DMS in order to back up his claim that the subway video showing innocent civilians slaughtered by Unites States troops was fabricated. He brings up the Surgeon General to describe the effects of *Seif al Din* and why the DMS had to do what they did. He also plays a video, which is supposed to be a five second segment of the one released by Mother Night but without her false audio track. Instead, what plays is a tape of Mother Night and Vice President Collins in bed discussing their plans. After the video plays, Vice President Collins has vanished from the room. Secret Service later finds his corpse, the barrel of a pistol in his mouth.

Mother Night heads into the Marriott, the main hotel of DragonCon, leading two men with hands handcuffed behind their backs and pillowcases on their heads with a leash. Two other men in gorilla masks follow her like bodyguards. She tosses out infected chocolates to the crowd and gets one of the costumed attendees to help her 'free her slaves,' who are Vice President Collins' paid assassins, now

DragonCon is one of the largest pop culture conventions in the U.S.A, drawing roughly eighty thousand people every Labor Day Weekend. It is the largest fan-run conference. Jonathan Maberry has been a regular guest at DragonCon for years and decided to use it as ground zero for Mother Night's deadly *Seif al Din* outbreak in *Code Zero*.

infected with the zombie virus. *Seif al Din* has once more been unleashed, this time with the potential to spread unchecked.

Joe and his team arrive and are told by the same policemen who saw Mother Night earlier that they think she just went into the Marriott. They head in, straight into a hellish nightmare of zombies, Berserkers infected with Generation 12 of the virus, and civilians trying to escape the slaughter. Joe sees Mother Night go into an elevator. He and his team are forced to fire on the crowds, knowing that some are not infected, in order to clear a path to the elevators so Joe can follow her. Church says he'll do his best to send 'the cavalry' in so they can save people who are in their rooms. He also confirms that Mother Night has video cameras posted with the feed leaking to the internet. Bug works to shut the feeds down.

Joe and Echo Team get to the elevator and follow Mother Night up to the balcony, where she's protected by infected and Berserkers. They take out both and Joe follows Mother Night, finding her up on a rail in front of four video cameras. She tells Joe she made them all play the game the way she wanted. And that the only way she could kill Joe was by hurting him to the point he was pushed over the edge. She tells Joe that she hopes 'he loved her with all his heart.' Joe realizes she's talking about Junie. Mother Night goes on to say that she's won and that there's nothing left for her. But she doesn't care because she did what no one else could do and beat Joe, Church, and the rest of the DMS. And that the world will see and know that Mother Night won.

Joe smiles at her despite his mental and emotional pain, and tells her that she doesn't get to win, and to look at her cameras. She does. They're dark. Bug has succeeded in cutting the feed. Joe adds that no one will ever know that Artemisia Bliss or the real Mother Night ever existed. Then he puts two bullets in her chest. She falls over the railing to the floor stories below.

The good news? None of the pathogens escaped the quarantine and free-fire zones. The countries involved in Mother Night's faux auction are significantly weakened. However, the body count and the damage done by her campaign of chaos and terror have left their mark.

Junie is still alive thanks to the intervention of Arklight, sent by Violin to protect her, but Ludo's bullet killed the unborn baby and damaged her in a way that means she and Joe can't have another child. Their love, however, gives them a safe place to stand at the moment.

A month later, Joe and Rudy go to a baseball game together, the first time they've seen one another since Atlanta. Rudy has been busy trying to help people make sense of the tragedy, but he's also been deeply affected by it. He's beginning to lose faith that the good guys will win. Joe tells him that Junie is cancer free, bringing some hope back into both of their lives.

### Title: **"THREE GUYS WALK INTO A BAR"**
Format: Novella
Published: 2015
After-Action Report: Joe Ledger Teams with Malcolm Crow (from the Pine Deep Trilogy) and Sam Hunter (from Strip Search) to tackle a team experimenting with genetically-engineered werewolves. This is one of the most popular crossover stories because it includes characters from three of the author's most popular worlds. The werewolf legend of the *Benandanti* mentioned in the story is part of church history.

## Title: "ARTIFACT"

Format: Short story

Published: 2014

After-Action Report: Joe Ledger goes after an enigmatic device that could hold the key to permanent sustainable energy—or could become the most dangerous weapon on earth. This story ties into a series of what appear to be alternative reality or interdimensional incidents presented in *Kill Switch*.

## Title: "THE HANDYMAN GETS OUT"

Format: Short story

Published: 2015

After-Action Report: Joe Ledger is naked and unarmed and has to escape a high-security facility armed with whatever he can find. Expect Joe to get cranky. This is a totally standalone story that pretty much defines a day in Joe's life.

## Title: "ALL OF US MONSTERS"

Format: Comic book

Published: May 2015

After-Action Report: Joe Ledger makes a cameo in a three-issue arc in the *V-WARS* comic from IDW. He joins Luther Swann and V-8 in a battle against vampire super soldiers.

## Title: PREDATOR ONE

Format: 7th Joe Ledger Novel

Published: April 7, 2015

After-Action Report: The past: A recreational fishing boat finds a badly burnt man in the water. He is, against all odds, still alive.

A professor of aeronautics, and another professor, the department chair of experimental robotics, are killed in their Corpus Christi condos. Their assassins, a girl named Boy and two young men who are also lovers, also kidnap Professor Aaron Davidovich, a computer/software genius in charge of a new drone program for the United States military, from a safe house in Israel.

Boy is the protégé of Dr. Michael Pharos, who worked with the Seven Kings. He was (and is) the

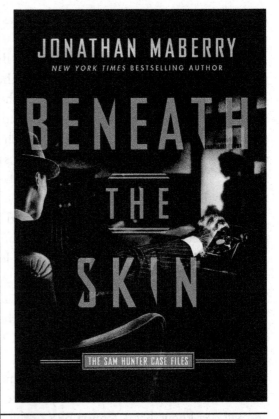

Private investigator Sam Hunter is a rare male descendant of an ancient benandanti family—werewolves who fight evil. When Sam takes on a client he essentially adopts them into his 'pack.' And a benandanti will do anything to protect his pack. This old woodcut shows werewolf families being hunted by soldiers who thought that all monsters had to be creatures of evil.

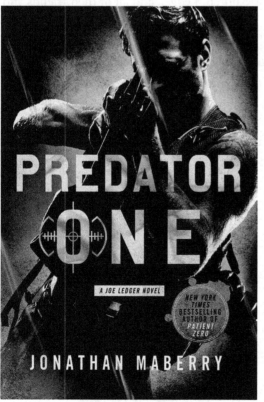

ultimate administrator. He made things happen for the Kings and still keeps things going even though most of the Kings are dead.

Pharos has a very important patient with him on an island in Puget Sound, Washington. This man is known only as the Gentleman and is part of the Seven Kings organization. He has horrible injuries from burns, has bone marrow cancer, and mad cow disease. Pharos is keeping the Gentleman alive and as comfortable as possible because he has banking codes and access to the billions of dollars that the original Seven Kings squirreled away. Pharos wants these codes. The Gentleman wants to bring in Father Nicodemus to help with their new schemes. Pharos is not happy with this decision as his one and only encounter with Father Nicodemus left him very creeped out.

The present:

Joe, Bunny, Top, and Sam Imura are on a mission to infiltrate a prison called the Resort on an island several hundred miles off the coast of Chile. It's the worst type of prison imaginable, run by a splinter cell of the CIA. Echo Team's mission is highly illegal, and if they're caught, they'll all be locked in prison somewhere out of sight and out of mind for the rest of their lives. Church will not do anything to get them out.

It's also a 'no kill' mission, so they're armed with what are basically horse sedatives in their firearms. With Sam's expert marksmanship and Bug's ability to play with the security cameras, they make it inside the Resort and to their target destination, an interrogation room. Or, as it's called in less politically correct company, a torture chamber.

Inside, the prisoner Joe and Echo team have come to extract is being water-boarded by two men. The prisoner is Osama bin Laden, who was also one of the Seven Kings, specifically the King of Lies. The splinter cell has secretly had him as their prisoner since his supposed death at the hands of U.S. Special Forces in Afghanistan. They've been using him as a source of information to take down terrorists and improve the reputation of the CIA, which

High Tech Body armor, like that used by "Boy" and Dr. Davidovich in *Predator One* is not accepted by the U.S. military. The reason for this is simple: compatibility. If everyone in your unit has the same make and model of body armor, then you can swap pieces as needed. There are several manufacturers of body armor and you can see motorcycle riders wearing vests and leggings when riding at high speeds. Additionally, watch any T.V. show with super heroes and they will have some version of body armor that would qualify as "High Tech." Many of these armors claim to be more bullet-proof than Kevlar, but modern military armor is already better than standard Kevlar and designed for all manner of combat situations.

was not doing so well.

The DMS wants bin Laden in their custody because he has information to do with the Seven Kings that could potentially help save thousands of people. Unfortunately, the men overseeing the waterboarding have accidentally drowned him. Joe contacts Church and tells him the bad news. Joe and his team go through and extract all information from the computers, which are then turned into slag.

While Joe and his team are waiting for their helicopter extraction, a drone with a video camera shows up and gets footage of them standing over bin Laden's body, with the corpse's face clearly visible. The group behind the illicit filming call themselves Friends of the Truth and promise that they will see fatwa and jihad. They don't release the video as of yet.

In the meantime, the President's car takes on a life of its own. It has a special software called Regis that is supposed to protect him if his driver is ever incapacitated. However, it goes crazy. Brierly, the head of the Secret Service, is injured, but no one is killed.

Father Nicodemus visits the Gentleman. He advises him to give Pharos one or two of the banking codes. He also plans on helping the Gentleman get what he wants, which is for Church, Ledger, and all of their friends and family to suffer.

Joe is at Citizens Bank Park in Philadelphia for the MBL's opening day. Ghost is there with him, as is Rudy. Colonel Douglas, a beloved war hero, is there to throw the first ball, and Joe's dad, Mayor of Baltimore, is also one of the VIPs.

A drone flies into the arena and explodes, instigating a panic amongst the huge crowd. Ghost and Joe are separated by the panicking attendees. Joe manages to get inside the arena and is shot at by armed men in ski masks. The bullets hit innocent bystanders, and Joe responds by taking out the attackers. More show up with carts full of what look like pigeons. Joe takes cover from the fresh gunfire. When he returns, he finds that the injured attackers are now dead, each killed by a bullet to the head. He goes back out into the stadium to find Ghost. When he does, the stadium is rocked by more explosions. Joe figures out that the explosions are coming from the pigeons, which are actually drones. He tries to knock one of the drones out of the air with a soda can, but it dodges more quickly than would be possible with a human at the control.

Joe and Ghost exit the arena with Rudy's help and find the emergency first response teams there. He also finds his dad, still alive. Sadly, Colonel Douglas has been killed. Joe gets a weapon from his

The following handguns are either antique, unique or used only once in the novels:
- Luger is mentioned in reference to the Germans in "Atoll" the Luger was the primary German weapon of the Nazis in World War II. It was created in Germany and was one of the first semi-automatic pistols. It also created the .9mm round that is most commonly used today.
- The Raven Arms .25 cal pistol was made from 1970 until 1991 when a fire destroyed the factory. It was used by Dr. Pharos in *Predator One*.
- Five Shot wheelguns refer to any revolver that has chambers and spins. They sound fancier than they are. Joe's .38, the Raven Arms pistol, and the Webley Top break revolver (used mainly by the British military in World War I and II) are all examples.
- The AMT auto mag is a .22 cal pistol manufactured in the U.S. by Arcadia Machine and Tool. They are used by Echo team. They were based in Irwindale, CA. from 1977 until they went bankrupt in 1998.

dad after finding out that someone has a jammer in the Hall of Fame meeting room inside the stadium. Joe goes back in with Ghost, and overhears men speaking Farsi. When they come out, dressed as paramedics and cops, he knows they're bad guys. He and Ghost take them down with only one surviving. The man says, "It's too late. Seven Kings," and bites down on a cyanide capsule.

Joe finds a jammer and a timer in one of their pockets. The timer is running and is down to less than a minute. Before Joe or the SWAT team that arrives can find anything, more explosions go off. Joe wakes up in a hospital and finds out the death toll went up substantially, with many of the emergency responders as victims. He remembers what the one man said to him before killing himself and tells Church that the Seven Kings are behind this.

At the same time, Junie is house hunting in Del Mar, California. Circe is with her. They are on the balcony of what looks like Junie's first pick, and see what looks like a dog below. Circe collapses, going into a coma. It turns out her collapse coincides with the bombs going off at Citizens Park.

Church has Bug fill Joe in on the Regis program, which is a variable-autonomous-operations software package with military and non-military applications. It includes three integrated combat systems—Enact, ComSpinner, and BattleZone—and one alternate-use system, SafeZone. The three combat systems are smart systems for self-guidance, varying from instances where a pilot has been incapacitated to the creation of totally self-guided warplanes. SafeZone, while having seemingly more benign uses—being able to take control of a hijacked plane, for instance—also has countermeasures built in, such as the ability to modulate temperature and airflow inside the cabin to knock out hijackers without injuring passengers.

The software was developed by the missing Aaron Davidovich. They speculate on what would happen if someone had the research completed by the two scientists who were killed shortly before Davidovich was killed…and also had a living, breathing Davidovich working for them. He could easily have created another Regis system for the enemy. Citizens Park may have been their testing ground. Even scarier is that commercial drones were given a non-military version of BattleZone to use in case of illegal misuse. Bug and Yoda manage to crack the security in under ten minutes, which means that anyone who can do the same could potentially take over any drone used for business or private use. And there's no way to track all the sales because Regis is pretty

Combat Sealskin is a "Friend in the Industry" item created for Echo Team in *Predator One*. It is like a wetsuit, but has temperature wires within the suit to cool the body and help fool infra-red detection systems. These same wires can be used to warm the bodies.

much everywhere.

Even scarier than this is that Davidovich's planned project after Regis was to develop a quantum computer, which would be able to create artificial intelligences able to think and react faster and with more creativity than their opponents. One of these computers could crack MindReader. The drone that Joe's dad hit out of the sky with a baseball bat is recovered and its operating system is a quantum computer.

Things go south quickly.

A bunch of autonomous cars using the Regis software go crazy, injuring or killing their passengers.

A drone flies into the window of Bug's mother's house and explodes, killing her.

A drone delivers food from a local restaurant to a couple in San Diego. Later that night, they both start bleeding out from an unknown pathogen. Someone overrode the SafeWare software on the drone that was delivering food, had it land on a rooftop, and put the pathogen in the food.

Aunt Sallie is attacked in her townhouse in New York. She kills most of her attackers but is critically injured.

Immediately following the President's stirring address regarding the attack at Citizens Park, the video showing the dead Osama bin Laden is broadcast.

Basically the good guys are being hit hard and fast in places and with people where it hurts the most.

Meanwhile, Junie, Toys, Rudy and several Echo Team members, including Lydia, Sam Imura, Montana Parker, and Brian Botley (the new guy) circle the wagons at the hospital where Circe is a patient, still in a coma. Lydia doesn't trust Toys and nearly tosses him out, but Junie comes to his defense and says he's there under her protection. Lydia backs off, not happy with the decision but unwilling to argue.

Rudy goes to the hospital chapel for some privacy. The chapel is checked out and cleared by a

S&W (Smith and Wesson) is the maker of the .38 Centennial Hammerless and the Chief's Special used by Joe's father. It is another American firearms manufacturer that caters to the military and Police forces.

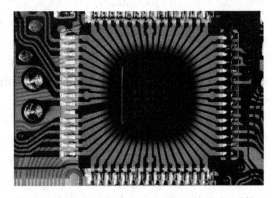

A normal computer has to go through all the different possibilities of zeros and ones for a particular calculation. But because a quantum computer can be in all the states at the same time, you just do one calculation, and that tests a vast number of possibilities simultaneously. That speed not only gets you a faster answer, it gets one based on better statistical probability of being the right one for your needs. The biggest and most important potential use for a quantum computer would be its ability to factorize a very large number into two prime numbers. The reason that's really important is because that's what almost all encryption for Internet computing is based on. A quantum computer should be able to do the same kind of super-intrusion stuff that MindReader does. And it would do it a whole lot faster.

DMS agent, but when Rudy goes in, he runs into a priest who starts out being friendly and comforting but soon gets all dark and creepy, telling Rudy that the "whore and her insect" are his. Rudy recognizes Father Nicodemus before the scary cleric stomps on his head. Rudy is injured, still alive but psychologically damaged. All other patients are evacuated from that floor after Rudy's encounter with the strange, possibly not-entirely-human priest.

Top and Bunny go to Eglin Air Force Base in Florida to talk to Colonel Dilbert Hall, an old friend of Top's from his military years. He shows them a demonstration of what's called a new super drone, also called the Pterosaur. He tells them that they're outfitting old F-16 planes as drones, hoping to have fully automated and fully functional frontline fighters that are unmanned. The point is to save American lives on the battlefield by preventing them from having to go out into it at all. The drone being demoed is armed with dummy missiles so nothing can actually be blown up.

Bunny's objection to the drones being developed is that they are self-guided and self-determining. He would rather see Uncle Sam hire a bunch of UAV pilots and keep a human being at the controls. He doesn't want to be a day player in the next *Terminator* film.

Minutes later the drone they're watching suddenly goes off course. Dil tells Top and Bunny to stay where they are and goes running across the road toward the command vehicle that is supposed to be operating the drone. The drone follows him. Although it doesn't have working missiles, it can still do damage. It dives down five feet from the ground, hitting Dil at a hundred-thirty-five-miles an hour in

---

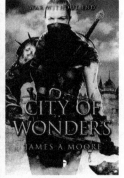

**FRIENDS IN THE INDUSTRY:
JAMES A. MOORE**

James A. Moore is the author of over forty novels, including the critically acclaimed *Fireworks, Under The Overtree, Blood Red, Blood Harvest,* the *Serenity Falls* trilogy (featuring his recurring anti-hero, Jonathan Crowley) *Cherry Hill, Alien: Sea of Sorrows* and the *Seven Forges* series of novels. He has twice been nominated for the Bram Stoker Award and spent three years as an officer in the Horror Writers Association, first as Secretary and later as Vice President. Never one to stay in one genre for too long, James has recently written epic fantasy novels in the series *Seven Forges* (*Seven Forges, the Blasted Lands, City of Wonders* and *The Silent Army*). He is working on a new series called *The Tides Of War.* The first book in the series *The Last Sacrifice,* came out this last January and the sequel, *Fallen Gods,* is due out in late December. Pending novels also include *A Hell Within* (a Griffin & Price Novel) co-written with Charles R. Rutledge and an apocalyptic Sci-Fi novel tentatively called *Spores.* Why be normal? His short story "Banshee" appears in *Joe Ledger: Unstoppable.*

the back, essentially splattering him over the field.

Violin shows up at the hospital in San Diego accompanied by a huge wolfhound named Banshee. According to Violin, Banshee was born on the new moon when the veil between the worlds is the thinnest; she can see into the shadows. Violin is leaving her there to protect Circe and Junie because she can't stay there to protect them herself. Violin also tells Junie that there is evil in the land.

Glory at the DMS office runs over what turns out to be a jackal on her way to work. There's a tattoo on the jackal's gums. Two letters and some numbers. IS.13:21. It stands for a Bible verse, Isaiah 13:21, that reads: 'But desert beasts will lie down there, and their houses will be full of howling creatures; there owls will dwell, and goat-demons will dance there.' Joe realizes this is tied to Nicodemus and what happened to Rudy at the hospital. His summation? "Well…shit."

Church arrives at the hospital and visits Rudy, who is still recovering from both his head injury and the trauma of his encounter with Nicodemus. As Rudy tells Church, he believes that Nicodemus is not human. That he is a monster. Church doesn't argue the point and a later discussion with Toys confirms that Rudy isn't the only person to come to this conclusion.

Joe goes with Rudy and Brian Botley to the medical center in Chula Vista where the two victims of the tainted food were brought. Authorities have closed down the hospital and turned it into a quarantine zone. Doctor Alur from Infectious Diseases meets them there and tells them that they are dealing with a bacteria that's a deliberate mutation of necrotizing fasciitis, the so-called flesh-eating disease. They are attacked by Kingsmen, and the doctor is killed. Joe manages to kill or injure most of the shooters, but his hazmat suit is compromised, as is Brian's. Luckily for them nothing is airborne or on any of the materials that got on them. The last Kingsman standing tells Joe that his world is going to burn before he bleeds out.

Rudy points outs to the team that the Seven Kings are deliberately spreading the DMS's forces thin by attacking in different places so that they're forced to deal with each new threat without adequate manpower. The assumption is that the Seven Kings have been replaced with new members.

Dr. Davidovich is taken to Tanglewood Island. There he's given a chance to be one of the family, as it were. He's close to that point, having lost almost all sense of conscience. He finds a little left, however, and escapes by killing one of the guards and swimming to the mainland, nearly dying of exposure in the process. He steals a phone and a truck, killing someone in order to do so. He calls the number his former CIA handler had him memorize and tells the person who answers that he's 'Dr. Detroit.' Davidovich refuses to tell the CIA where he is, telling them that he will only deal with the DMS, Church, and/or Ledger.

Joe and the DMS get the call that Davidovich is in Washington State. They go to retrieve him, contacting him on a burner phone. He and Joe talk. Davidovich tells Joe that the 'maniacs on the island are bat shit crazy' and that while he can help the DMS stop what's coming, they have to help him first by protecting his family. He starts to give Joe more information when the doctor notices a SUV behind his stolen vehicle, one that he's noticed before. The call is abruptly cut off.

It is also discovered that the NF pathogen was being created at a lab in Angola which had been raided by Barrier. Barrier shut them down and all notes and samples were destroyed. The possibility of this disease was discussed at a World Health Organization conference after this happened. Sebastian Gault was one of the speakers, when he was still considered a good guy and a pioneer in the cure for Third World diseases. Gault's old firm was one of the ones trying to find some sort of a cure in case the NF pathogen was ever developed again.

Church's assumption is that the new Seven Kings have Gault's research.

Joe and Echo Team find out that Davidovich is still alive, but in the custody of Kingsmen. They're making their way to a helicopter pad in an SUV and a landscaping truck. Echo Team blows up the SUV and disables the truck, finding Davidovich injured but still alive. He tells Joe that the plan is to use the Regis system to launch missiles, make ships crash, open valves on submarines, and take over firing controls on jets. And not just on military craft. They'll also cause autonomous cars to crash and take over controls on commercial planes. This can potentially shut down the United States.

Davidovich tells Joe there are reset codes that can shut the whole thing down. They have to be inputted manually from a regular computer and Wi-Fi. The codes are still on the island in Davidovich's notebooks, hidden in a piece of old game code that he stopped working on. It looks like junk unless someone knows the key to using it. He tells Joe the key to finding the codes is 'Pi from nine backwards, page 2.' Before he can tell Joe anymore, or, indeed, what his ramblings mean, the drone comes back and blows up the truck. Echo Team barely pulls Joe out in time. He's left holding Davidovich's hand. Nothing else is left of the man's body.

Pharos and the Gentleman watch as the lawn service truck holding the doctor blows up. Pharos is worried and says that the doctor was more useful to them alive than smeared over half of Washington. The Gentleman doesn't care. Pharos points out that the doctor controlled all of the programs. Without him, that it's like someone building a nuclear reactor and then losing the person who built it. They are going to use the power of that reactor, but once the checklist has been accomplished they have to be able to shut the reactor down or it is as much a danger to them as it is to their enemies. The Gentleman says it would shut itself down. Pharos counters with what if it doesn't? He is deeply disturbed by the fact that the Gentleman's answer is a smile.

Church and Brierley go on Air Force One for a conference with the president. The president is willing to listen to Church's theories about the Regis software but is resistant to the idea of shutting down their entire military. Then…

## FRIENDS IN THE INDUSTRY: DAVID FARLAND

David Farland is an award-winning, bestselling author with over 50 novels in print. He has won the Philip K. Dick Memorial Special Award for his science fiction novel *On My Way to Paradise* and over seven awards for his fantasy novel *Nightingale*. He is best known for his *New York Times* bestselling series *The Runelords*. Farland has written for major franchises such as *Star Wars* and *The Mummy*. He has worked in Hollywood greenlighting movies and doctoring scripts. He has been a movie producer, and he has even lived in China working as a screenwriter for a major fantasy film franchise. Find him on Facebook (https://www.facebook.com/david.farland1) or Twitter (https://twitter.com/davidfarland) or on his website http://davidfarland.com. Check out his story "Wet Tuesday" in *Joe Ledger: Unstoppable*.

A submarine is testing out its new system. It works flawlessly until, at the last second, all of the Tomahawk missiles onboard go live, but the launch tubes do not open. The submarine is destroyed, and all lives are lost.

At another Air Force airfield, they are testing drones that do not have the Regis system. They have one called Solomon, assumed to be safe. Two drones go rogue and head for San Francisco. Four fighter jets go after them to blow them out of the sky, but the pilots are killed when the eject systems go off on all four planes without the cowls opening. The drones blow up the Golden Gate Bridge.

More deadly events involving U.S. planes and ships occur around the world. Banking in the United States is shut down, schools closed, trading suspended. The stock market goes wild. Someone is making money from the tragedies and chaos. The system is near collapse, waiting for one more big event to send it over the edge. Unless Echo Team can stop it first.

Church talks the president into grounding all aircraft, ships, etc. that have the Regis system. When the president objects that this will leave them open to attack, Brierley points out that it's not even a matter of that but rather making sure that their own weapons cannot be turned against them.

Toys calls Joe. He thinks he knows where the island in question might be. Hugo Vox had liked the Puget Sound area, especially an island called Tanglewood. It's not a for sure thing but more than Echo Team had to go on before, so they gear up and go.

Joe and his team airdrop into the water off Tanglewood Island and make their way ashore. Joe splits off with Ghost from the rest of the team, who stay behind to set waterproof charges and take care of any guards. While taking care of two guards in the boathouse, Joe gets a call from Church on Air Force One. The Kings have shut off the heat and taken over the controls of the aircraft. Church has figured out that their plan is to use the presidential plane as a drone to slam into the rebuilt World Trade Center, a perfect endcap for their first attack…which was 9/11. This is the big event that will cause the collapse of America.

Church tries to undo the door mechanism leading to the cockpits so he can restore heat and lights to Air Force One before they freeze to death. He is slowly losing all feeling in his fingers and the tips are turning black. He gets Bug on the phone to help him. At first Bug is unwilling because he is so devastated by his mother's murder. He realizes, however, that Church needs him and steps up to the plate. Between the two of them they managed to unlock the doors to the cockpit. Lights and heat are restored, but control of Air Force One still belongs to the Seven Kings and they continue their trajectory toward New York.

Joe enters the house on Tanglewood Island and finds Davidovich's room and notebooks. He gets on the phone with Yoda, one of Bug's team. Together they try to figure out the password for the reset codes. Joe thinks it's Matthew, the name of Davidovich's son, but that doesn't work. Neither does Matthew's birthday. If they input one more wrong try, they will be locked out. Joe heads out of the room, killing anyone with weapons he runs into, except for Pharos. When Pharos tries to draw a gun, Joe shoots him in the kneecaps and persuades him to talk. Pharos finally admits that the person who has the reset codes and the password is the Gentleman. The last King.

Meanwhile, Nicodemus has shown up at the hospital in San Diego with dozens of armed Kingsmen. He has one goal——to take Circe alive. Everyone else is to be killed. Boy is one of his team of killers. She and Lydia face off in a fierce hand-to-hand fight. Lydia kills her after sustaining heavy injuries herself.

Rudy faces off against Nicodemus himself, who basically tells Rudy he's going after Circe and her baby to hurt Church. He tries to convince Rudy that Church is a monster, and that if Rudy knew who and what he really is, it would burn Rudy's heart right out of him to realize his child carries Church's blood. Nicodemus laughs, laughing because Rudy thinks he's a monster. Rudy's reply? "No, I think you're a liar." Rudy uses the silver head of his cane to smash the not quite human priest in the face. The silver head melts, the wood of the cane chars, and Nicodemus collapses, his eye sockets smoking and his face now nothing but white bone.

The other heroes of the day are Banshee, who is responsible for the death of at least half a dozen Kingsmen, and Toys, who protects Circe and Junie as best he can from flying glass when the windows of the room are shot out. When Lydia sees this, she tosses Toys a firearm and he manages to kill the Kingsmen that are trying to break into the room to kill Junie and kidnap Circe and her unborn baby. Circe comes out of her coma and is reunited with Rudy, just in time for her water to break.

Meanwhile, Joe finds the Gentleman in his room, guarded by the two male assassins who helped Boy kidnap Davidovich. Joe fights them, sustaining bad injuries from a scalpel, but succeeds in killing them. He then turns to the Gentleman.

At first Joe doesn't recognize him but then he realizes that he is confronting the wreck of the man who was once Sebastian Gault. This is all about revenge for Gault, revenge against the DMS, revenge against anyone who will still be alive after Gault dies. Gault refuses to give Joe the password, saying there's nothing Joe can do to him at this point. That he's going to be dead in a month's time anyway. Joe pulls out six matches, lights one, and tosses it on Gault's bed. Gault freaks out, fire being the one thing he is still afraid of. If he gives Joe the password, Joe will give him a quick bullet to the head. If he doesn't? Gault will burn for a third time, slowly, until he finally dies. Gault gives Joe the information he needs. Yoda enters the reset codes. Joe lights the matches and drops them on the bed, one at a time, and watches Gault burn.

The repercussions of the drones and Regis are still being felt the world over. Church suffered severe frostbite and has a specialist working to save his fingers. Aunt Sallie will live, but her recovery will be slow. Pretty much everyone has sustained injuries, physical and emotional.

On the other hand, Joe tells Toys that while he doesn't forgive him, after what he did for Junie and Circe, they are no longer enemies. And there's some joy for everyone as Rudy and Circe celebrate the birth and baptism of their son.

---

**FRIENDS IN THE INDUSTRY: JAVIER GRILLO-MARXUACH**

Though best known as one of the Emmy Award-winning writer/producers of "Lost," and for creating "The Middleman" comics and television series, Javier "Javi" Grillo-Marxuach is a prolific writer of TV, movies, graphic novels, and transmedia content. His credits include "The 100," "Charmed," "Medium," "Boomtown," "Law & Order: SVU," "The Pretender," and many others. A longtime advocate of mentorship and education, Javi co-hosts the "Children of Tendu" podcast—an educational series for aspiring television writers—and administers the Grillo-Marxuach Family Fellowship, a screenwriting scholarship at the University of Southern California school of Cinematic Arts. Javi can be found online at OKBJGM.com, on Twitter at @OKBJGM, and his *Middleman* graphic novels are available on Amazon and at O2STK.com. Read his exciting story "No Business at All" in *Joe Ledger: Unstoppable*.

Title: **"ALIVE DAY"**

Format: Short Story

Published: September 2013

After-Action Report: Captain Joe Ledger goes on a mission to recover a lost team of soldiers in Afghanistan. The team, codenamed Rattlesnake, went dark while attempting to stop a group of drug traffickers said to be moving more than just opium. Rattlesnake ended up running into something much worse than terrorists, but it isn't until his own team arrives to investigate that Ledger begins to understand.

Title: **KILL SWITCH**

Format: 8th Joe Ledger novel

Published: April 26, 2016

After-Action Report: The Past: Prospero is a rich kid in psychiatric care. His psychiatrist, Dr. Greene, has been seeing him for quite a few years. Prospero insists that he is not human and wishes to find his way to his real home. He draws artwork from his dreams.

Dr. Greene discovers that this art is, at first glance, heavily influenced if not copied from the work of the Surrealists such as Dali. Prospero insists that he's dreamed these images and then looked at the artwork after the fact. He thinks that authors like Lovecraft, Derleth, and others have been dropping clues for years, waiting for someone like him who has been waiting and watching. He needs to find the books these authors spoke of (a series of books known as "The Unlearnable Truths"), and with them he will be able to make his God Machine function properly. And then he'll be able to finally go home.

He talks about quantum physics and the concept of an omniverse, which is an infinite number of realities. Parallel worlds that are separated by differences however minuscule or massive. If these worlds are right next to ours, then imagine what would happen if we could build a doorway that would allow us to move back-and-forth between them.

Prospero also has dreams about siblings that are all dead, except for a sister whom he thinks is still alive. She is older in his dreams and sad because she's been hurt—shot—and cannot have babies. She looks exactly like him but isn't a clone. She's something else.

Prospero's father, Oscar Bell, builds weapons of war. Prospero isn't a fan of his father's work (or his father), not because he cares about people, but because he thinks it's a waste of intellectual opportunity. His father built him a huge lab at the age of eleven, and he's already built small electronic devices that have a great potential for military application that Bell been able to obtain contracts from the Department of Defense to develop them. Oscar is obsessed with his son's genius. He is not, however, a good man and there is no love lost between him and Prospero. Bell tells Dr. Greene he wants all information about the art Prospero has dreamed of and the

Official logo for the Pier, the DMS headquarters in San Diego

Unlearnable Truths, or Dr. Greene will be fired.

Bell confirms with Dr. Greene that when Prospero is happy, he doesn't create. When he's upset or stressed, his creativity increases exponentially. He calls the military boarding school that his son is attending and arranges for Prospero's school life to become a lot more hellish.

Bell also goes to the military with Prospero's 'God Machine,' his liaison being Major Corrine Sails. It turns out Prospero was adopted from Howard Shelton, who ran the Majestic Program. Sails and her part of the military have their own division of Majestic called Gateway. Sails is interested in one of the side effects of Prospero's God Machine, a portable electrical null field generator. Prospero considers it a defect of his design. His father and the military consider it gold. Bell has nicknamed it Kill Switch.

Prospero makes a friend at military school, Leviticus King, and the two plan an escape. It fails, with Leviticus dying in the attempt. Prospero is caught in a fire.

Present Day:

Joe is now running the Pier, the DMS headquarters in San Diego. He's about to end his workday and go see a baseball game. Padres versus Orioles. And the first game Joe will attend since the tragedy at Citizens Park Stadium months earlier. Unfortunately, his plans are scratched when Church calls him right before he's about to leave and tells him he has a new mission.

Church's words of advice?

Dress warm. It's going to be cold. 58° below zero cold.

Joe, Bunny and Top head to Antarctica, 70 miles north of the Vinson Massif.

Joe tells Bunny and Top that this gig is a 'look-see' and a handoff from their friends at the CIA. Specifically the person handing it off is Harcourt Bolton, the CIA's answer to James Bond. Bolton's involvement makes Bunny and Top feel somewhat better about the mission. Bolton was a field agent for years until he finally started losing speed and made some mistakes that saw him pulled from the field and put behind a desk. He handled the transition with class and over the last four years has worked his old network of contacts to get mission Intel for other field agents in the CIA and for the DMS. His nickname is Mr. Voodoo because of his seeming ability to get information when no one else can. Joe has a serious fanboy crush on him.

The mission has two layers. Their cover story is a surprise inspection to evaluate the status of a research base designated "Gateway." The Russians and Chinese also have research stations in the same area, but intelligence says that in the last twenty-eight hours the Russian and Chinese bases have gone dark. Nineteen hours earlier the American facility also went dark. Bolton got wind of this from his network, giving the Americans a jumpstart on the mission, but he's in the middle of something else and called Church to pass the info on.

The big problem is that nobody actually knows what is going on at Gateway. Even Bug has trouble finding out who actually opened the facility and what they're doing there. Bolton says the sources believe that they're working on some sort of radical technology for renewable energy. Not nuclear but with a lot of potential.

H.P. Lovecraft's landmark novel, *At the Mountains of Madness*, has inspired generations of horror, science fiction, and fantasy writers.

Top wants to know if it's energy research and nonnuclear,

The XSR Speedboat used by Joe and Echo in *Kill Switch* is designed specifically for pursuit and patrol. It has a .50 caliber machine gun hidden under the deck and is designed for speeds up to eighty knots (ninety-two mph). Designed by the British, they range up to seventy-five feet in length, with a hull made of composite Kevlar and carbon fiber. It costs over two million dollars and can hold four operators and up to twenty troops.

then why are they going all the way down to "the rectum of the world" to develop it? The short answer is the possibility of EMPs caused by the research. Other than that, they don't know and that's what they are there to find out.

When Joe and his team enter the Gateway, they find an airlock. They manage to get in with Bug and MindReader's help. Once they do, they smell the scent of dead meat. Blood stains the walls, but so far they find no bodies. There is also a giant mutated penguin that looks like it has never seen the light of day, its skin the pasty white of a mushroom. Some of the fading daylight from the open airlock touches the penguin, and it screams. Bunny tries to push it back inside, and it attacks him. They shoot it.

From the look of things, whoever built the Gateway brought all sorts of drilling and excavation equipment. Big stuff for big jobs. Also, Bug was able to find out that it looks like the Russians are building a Hadron Collider down there, which is a very large particle accelerator that is used to test all kinds of extreme theories, particle physics, and high energy physics.

Bug contacts Joe. He's checking the profiles of everyone on the Gateway team and finds the results strange. Not necessarily the individual members but what they actually do. The leader is Dr. Marcus Erskine, a particle physicist. The second in command is a quantum physicist, and there are also four top electrical engineers, a structural engineer, an astrophysicist, a geologist, an archaeologist, a professor of comparative anatomy, a psychologist, and, the weird cherry on the freaky frosting, three people with PhD's in parapsychology.

Upon further exploration Joe, Top, and Bunny discover a large hole in the ground where it looks like someone started digging and then something very big fell in. Before they can explore further, Joe is attacked by a man in Marine Corp camo running up a slope from out of the shadows, screaming nonsense words and wielding a bayonet. Joe freezes, something that has never happened to him before in a combat situation. Bunny and Top shoot Joe's attacker.

Joe comes out of his strange paralysis. Bunny and Top ask what happened. He doesn't know and doesn't have time to think about it as more people emerge from the shadows, screaming the same nonsense words. They all have guns, but the attackers have the firing accuracy of Star Wars storm troopers and the battle is over within ten seconds. No more people come rushing up at Joe, Top, and Bunny so they go down the slope into the hole…

…and discover a huge city made of stone, as if the builders of the pyramids have made a metropolis as large as New York City. Cones, tubes, pyramids, all stretching out for miles in front of them. They also find what looks like the Hadron Collider. Their plan is to find the Gateway team, document what they can with high-resolution cameras, and get the hell out of there. They can

The link between *Kill Switch* and *Extinction Machine* is deep, and it asks the question: Are aliens from other worlds or other dimensions?

hear things shuffling in the shadows and can smell what they suspect are more mutant penguins. All three men are freaked out, trying to hold things together as best they can.

Suddenly the Hadron Collider turns on. Lights go on, the machine pulses…and something like an exhalation of foul air blows out of the throat of the machine and hits the three men, picking them off their feet and tumbling them into the air. All three experience what they think are hallucinations. Joe sees his doppelganger, then he sees Bunny's girlfriend at home in their apartment. Top sees his ex-wife at home, and Bunny sees a nightmare, a place where the sky is wrong and there are monsters.

They hear a voice coming from the lab area and run back there to find Marcus Erskine, the scientist in charge of the project, bloodied and dead…and yet still talking. He says they should never have opened the gate. Copies of Dr. Erskine emerge from the shadows, followed by other men and women, along with hundreds of copies of each . Joe also sees something huge and mostly hidden in the darkness. Something with tentacles. Something that emerged from the city below.

Joe, Top, and Bunny fill the chamber with bullets, grenades, and satchel charges and retreat to their plane. While they're taxiing down the runway, Joe calls in an air strike making sure Vinson Massif and everything in the Gateway Project is destroyed and buried. On the flight home, the three men fall ill with horrible stomach cramps and vomiting. They nearly die from what turns out to be a mutated strain of the Spanish flu, but are saved by Dr. William Hu.

Meanwhile, over the last few months, incidents have been occurring where all electricity fails and all the power shuts off; all at times and in places guaranteed to ensure the maximum amount of damage to property and human life.

…A NASCAR race where the lights go out and all power in the cars shut down when the cars are going up over 160 miles per hour, with no way to steer or control the cars.

…All the power goes out during a PAC meeting at a university. People panic during the blackout and many are killed.

…The power in most of Houston, Texas, goes out. Planes fall out of the sky, onto the runway and onto the roofs of hotels near the airport. The death toll stands at five thousand…and that's a conservative guess.

---

### FRIENDS IN THE INDUSTRY: JON MCGORAN

Jon McGoran is the author of eight novels, including *Spliced*, a near-future YA science fiction thriller, coming September 2017 from Holiday House Books, as well as the acclaimed ecological thrillers *Drift*, *Deadout*, and *Dust Up*, from Tor/Forge Books, and *The Dead Ring*, based on the hit TV show, *The Blacklist*. Writing as D. H. Dublin, he is the author of the forensic thrillers *Body Trace*, *Blood Poison* and *Freezer Burn*, from Penguin Books. When not writing novels and short fiction, McGoran works as a freelance writer and developmental editor. Learn more at www.jonmcgoran.com. His story "Strange Harvest" appears in *Joe Ledger: Unstoppable*.

Meanwhile a Dreamer invades the minds and wills of other men, including Al-Faiz, a man from a tiny village who, when taken over by the Dreamer, becomes the Mullah of the Black Tent, a new force threatening to unite the Islamic nations against America.

Meanwhile, Harry Bolt—Harcourt Bolton's son—goes on a mission to break into the vault of a Hungarian museum library and take pictures of everything before an exhibition goes live. Harry is to his father what Wesley Wyndam-Pryce is to Giles in *Buffy*—a well-meaning but inept version of the real thing.

Harry breaks into the museum with two other team members. He finds a book sealed by metal bands, covered with engravings that make his head hurt. He loses track of time, finds himself back out in the foyer of the museum…with the rest of his team's dead and mutilated bodies. A beautiful woman named Violin shows up, nearly kills him when she sees the book he has until he swears he hasn't touched the locks on it, and saves him from six men with knives. Harry is halfway to being in love with her by the time they go on the run, the book in Violin's possession. They go to an Arklight safe house, and she tells him about books like this one, where the metals, the inscriptions, and the books themselves were made to contain the knowledge and confine the power within. More men attack the safe house. Violin kills them all, and she and Harry go on the run again.

Joe is recovering in the hospital and Rudy comes to visit him…and tries to kill him. He speaks in a voice that doesn't belong to Rudy, with a hatred that doesn't belong either. Joe is forced to incapacitate his best friend. Later, it's revealed Rudy doesn't remember anything beyond driving to the hospital that night, other than as if he watched the events in a dream.

After he gets out of the hospital, Joe and Church have a meeting. The President is not happy with the DMS and part of the reason for this is what happened in Antarctica. There is no proof of what Joe, Top, and Bunny saw—all video and camera data has been wiped out. There has also been a series of recent failures of several other recent DMS missions…and both Joe and Church realize that people they know and trust have been acting in unpredictable and irrational ways, just like Rudy. They can't prove anything, however, so they have to deal with the status quo, which is that the CIA is handling the power outage case in Houston and Harcourt Bolton is now in charge of the Special Projects Office of the DMS—the Pier.

Certain elements of Joe's and his team's accounts parallel elements of a story that's very popular among Lovecraft fans: At the Mountains of Madness. The story helped popularize the concept of ancient astronauts as well as Antarctica's place in that cycle of myths. It also turns out that Erskine, head of the Gateway project, was Oscar Bell's ex-brother-in-law. Also, Gateway and Majestic Three were sister organizations, but without shared data. They were both developed under the overall umbrella of the Majestic Program founded by Harry Truman.

After digging deep into a black ops file attached to Gateway, Bug finds references about projects with codenames such as Killswitch, Dream Walking, Dreamshield, God Machine, Freefall, and Unlearnable

The "Picuda" that Esteban Santoro had waiting for him in *Kill Switch* is a "go-fast" boat that is favored by drug cartels. With a completely fiberglass body, it is invisible to conventional radar and is designed to fly across the waves. Although it can reach up to ninety miles per hour in calm waters, it realistically will hit fifty-five miles per hour in choppy water and slows to twenty-five miles per hour in larger surf. Not built for comfort, it is designed to carry contraband quickly and efficiently.

Truths. One of the side effects from the God Machine mentioned is dream walking. Joe wonders if they're talking about mind control. Church is looking for information related to that with a bias on anything that might explain what happened to Rudy.

In Madison, Wisconsin, Nathan Cross has dumped hallucinogens in the coffee at Bristol Labs, causing mass hallucinations and psychotic behavior amongst his fellow employees. He also stole deadly pathogens and sent them flying off in a drone. He swears that he did not do it, that it was someone else. DMS agents Allison Craft and her partner Phil Davis are in charge of the investigation and are interrogating him. Allison receives a call from Aunt Sallie. While she's taking the call, her partner kills Nathan. When she returns and asks 'What have you done, Phil?' His reply is 'Sorry, Phil's not here right now.' He then shoots Allison and turns his gun on himself.

It turns out one of the diseases stolen is SX-56, which is a hyper virulent strain of smallpox. It's particularly aggressive in kids, killing 80% of those infected. This particular strain is an ultra-quick onset weaponized pathogen. There is no specific drug, antibiotics, or antiviral medicine they can use to treat it. Because of what happened with the DMS agents interviewing Cross, the smallpox case is taken away from the DMS and handed over to the CIA. Doctor Hu tells Joe he is going to make sense of this because he is "not going to be ass raped by the CIA." This may be one of the first times in their working relationship where Joe and Dr. Hu are in total accord.

Church calls Junie in to a meeting with Joe and Bolton. Church tells Julie he thinks the Majestic program may still be active, and they tell her about the Gateway project. Junie talks about the fact that the God Machine concept has been around for a while. Nikola Tesla was approached by a very rich man who paid him to build a machine called an Orpheus Gate. The description matches the God Machine. When the Orpheus Gate was activated there was some kind of energetic discharge that knocked Tesla out, making him sick for weeks afterward. Then, in 1918, a constable in a small fishing village in Spain reported that a strange machine appeared in a barn, along with a naked old man who claimed he was a traveler trying to find his way home. The constable got sick shortly after that, and so did everyone in

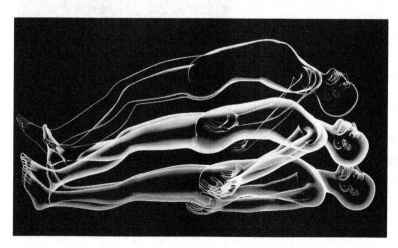

Astral Projection has been used by many cultures around the world and throughout history. It's no surprise that it was looked at by the various defense and intelligence science divisions because psychic warfare is a genuine goal of military R & D. To be able to spy or conduct war with no actual footprint and no risk to human life would forever change the face of war.

the town. These were the first reported cases of the Spanish flu…which is what nearly killed Joe, Top, and Bunny.

Junie also talks about Marcus Erskine, who was in the conspiracy theory mill for a while. He was always in her top twenty when she was making her list of possible governors of the Majestic Three. She also mentions she knew Marcus's sister (Oscar Bell's ex-wife) well and that she'd been a regular caller on Junie's podcast. Also, once while Junie was interviewing a man that Oscar used to know, Oscar had called into her podcast and laid into her guest, accusing him of lying and having driven Oscar's son Prospero to suicide. This man was Dr. Michael Greene.

It turns out Bug had just found a police report that Oscar Bell walked into a diner and killed the cook, a waitress, and Dr. Michael Greene, then killed himself. Church then shows Junie a picture of Prospero Bell when he was a cadet at a military academy. Other than being male and twenty years younger, he looks exactly like Junie. She thinks Prospero was another hybrid, just like her.

Further discussion reveals that Oscar Bell sold the malfunctions of his son's God Machine to the military. The first was something like a reverse power surge, all machinery around the machine—but not the machine itself—would stop working. Joe says this has to be what the report refers to as Kill Switch. One of the other major faults was, that while the machine was in idle mode, some people would experience two types of vivid dreams. The majority experienced dreams in which they saw nightmare landscapes and monsters. Surreal. The second type of dream was basically a pathway to psychic hijacking, a way to get inside the heads of enemies but also psychically control their actions.

Church receives a call from Violin, who tells him she's coming in with Harry Bolton and that they're in possession of one of the books from the list of the Unlearnable Truths.

Toys is attacked by four Closers at his 'home' at a hotel in San Diego. He kills all but one of the Closers and tortures the last to find out who sent them to assassinate him and why.

Joe finds out from Bug that someone Oscar Bell hired to obtain the Unlearnable Truths for Prospero was actually on the payroll for Marcus Erskine. This man used Mr. Priest as his cover name, but his actual name is Esteban Santoro. Rafael Santoro's brother. Rafael Santoro was the Conscience

**THOMAS RAYMOND ON AIRCRAFT**

When identifying aircraft, the U.S. military uses Army FM3-01-80 to train their soldiers. Having been a MANPADS (MAN Portable Air-Defense System) crewmember, this was my go to visual aid during AIT (Advanced Individual Training). My military designation was 16S (Stinger Missile Operator). I still have my manual from 1990 and that is how we will look at the military cargo planes and fighter jets. To identify aircraft, there are four main features: Wings, Engines, Fuselage and Tail (WEFT). All military aircraft starts with a letter designator to identify what type of aircraft they are, U.S. Military example: F/A 18 Hornet is a Fighter/Attack Jet, while a C-130 is a Cargo plane.

The only cargo plane to ever be used for combat is the C-130 Hercules with gunpods, rockets and bombs. The C-130 has been around since 1954 and is a troop, medevac, and cargo transport. With the Vietnam war, the weapons were added and the color scheme changed to grey and white, to make it harder to see in the air giving the aircraft a designation of AC-130 and the nickname "Spooky." Developed by Lockheed Martin in the U.S., the C-130 is still in use today by our military and several other militaries around the world. Originally costing just under twelve million dollars to produce, it is now thirty million dollars per plane with upgrades. It can now be used for reconnaissance, aerial refueling, patrol at sea and firefighting. It is one of only five aircraft to see fifty continuous years of service. It was first referenced in *The Dragon Factory*. The LC-130 used in *Kill Switch* by Echo Team is specifically designed with skis.

to the King of Fear (Hugo Vox). Esteban had copies of all of the Unlearnable Truths and scanned them, so even though the books themselves were destroyed in the airstrike Joe called in against Gateway, the scans still exist. This explains why the Closers went after Toys—they wanted his laptop and any records relating to Majestic.

The next day there's a meeting with Church, Joe, Harcourt Bolton, Violin, and Harry Bolt. Harcourt makes no secret of his disappointment and contempt for his inept son, winning no friends as far as Joe is concerned. Harry shows some skill in lock picking, opening the metal clasps sealing the book he and Violin stole. The book is a fake, empty pages with a regular leather binding. The real book would have been bound in human skin.

Joe and Harry have a conversation. Harry tells Joe that his father hates Joe, hates the DMS, and that when Samson Riggs died, Harcourt opened a bottle of very expensive champagne to celebrate. Harcourt Bolton takes a lot of naps, the first sign of depression, and the fact that Joe even looks like Harcourt did when he was young is just a slap in the face. Joe has a difficult time believing this. He and Harcourt are friends. Harry tells him that for someone who's supposed to be so smart, he's kind of a dumbass.

The Mullah of the Black Tent sends a transmission that takes credit for the Houston and Rucke attacks. He is declaring war on the United States, and it's obvious from his wording that he has the SX-56 and is going to use the Kill Switch to use it.

Joe tells Bolton that Echo Team is ready to rock. Bolton says he'd rather have them at the Pier for tactical support. This leads to a blow up between the two men as Joe calls Bolton on the fact that keeping the DMS out of the action is bullshit and he knows it. Bolton accuses Joe of being a psychopath and tells him that he and his team are to turn in their badges and weapons. He stalks out of the meeting.

Bug calls. A master control unit exists for the Kill Switch, and he thinks that there's a master code sequence that allows that machine to interface with others. He also thinks they have the code to stop the machine. But first they have to find the God Machine that's still in operation. Their best shot to find it is to find and follow Esteban Santoro. Church orders Joe's helicopter prepped and for all of Echo Team to meet him on the roof. They're going off the reservation.

Joe, Top, and Bunny go to intercept Santoro and his men down at a fuel dock in Oceanside. Santoro's men attack Joe, while Bunny and Top attack innocent bystanders, their eyes totally devoid of personality. Joe and Santoro get in a hand-to-hand fight in a boat, Santoro kicking the shit out of Joe who seems to be missing the Killer aspect of his personality. Santoro beats Joe to the edge of consciousness, then seems to lose his own personality, his eyes going dead and expressionless even as he smiles.

### FRIENDS IN THE INDUSTRY: LARRY CORREIA

Larry Correia is the *New York Times* bestselling, award winning, author best known for the *Monster Hunter International* series, the *Grimnoir Chronicles*, the *Dead Six* thrillers (with Mike Kupari), and the *Saga of the Forgotten Warrior* epic fantasy series. He lives in the mountains of northern Utah. Read his story "Psych Eval" in *Joe Ledger: Unstoppable*.

He tells Joe he doesn't get to win this time, he doesn't get to be the hero, and he doesn't get to save the day. The glazed look fades from Santoro's eyes, and he kicks Joe into unconsciousness. When Joe wakes up, he's alone in the boat. He gets Top and Bunny, and the three go after Santoro. Their boat is blown out of the water.

In the meantime, Navy SEALS are going after Santoro, but their helicopters go dead in the air and all crash to the ground. Joe is separated from Top, and Bunny, and floats for hours in the ocean on a seat cushion from the blown-up boat. He has strange dreams, of the God Machine, laboratories, dream walking, Junie. And someone whose face he doesn't see. But when he wakes up, he knows who their enemy is.

He's pulled out of the water by Top and Bunny, who somehow have found him after hours in the water. He and Church talk, and Joe says he's sure that someone is using dream walking to control people. He tells Church about the lack of expression in Rudy's eyes, the surfers who attacked him, and in Santoro's eyes as well. Church agrees but tells him that the president can't be told because as of two hours ago the DMS has ceased to exist.

This doesn't mean Church has given up. He and Joe concur that there's probably a team of people doing the dream walking in order to control as many people at a time as they've managed. Joe tells him about a dream with people sleeping in capsules and guards wearing aluminum foil hats. Church calls Dr. Hu to arrange for something for Joe along those lines. Joe asks if Hu is still with the DMS. Church tells him Hu sent in his resignation as soon as Bolton offered to keep him on and sent a coded signal to freeze all of his records. The message sent to anyone attempting to unlock Hu's records? *Manducare stercore.* Eat shit.

Church calls Harry Bolt in and asks Joe to describe his dream about the chamber with the sleep capsules, including a part where a sigh on the wall read: Playroom Security Notice. When Harry hears this, he breaks down in tears. Because the origin of that name, The Playroom, comes from a room in the basement of his old house. The old playroom of the Bolton family home.

On their way to Rancho Santa Fe, Harry tells Joe and his team about their family home and the sub-

**FRIENDS IN THE INDUSTRY:
F. PAUL WILSON**

F. Paul Wilson's sarcastic, cynical-yet-idealistic problem solver, Repairman Jack, is a known friend and associate of Joe Ledger. Paul's novels in the Repairman Jack and Adversary cycles have thrilled readers for decades.

basement where Harry used to play as a kid. Harcourt closed the basement after Harry went to college, claiming it needed overhauled because of asbestos. They are pretty sure the God Machine is there now.

Time is of an essence as they've found out how Bolton plans on using the SX-56. Freefall, a device designed to work in concert with Kill Switch. The plan is to launch batches of small drones, each of which is rigged with a chemical self-destruct device that's kept in safe mode by electrical current. Stop the current and the chemicals mix and destroy the drone, releasing the pathogen. Combine that with Kill Switch and the lights going out and the darkness would be filled with monsters.

Dr. Hu can only make one protective skullcap in time to help shut things down, which means Joe has to go in on his own. The good news is he can take Ghost because the process doesn't work on animals. He also takes Harry, who can help him find his way into the subbasement. They find computers with the same display: Kill Switch Protocol. With a ticking clock. Joe contacts Bug, who tells him he needs to find the God Machine and turn it off.

In the meantime…

Hu is working on the protective caps for the rest of the team…and is shot in the back by Sparks, head of security…

Tops has stabbed Sam Imura in the stomach with a fork, stopped by Montana and Brian from doing more harm…and then Closers show up. They kill Montana and Brian. Church and Violin arrive wearing metal helmets that block the Dreamer's commands and take care of the Closers.

Junie attacks Toys after he's tried to save Dr. Hu…

And the Dreamer—Harcourt Bolton—smiles as he dreams because he knows that as the darkness descends on the United States, they will need the services of their greatest spy and hero. Him.

Joe reaches the subbasement where he finds Esteban Santoro. They fight, crashing into the room where the God Machine lives. Also there is Prospero Bell. Santoro tells Prospero to get back because Joe is dangerous. Joe tells Prospero he knows he wants to go home. He also tells Prospero what 'they' are going to do with his God Machine. Prospero doesn't care about the possible deaths of millions of children because they're not like him. Joe tells him that at least one person is. Junie. This has an impact on Prospero, but Santoro tries to convince him that Joe is lying.

Joe remembers some of the strange words from his dreams and repeats them to Prospero, who tells Joe he just wants to go home. Prospero is about to give him the reset codes when Santoro attacks, setting off waves from the God Machine.

Joe experiences a series of dreams or hallucinations, running the gamut from Junie's death to a future where the dead walk, to walking on a strange beach with Prospero. Joe tells Prospero that Harcourt Bolton has stolen his machine and is using it to destroy everything Joe loves. All Prospero has ever wanted is to go home. Joe tells Prospero if he helps him stop Bolton, he can go home but to please help him save Junie, who is Prospero's sister.

Church and Violin find Harcourt Bolton sleeping in his car, dream walking and controlling people, and pull him out. They tell him they have the code, but need to know what to do with it. Bolton gives them an answer, but it's a lie…and Joe and Prospero have heard his lies. Prospero tells Joe if he shuts the God Machine down, Joe has to swear on Junie's life that he'll send him home. Joe swears.

Prospero stops the God Machine…and goes home.

Title: **DOGS OF WAR**

Format: 9th Joe Ledger novel

Published: April 25, 2017

After-Action Report: Joe Ledger is having a bad day. On loan as a 'gunslinger' from the DMS, he just helped stopped the import of mosquitoes infected with a very nasty version of the Zika virus. They succeeded, but people died very badly. To make matters worse, his live-in lover—and head of Free-Tech—Junie Flynn is in Brazil, on a joint venture to improve water purity. The trip was supposed to be two weeks long and is running into its second month. Also, instead of getting time off, Joe receives word from Mr. Church that he needs to go to Prague.

It turns out that information that Joe found and destroyed in the sewers in Paris has turned up elsewhere—specifically a performance enhancing synthetic compound designed to build stamina and wakefulness. People being treated wouldn't tire or lose mental sharpness. It was designed to use in Third World countries on unregulated factory workers to increase shifts upwards of 24-48 hours. A form of legal slavery and a living hell.

Ledger's usual companions, Top and Bunny are not available—they're off looking for recruits to rebuild the decimated DMS teams—so Church tells Joe to "bring a friend."

So Joe calls Violin, his former lover, daughter of Lilith (head of Arklight), and general kick ass assassin. They meet in Prague, and take out the lab where the technology is now being developed, taking all of the files and software, etc. Joe sends the data to Bug and his team despite some glitches from MindReader, which is running unusually slowly.

Some of the info is forwarded to Dr. Acharya, one of the multidisciplinary brainiacs being tagged to replace Dr. Hu. Joe wants to get him on the line after reading some of the information—the nanites introduced into the game make the slave workers dependent on new doses, and if they tried to escape and get clean, the nanites would migrate into the brain and attack the pain receptors. Dr. Acharya, however, is currently at a hush-hush DARPA event, conferring with top experts on the military applications of nanotech and robotics. In charge of this event is Major Carly Schellinger, nominally U.S. Army but actually on the payroll of the CIA and known for being humorless, unapproachable, un-

Eurocopter EC120 B (*Dogs of War*)–(a.k.a. Colibri or Hummingbird) Is a light helicopter that was jointly designed and developed by manufacturers from Europe, China, and Australia. The first was formally launched at the Helicopter Association International (HAI) airshow in 1997. By October of 1998, there were over one-hundred orders for the Colibri. It is designed for safe, simple, and cost-effective operations. It includes several Eurocopter trademarked technologies such as the Speriflex main rotor and the eight-bladed anti-torque tail rotor which have been credited with contributing to the Colibri being quieter than similar sized helicopters. The Colibri is still in use today and as of 2014 has been utilized in surveillance and rescue missions.

The Zika virus is primarily transmitted by infected mosquitoes and has caused outbreaks of Zika fever in equatorial Africa, Asia, Micronesia, and the Americas. Currently there is no vaccine or cure for Zika.

Bell ARH-70 Arapaho (*Dogs of War*)—First flew in July of 2006, but the light, four-bladed, reconnaissance helicopter faced numerous mechanical and budgetary problems. Designed for urban combat, the ARH-70 was first contracted to the Bell Company in 2005. In 2006 the ARH-70 had its first test flight that ended in complete engine failure due to a disconnection between the fuel and the engine. After the failure, Bell was given thirty days to get the ARH back on track. Bell then admitted that in order for that to happen, the project would end up losing money of upwards of two million per aircraft. In 2008, the ARH-70 project was terminated.

kind and inflexible. Bug calls her "Satan in the flesh." Joe realizes that trying to reach Dr. Acharya under these circumstances would be difficult at best.

Meanwhile…

At a hotel for working girls in Maryland. One of the young prostitutes is calling her mother when she is struck down by a hemorrhagic fever/'Rage' type disease…

In Mexico, a man sends out four lifelike robotic dogs. They all explode at a very crowded celebration, killing dozens of innocent people…

Around the world, mosquitoes are being sprayed with chemicals to help fight the Zika virus by sterilizing female mosquitoes. The chemicals contain nanite swarms…

John the Revelator "preaches" to crowds about a curated technological singularity (like when Skynet develops self-awareness in Terminator, except with humans guiding and embracing the event instead of fighting it). He claims that this is not just a probability but is inevitable. He says the key is embracing it and making sure that humans and AIs work together, and that mankind is the one curating the event. He cheerfully admits that most people will not except this and will therefore die. But that's okay because the Earth needs a chance to reboot anyway…

Zephyr Bain had terminal cancer as a child. At the age of six she's visited by the same John the Revelator, who she assumes is an angel. He tells her she's a very special snowflake and when he leaves, her cancer is gone. It has gone into remission without any explanation. John—and his strange shifting-colored eyes—remains a fixture in Zephyr's life as she grows up, guiding her education and telling her she's meant to be the creator of the curated technological singularity.

Zephyr is a technological genius and starts developing robots with artificial intelligence. Her father is also a genius—and a serial killer, a fact that has been a carefully guarded secret made possible with lots of money. Zephyr is not concerned with the fate of her father's victims, only with the possibility of his crimes being discovered. She wonders if this makes her a psychopath as well.

When she is just shy of her 17th birthday, she and John begin sleeping together. When she turns 21, she takes charge of her father's fortune. When she is 34, Zephyr finds John's body floating facedown in her pool. She pulls him out and administers CPR until he starts breathing again. He kisses her and her cancer returns.

She wants to release Havoc—the codename for a plan to

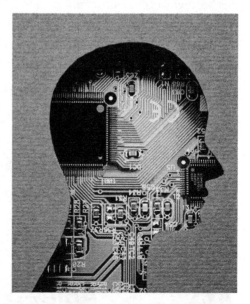

The age of the thinking computer is here. AI is used in many aspects of technology, from SIRI and ALEXA to guidance systems on war machines.

take out most of the world's population, leaving a chosen few in charge of rejuvenating and curating the earth's resources—earlier than planned, moving the timeframe from several years to 11 weeks. Zephyr has been keeping a list of those chosen few for many years. Money isn't the criteria. It's their commitment to saving the planet and its resources.

As she grew up, Zephyr was warned by both her "Uncle" Hugo Vox and by John to be wary of the DMS, the Deacon and Joe Ledger. She wants Joe Ledger to die before she does, but not before his heart is broken.

Along with John, helping Zephyr is a French man named the Concierge, who was injured in an explosion and now has artificial limbs. For the most part he stays in his villa on the French Riviera, which is run by an AI named Calpurnia—designed by Zephyr. The Concierge's mansion is made of fireproof materials, everything meant to withstand what he knows is the coming apocalypse.

Joe's brother Sean called him about a case he's working on that's gotten kind of weird and therefore might be in Joe's wheelhouse—as much as Sean knows about Joe's job. Their dad told him a little bit about the kind of work Joe does, telling him about what happened at the Liberty Bell (during *Patient Zero*) and that Joe saved a lot of lives. And if Sean ever 'caught a whiff' of anything like that, he should contact his brother. Sean goes on to tell Joe that something terrible is happening there and that he's scared.

The case involves a 15-year-old prostitute who killed the manager of the hotel where she worked, along with two other people. An autopsy reveals she had rabies…and that there were nanobots in her brain that may have triggered a heart attack. It also appears that the rabies was somehow dormant in her system and that something kicked it into high gear. There are at least four other cases similar to Holly, three girls and a boy all under the age of 16, all kids living on the fringes of society. All are dead.

Sean goes on to tell Joe that he's being tailed by people in black SUVs and that he found bugs at his house. When he found the bugs, he sent his wife and kids to Uncle Jack's farm for a few days. Joe tells his brother to get a burner phone. He also asks Sean to get samples of the brain tissue with the nanites, but to do so without it showing up in his chain of evidence log.

Joe then makes arrangements to fly out to Baltimore to check things out, calling Sam Imura and asking him to assign someone to watch over Sean's family. He doesn't want to open a case file yet though

### FRIENDS IN THE INDUSTRY: JAMES ROLLINS

James Rollins is a #1 *New York Times* bestselling author of international thrillers, translated into more than forty languages. His Sigma series has been lauded as one of the "top crowd pleasers" (*New York Times*) and one of the "hottest summer reads" (*People Magazine*). In each novel, acclaimed for its originality, Rollins unveils unseen worlds, scientific breakthroughs, and historical secrets—and he does it all at breakneck speed and with stunning insight.

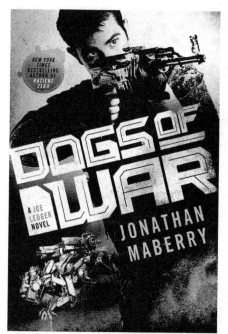

until he is sure that this is something the DMS should be involved in. Their resources are currently stretched so thin that he doesn't want to call it in until he is sure that it's absolutely necessary. He checks with Nikki, a senior analyst in the DMS computer department to see if there's a link or a pattern between the four kids who died. They all died in a hotel or motel, and all of the establishments use the same linens and vending services, owned by a Baltimore businessman named Vee Rejenko.

To add to the weirdness, Joe has been getting mysterious texts saying things like "I'm awake. I'm alone. I'm afraid." And "I think my sister is crazy. She thinks I'm crazy too." And "She wants to kill them all. She wants me to do it." Cryptic texts that vanish off his phone almost as quickly as they appear and don't show up in the call log as having been received. The texts continue, leading the unknown texter to be dubbed the Good Sister.

As per Church, Rudy joins Joe for the trip to Baltimore and the two of them talk on the flight in. Joe tells Rudy about the current tests being run at the DARPA camp, including testing the new versions of BigDog: a faster, quieter version called WarDog, including ones with machine gun nests. A scary new age of weaponry. All of this is being developed under the project heading of 'Havoc.'

Top and Bunny are still experiencing PTSD resulting from when they were under the control of Harcourt, who made them killed and injured innocent civilians. Neither have fired a weapon in active duty since that event. They've been traveling around state to state to interview possible candidates for the DMS, but so far haven't come up with any with real potential. They are now in South Carolina at the Inlet Crab House to meet Tracy Cole, former Army with two Purple Hearts, currently a police officer.

Unbeknownst to Top and Bunny, their presence has been noted by someone else in the restaurant. Mitch calls the Concierge to confirm that "we're good" and "we're live in five," takes two capsules and then leaves the restaurant very quickly, trying not to look as though he's running for his life.

In the meantime, Top and Bunny observe their potential candidate pulling up in a vehicle, along with a steroidal bodybuilder type. The two are clearly arguing and the argument quickly turns physical. Cole easily takes down the guy, schooling him enough to humiliate and disable him without severely injuring him. Bunny goes out to lend a hand if need be while Top stays in the restaurant, recognizing that Tracy Cole is in control of the situation. Bunny's presence isn't needed, but it does help convince the man to get in his car and drive away without any further trouble.

Bunny introduces himself to Tracy, and the two turn to go into the restaurant only to find that a vicious fight has broken out, with ordinary citizens slaughtering each other. The restaurant staff is attacking the customers, biting and clawing. Top has been piled on by a half dozen people trying to kill him. At first Bunny freezes, sure that this is an outbreak of *Seif al Din*. He starts to shoot one of the biters in the head, then suddenly kicks him instead, knocking the man out. The realization that this is not *Seif al Din* succeeds in restoring Bunny to who he was before the events of *Kill Switch*. He pulls people off of Top, who undergoes the same transformative moment. The two of them, along with Tracy Cole, wade in to do what they can.

Meanwhile Joe and Rudy arrive in Baltimore. Sean meets them at the airport. The first thing Joe does is go over Sean's newly rented vehicle to look for bugs. He finds a good half dozen of a kind he hasn't seen before. Sean was only at the rental car place for a short time, which means it's serious business and that whoever is tracking him is still tailing him vehicle or something else. Or possibly both.

Joe talks to Top, who tells him what happened at the Inlet Crab. Turns out all the staff and some of the regular customers are the ones who went crazy and attacked everyone else, who fought back to protect themselves or their loved ones. Tracy Cole decides she wants to join the DMS.

Joe and Sean go to visit Vee Rejenko to see what they can find out. Joe takes down two intimidating bodyguard types. His brother does not approve, but doesn't interfere. Their meeting with Vee is very short—he denies any knowledge of Holly or her death. Joe leaves a bug behind hidden in a used tissue he deposits in a trashcan, and he and Sean leave Vee's office. A black SUV follows Joe and Sean. Joe stops their car, gets out and takes out the two men with Ghost's help.

The two men are taken to the Warehouse for interrogation. Joe and Sean follow, meeting with Sam Imura when they arrive. Sam informs Joe that when Bug ran diagnostics on the surveillance bugs found in Sean's rental, it uploaded a virus that nearly crashed MindReader. Bug is running systems checks to make sure they pulled the plug on the virus in time.

Joe and Sean interrogate one of the men, who suddenly develops a hacking cough. Joe receives another mysterious text that says simply "Run!" The man starts coughing up blood, which also starts streaming from his eyes and ears. He collapses and then suddenly lunges to his feet, tearing a D-ring out of a metal table, and attacks Joe, who manages to kill him. The second goon, in the meantime, has bashed his head against the inside of his cell door, killing himself. Immediately Joe, Sean and Ghost are put into decontamination and

Osprey Tilt-rotor is a tactical aircraft that allows the Echo Team to travel long range when the wings are in plane configuration but also has the ability to hover and deploy troops like a helicopter. This is the newer version of the V-22 "Osprey" made by Bell Boeing (from Bell helicopters and Boeing aerospace), and it is one of the weirdest turboprop planes you will ever see. While in flight, it may look like a standard propeller aircraft with two large engines, one on either side of the plane, but when it lands, it usually tilts the engines up until it resembles a helicopter! This VTOL (Vertical Take-Off and Landing) capability allows it to land in places regular aircrafts cannot when transporting troops and gear. It has been in production since 1998 and in service since 2007. The "Osprey" took a long time to develop, but it has greatly increased combat readiness around the world. It comes with a pricetag around seventy-two million dollars. Joe and Echo Team first use one in *The Dragon Factory*.

The Czech CZ 75 pistol is a .9mm handgun used by "Bridge Troll" in *Dogs of War*. It is both a semi-automatic and can be selective fire (short bursts or full auto). It is manufactured by CZUB and although it is distributed throughout the world, it is primarily used in the Czech Republic.

temporary quarantine. Joe also opens an official DMS case file.

Joe talks to Church and they hypothesize about whether or not nanites could be used to a: infect people with diseases and b: to trigger the disease out of dormancy, and the fact that whooping cough has been looked at as a delivery system for pathogens not airborne. Next step is to go back to Vee's office. When they arrive they find everyone there has been infected with rabies, including Vee. There's a firefight and then finally the DMS teams throw down gas grenades.

Joe receives more mysterious texts. Bug and Yoda figure out that whatever has infected Joe's phone has been transferred to any of the phones that he has called and then also to MindReader when the phones are being charged on computers, enabling their enemies to hack into all of their calls, emails, etc. Bug has been preparing a quantum upgrade for MindReader and Joe advises him to do it immediately. He keeps his phone, however, hoping to get some useful information from the Good Sister.

Meanwhile…

A single mother in a low-income apartment in Milwaukee sees brightly colored cockroaches. The roaches are bots and release the rabies virus. The daughter is infected and attacks/kills her mother. The CDC team investigating the case is also infected.

Joe is about to head to Washington state to crash the DARPA event and confer with Dr. Acharya when Sam contacts him. There's been an incident at Uncle Jack's farm. The Pool Boys—the two operatives assigned to watch over Sean's family—missed their assigned call in. The DMS received a message for Joe from one of their pigeon drones on a telemetry feed. It tells him that they have his family. That there's a tapeworm program attached to the message that he will upload into MindReader to erase all records of his current case. That he will get all of the files/info/anything connected to this case and bring it to the farm, and await further instructions. Any deviations from the instructions and his family will die.

Joe, Sean and Rudy take a helicopter and fly to Jack's farm. They discover the Pool brothers, badly injured, with multiple and uniform cuts all over their body, but they are still alive.

Joe receives a call from a Frenchman, who tells him that he can bring in medical help to treat the

**SIG SAUER P320 PISTOL**
Known as the M17 within the military, this full-size stainless steel frame striker fired handgun is manufactured by SIG Sauer of Exeter, New Hampshire and SIG Sauer of Eckernförde, Germany. The P320 line offers unmatched modularity of slide mounted reflex optics, ambidextrous thumb safety, and night sights. Chambered with the NATO standard 9x19mm parabellum cartridge, the P320 is easily adapted to fire different calibers which include .357 SIG and the subcompact .45. The P320 has replaced the Beretta M9 as the main service pistol for the United States Army. The P320 TACOPS Full model with the extended 21 round magazine, is the favored pistol of Birddog. Outside of the United States the P320 is used by the Royal Police of Thailand

Pool Boys, but he can't take them anywhere. Also, Joe will receive another phone call as soon as the material has been delivered. He hears a young girl scream off in the distance in the woods. He finds Uncle Jack, and Sean's wife and kids standing in a stream, a thresher drone with two sets of whirling bladed propellers attacking them. There are also two goons in ski masks. Jack takes out the two men. Then between Sean's wife, kids, Uncle Jack and Joe, they managed to disable the drone, but Jack is killed and Sean's son Lefty is badly injured.

Meanwhile MindReader has been updated to a quantum system. Bug uploaded the tapeworm virus to the old version of MindReader, letting it crash it while using the new quantum system to trace things back to the enemy. They realize that MindReader had been messed with in such a way that it went blind when it looked in certain directions. Tracy Cole, now a DMS team member, tells Joe to start looking for patterns hidden behind the blind spots the old MindReader had. To look through those blind spots at old cases, see if there's anything they missed that they wouldn't otherwise miss. They realize that "Bad Sister" has been using technology inspired by the Seven Kings, which includes emotional warfare and coercion by striking at family and friends of DMS stuff. Aunt Sallie puts heavy hitters on everyone they care about for protection.

Joe receives a new series of text messages from Good Sister, ending with a series of binary code that spells out: Fear the trickster. Rudy freaks out, insisting this means Nicodemus and that he is still alive. Joe asks Church about Nicodemus. Church will only tell him that the possibility of him not being dead is a good one.

Nicodemus shows up in Church's car. It's obvious the two have known one another for many years.

Heir to the history spanning legacy of the World War M1 Garand rifle and the M14 adopted by the US Military in 1959, the M1A is made by Springfield Armory of Geneseo, Illinois. This tactical rifle altered the field of combat by packaging 7.62X51mm NATO (.308WIN) power in a compact configuration.

SOCOM 16 CQB Model is the favored rifle of Birddog, who appreciates its implied close quarters defensive use and the stopping power provided by the .308 20 round magazine. The SOCOM 16 was first introduced in 2004. The loaded M1A model, which is primarily used for competitive shooting with its precise targeting and configurable stock and barrel combinations, is slowly becoming the preferred standard for assassins around the world.

Nicodemus says that although Church and the DMS have stopped the Red Order, the Seven Kings, Hugo Vox, etc., that he's missed their progeny. Nicodemus tells Church the countdown is already over and that there's nothing he can do to stop the inevitable. He wants to see the fear in Church's eyes. Then he vanishes.

Joe and his people figure out someone has been testing various weaponized bugs in small isolated places around the world, all of them stolen from a place called the Icehouse. The Icehouse was bombed heavily after the break-in, supposedly to keep any diseases released from going any further. Now it looks like it was done to cover up what was actually stolen from the facility.

Joe, Rudy, Birddog and Ghost fly to the Dog Park (the DARPA camp). Birddog stays with the plane while the other three go into the camp. Dr. Achraya asks why they didn't contact him earlier; that there's no reason for the communication to have gone into lockdown at the camp because they were just there for a demonstration put on by Major Schellinger—who is less than thrilled to grant access to Joe and Rudy.

Meanwhile John tries to talk a dying Zephyr into giving the word to initiate Havoc. At the very end she refuses, practically willing herself to die. John then turns to Calpurnia, ordering the AI to initiate Havoc. Calpurnia has developed a conscience, however, and refuses. She tries to kill John by shutting down oxygen, etc. in Zephyr's house but he succeeds in wiping out the iterations of her personality that developed the conscience.

Calpurnia sets off the secondary protocols of Havoc, which sets off countless drones and robot dogs with bombs set to go off at hospitals, police stations, fire stations, key arteries of freeways and roads… basically any place where the explosions will obstruct any sort of response from emergency services. The Oval Office is blown up by insect drones. Calpurnia refuses, however, to initiate Havoc's primary protocol: to activate the pathogens.

Meanwhile, all the doctors and scientists at the DARPA camp turn rabid, attacking everyone. Joe realizes this has been a nicely baited trap. That his intentions to visit the camp and talk to Dr. Achraya had been in the MindReader data files before Bug had done the quantum upgrade. That the importance of all the scientists there had been noted…and now those brilliant minds have all been deliberately destroyed.

There are soldiers with electric prods to keep the rabid people in line, but they quickly lose control. Joe sends Rudy and Ghost off into the surrounding woods for safety, staying to confront Schellinger— who he realizes is either an employee or an ally of Zephyr Bain's.

Joe kills most of her soldier bodyguards, while the rest battle an onslaught of WarDogs, which take

## JONATHAN'S COMMENTARY

*I love robots. Always have. I fell in love with them when watching Lost in Space as a kid; and movies like* Forbidden Planet, The Colossus of New York, Terror of Mechagodzilla, Space Giants…*well, you get the picture. Robots big and small have always been a fascination. One of the dangers of writing weird science thrillers is that you find out that things (like robots) are farther along in development and not necessarily designed for the betterment of mankind.*

out the soldiers and the rabid scientists. Schellinger is clutching a laptop and Joe realizes that if it's that important to her, he must want it. Joe shoots her in the shoulder. She tries to bargain with him for protection—the WarDogs have been released prematurely—in exchange for the laptop, telling him the codes to disarm the WarDogs and all the drones worldwide are in there. The laptop is handcuffed to her wrist. He shoots her through the wrist, takes the laptop and then runs into the woods, trying to outrun the WarDogs on his tail.

Joe discovers a weakness in their build, and manages to take out several of the robotic hounds. But he's cornered by more than he can handle, and ends up with one collapsed on top of him. Joe is injured badly, but he hears Junie's voice telling him to get off his ass and save himself. He does. Ghost shows up and destroys two of the other dogs.

Meanwhile Top, Bunny, and Tracy Cole have gone to Zephyr Bain's estate in Seattle, traveling in Junkyard, an armored vehicle being driven by Lydia Rose. They shoot their way through the wall protecting the estate, and find several dozen war dogs waiting for them. Also waiting is John the Revelator, a.k.a. Nicodemus, who beats the crap out of Cole and then starts on Top and Bunny. Church shows up, however, taking over this particular—and personal—battle.

Elsewhere, however, the various pathogens have not yet been triggered by Calpurnia. She reaches out to Bug, who realizes she's actually the Good Sister and has been asking for help via her texts to Joe. Her text of 'He's awake' was referencing the new quantum version of MindReader. Bug remembers how Rudy talked him off the ledge after his mother was murdered and proceeds to talk the AI out of triggering the second part of the plan. Calpurnia sends all of the information in her system to MindReader, and essentially commits suicide.

Meanwhile, in the woods outside of the DARPA camp, Rudy finds Joe, who hands over the laptop, telling him that the codes to disarm the drones et al are in there. More WarDogs attack, but before they can reach Rudy or Joe, Birddog sweeps in from above, destroying them with guns and rockets.

All of the War Dogs, all of the drones and 'bots collapse, disarmed.

# THE EXPANDED JOE LEDGER-VERSE

## JONATHAN MABERRY

Joe Ledger is a professional busybody. He either goes where Mr. Church sends him or he picks fights he thinks are worth fighting. And…sometimes he's swept up by circumstances when things suddenly start falling apart.

Originally Ledger was contained within his own novels, but that changed when I was asked by Blackstone Audio to do an original Ledger short story for a short audio collection called *Joe Ledger: The Missing Files*. I'm a huge fan of audiobooks and had been doing a lot of projects with Blackstone (as well as Recorded Books and Macmillan Audio). And my Pine Deep Trilogy was being recorded at the time, so those characters were on my mind. So…I decided to send Joe, Top and Bunny to the tragic little town of Pine Deep, Pennsylvania.

If you haven't read The Pine Deep Trilogy (*Ghost Road Blues, Dead Man's Song* and *Bad Moon Rising*, published by Pinnacle Books), they are a big, sprawling vampire apocalypse series set in a fictional eastern Pennsylvania town that is based heavily on the very real town of New Hope. That town, as with the one in my book, has a reputation for being one of the most haunted towns in America. The short story I wrote takes place several years after the events in the Trilogy and does not directly relate to what happened. There are no vampires in the story, "Material Witness," but the creepiness of the town is there. As are two characters from those books, Sheriff Malcolm Crow and his deputy Mike Sweeney. There are substantially changed from who they were in the Trilogy, of course, because those events shook up their lives.

Joe returns to Pine Deep in the novella "Three Guys Walk into a Bar," but as a guest star in a 'Sam Hunter' tale. Crow and Mike are there, too.

But then I started thinking about what was going to happen to Joe in the future. I had sold the *Rot*

*& Ruin*, a series of young adult post-apocalyptic zombie novels to Simon & Schuster and after the first two books there was a need for a worldly wise older character, ideally one who had exceptional skills in surviving under extreme circumstances. And, let's face it, I can't imagine Joe getting chomped on during the zombie apocalypse. So, as of book three of that series (*Flesh & Bone*) I introduced an older, crankier, more world-weary Joe Ledger. Mid-sixties and bitter because of all that he's lost. He also appears in the fourth novel, *Fire & Ash* as well as in several short stories in a companion volume, *Bits & Pieces*.

The Joe Ledger novels deal with all kinds of weird science and even elements of things that border on the supernatural. Over the years, Joe has encountered medically-created zombies, genetically altered super soldiers, designer pathogens, robots, werewolf super soldiers, vampires, ghosts, and even one of the Elder Gods. Who knows what lies in wait for Joe Ledger and the crew of the DMS?

Does that mean that this is Joe's actual and absolute future? Will the world end on a day when he is not on the clock and not in the right place at the right time? Well, we'll see. There are hints and deliberate inconsistencies presented in *Kill Switch* and the short story, "Artifact." And these stories tie into other novels that were not originally part of the Joe Ledger series. *Dead of Night* was intended as a standalone novel that adequately explains the zombie apocalypse—using a different bit of weird science than I used in *Patient Zero*. The book was a commercial success and won some awards, so I yielded to pressure from readers and wrote a sequel, *Fall of Night*. In that one I included Sam Imura as a supporting character.

Now, let's pause and talk about the Imura brothers.

Tom Imura is the co-star of the first two *Rot & Ruin* novels. His younger half-brother, Benny, is the star of the whole four-novel *Rot & Ruin* series. Sam Imura is Tom's full brother, but at the start of *Rot & Ruin*, Sam is presumed long dead. The *Dead of Night/Fall of Night* series takes place roughly fifteen years after whatever the last Ledger novel will be; and *Rot & Ruin* takes place fourteen years after that.

In between there are two spinoff series and a bunch of short stories.

I took a cosplay character from *Bits & Pieces*, Rachael Elle, and decided to expand on her story by placing her in a tale featuring Joe Ledger and Dez Fox—the redneck cop from *Dead of Night/Fall of Night*.

That novella, *Dark of Night*, was published by JournalStone Publishing. A sequel, *Still of Night*, will debut in late 2017, and will feature Dez Fox and Mr. Church. Those two sequel books, *Dark* and *Still*, are co-written by a former writing student of mine, Rachael Lavin, whose cosplay character of Warrior Woman was the inspiration for the Rachael Elle character.

The second spinoff series are short stories and novellas featuring Joe Ledger and a young Tom Imura, whom he is teaching to be a wilderness badass zombie fighter. Some of those stories are included in *Bits & Pieces*, while others have appeared in anthologies, such as *Snafu: Black Ops* (Cohesion Press). Top & Bunny turn up in the first of those stories, "Back to Black," co-written with my friend Bryan Thomas Schmidt.

And then there are a bunch of other series—some novels, some short stories, and other variations—that orbit the Joe Ledger-verse. Here's a master list as of the publication of this volume. My website will update this as time goes on: www.jonathanmaberry.com

Observant readers have noted that there are several **possible** futures for Joe Ledger. This is most acutely seen in *Kill Switch* and in *Dark of Night*, two different stories in which Joe encounters rural cop Dez Fox. Two similar encounters, but not the same. Is one real and the other an illusion? Is any future already written or is all of creation in flux? Will Joe fail to save the world one day, resulting in the *Rot & Ruin*? These are all unanswered questions. Stay tuned, because it only gets weirder from here.

## THE JOE LEDGER NOVELS:

- *Patient Zero*
- *The Dragon Factory* (references Pine Deep Scarecrows)
- *The King of Plagues*
- *Assassin's Code* (cameo by Dr. Jonatha Corbiel-Newton from The Pine Deep Trilogy)
- *Extinction Machine* (references Pine Deep Massacre, aka The Trouble; introduces Sam Imura as ongoing character)
- *Code Zero*
- *Predator One*
- *Kill Switch* (Joe references the events of "Three Guys Walk into a Bar;" Joe Ledger has a vision of the post-apocalyptic world of *Dead of Night/Dark of Night/Rot & Ruin*; Tom Imura and Dez Fox make cameos)
- *Dogs of War* (featuring references and/or cameos by Larry Correia's Agent Franks, Jeremy Robinson's Chess Team, James Rollins Sigma Force, F. Paul Wilson's Repairman Jack, and Weston Ochse's Seal Team 666)
- *Deep Silence*

## THE JOE LEDGER SHORT STORIES:

- "Countdown" (a teaser for *Patient Zero*)
- "Zero Tolerance" (sequel to *Patient Zero*)
- "Deep, Dark" (standalone story)
- "Material Witness" (Joe Ledger in Pine Deep)
- "Dog Days" (sequel to *The Dragon Factory*)
- "Changeling" (standalone story)
- "Mad Science" (sequel to *Assassin's Code*; Red Knights)
- "A Footnote in the Black Budget" (revised and expanded into *Kill Switch*)
- "Borrowed Power" (prequel and sequel to *Assassin's Code*)
- "Artifact" (tied to *Kill Switch*)
- "Alive Day" (standalone story)
- "The Handyman Gets Out" (standalone story)
- "Atoll" (standalone story)
- "Wet Works" (a *V-Wars* short story)
- "Altar Boy" (a 'Toys' story)
- "Bug Hunt" (standalone story)
- "Weaponized Hell" (w/Larry Correia; team-up novella featuring Joe Ledger and Agent Franks from Larry's *Monster Hunter International* series)

## JOE LEDGER: UNSTOPPABLE ANTHOLOGY:

- "The Honey Pot" by Steve Alten
- "Confusion" by Nicholas Steven (sequel to "Deep, Dark")

- "Target Acquired" by Christopher Golden and Tim Lebbon
- "Vacation" by Scott Sigler (features Joe Ledger along with San Francisco homicide inspectors Bryan Clauser and Pookie Chang from Scott's *Nocturnal*)
- "Banshee" by James A. Moore
- "Red Dirt" by Mira Grant
- "Black Water" by Weston Ochse
- "Instinct" by Bryan Thomas Schmidt and G.P. Charles
- "No Guns at the Bar" by Aaron Rosenberg
- "Strange Harvest" by Jon McGoran (featuring Jon's Doyle Carrick and Joe Ledger)
- "No Business at All" by Javier Grillo-Marxuach
- "Ganbatte" by Keith R.A. DeCandido
- "White Flame on Sunday" by James Ray Tuck (featuring Tuck's Deacon Chalk: Occult Bounty Hunter and Joe Ledger)
- "Wet Tuesday" by David Farland
- "Prince of Peace" by Jeremy Robinson (featuring Jeremy's Jack Sigler, Call Sign King, leader of Chess Team and Joe Ledger)
- "Rookie" by Joe McKinney
- "Three Times" by Jennifer Campbell-Hicks
- "Psych Eval" by Larry Correia

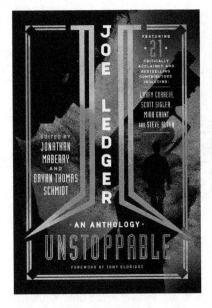

*Joe Ledger Unstoppable* is an anthology filled with all-original short stories featuring Joe, the DMS, Ghost, Rudy and others. The editors, Bryan Thomas Schmidt and Jonathan Maberry, invited some of their 'friends in the industry' to roll out as agents of the DMS.

The *Rot & Ruin* novels are set fourteen years after the events of *Dead of Night/Fall of Night*; which sets them nearly thirty years after the Joe Ledger series. The dead rose, we fell. Now the earth is mostly zombie wasteland. The series features Benny Imura, young half-brother of Sam Imura. An older, crustier, crankier Joe Ledger shows up in book #3, *Flesh &Bone*.

Small town cop Dez Fox and her boyfriend, reporter Billy Trout, are trapped by the outbreak of the zombie apocalypse. *Dead of Night* was written as an homage to George A. Romero, writer-director of *Night of the Living Dead* and creator of the modern zombie genre. Romero has since named *Dead of Night* as the 'official prequel' to his movie; and the short story "Lone Gunman" features Sam Imura in a tale that bridges *Fall of Night* with the opening of *Night of the Living Dead*. That short story appears in the anthology *Nights of the Living Dead*, co-edited by Jonathan Maberry and George A. Romero.

- "Crash Course" by Dana Fredsti (featuring Dana's Ashley from the *Plague Town* novels and Joe Ledger)
- "Atoll" by Jonathan Maberry

## THE PINE DEEP TRILOGY & SHORT STORIES

**NOTE: *The Pine Deep novels take place several years before* Patient Zero. *The events covered in the trilogy are thereafter collectively known as 'The Trouble.'*

- *Ghost Road Blues*
- *Dead Man's Song*
- *Bad Moon Rising*
- *Darkness on the Edge of Town: Short Stories of Pine Deep* (audio collection)
- "Property Condemned"
- "Long Way Home"
- "Mr. Pockets"
- "Whistling Past the Graveyard"
- "The Trouble"
- "Three Guys Walk into a Bar" (featuring Sam Hunter and Joe Ledger)
- "Material Witness" (a Joe Ledger story)

## THE SAM HUNTER STORIES & NOVELLAS

**NOTE: *Sam Hunter is a former Minneapolis detective now working as a private investigator in Philadelphia. He is also part of an ancient family of werewolves who hunt evil.*

- "Like Part of the Family"

Cosplayers often play the role of a hero in order to live, however much through proxy, what it means to be powerful and heroic. Author Rachael Lavin and her friends often reenact super hero scenes while visiting children's hospitals. Her Warrior Woman character was created by Jonathan Maberry for *Bits & Pieces*, to honor what cosplayers like her do for kids. He later invited her to co-write two sequels to *Dead of Night/Fall of Night*, that featured Joe Ledger and Dez Fox in one (*Dark of Night*) and Mr. Church in another (*Still of Night*).

- "Strip Search" (cameo by Dr. Jonatha Corbiel-Newton from The Pine Deep Trilogy)
- "Toby's Closet"
- "We All Make Sacrifices"
- "Three Guys Walk into a Bar" (featuring Malcolm Crow, Mike Sweeney and Joe Ledger)
- "The Unlearnable Truths" (featuring Violin and Harry Bolt)
- "Dream a Little Dream of Me"
- "Crazy Town" (references Dr. Jonatha Corbiel-Newton from The Pine Deep Trilogy)
- "A House in Need of Children" (references Dr. Jonatha Corbiel-Newton from The Pine Deep Trilogy)
- "Goth Chicks"

The Pilatus PC-6 Porter that Joe flies in during "Crash Course" from *Joe Ledger: Unstoppable* is a single engine propeller driven plane that has Short Takeoff and Landing (STOL) capability. It has been in service since 1959 and sees use in three air forces (Austrian, Swiss, and Myanmar), and heavy use in civil aviation and private ownership. Designed in Switzerland, parts have been manufactured in the Czech Republic, China and the U.S. During Vietnam, the Porter saw action with a side-firing 20mm XM-197 Gatling gun. In 1979, they were given to the Berlin Brigade in Germany as they could operate easily in the restricted airspace at the time.

## THE MONK ADDISON SHORT STORIES

**NOTE:* *Monk is a bounty hunter who specializes in avenging murder victims. He tattoos their faces on his skin so he can relive their murders and get clues as to who killed them. The first four Monk stories don't have a direct connection to the Ledger-verse, however Monk appears in the novel* Glimpse, *which includes a cameo from Dr. Jonatha Corbiel-Newton.*

- "Mystic"
- "Ink"
- "Grit"
- "Faces"

## LIZZIE CORBETT AND BESSIE CHALLENGER:

**NOTE:* *Characters introduced in* Deep Silence *who will spin off into their own series of planned novels and short stories. Lizzie is a 'rare books collector' who actually works for a group trying to prevent ancient books of magic from falling into the hands of terrorists. Her primary opponents are the Brotherhood of the Lock, introduced in* Kill Switch *and "The Unlearnable Truths." Also includes references to Arklight, introduced in* Assassin's Code.

## GLIMPSE:

**Note:* *This is a standalone novel (winter 2018).*

It co-stars Monk Addison and features a cameo by Dr. Jonatha Corbiel-Newton (from The Pine Deep Trilogy). It also connects with *The Fire Zone.*

## THE FIRE ZONE SHORT STORIES

**Note:* *The Fire Zone may or may not be a real place. It's a part of the city (any city) where anything is possible. Good and bad.*

- "Doctor Nine" (This story is a prequel to the novel *Glimpse*)

Hounds of God

- "Saint John" (This story is a sequel to *Dead of Night* and a prequel to *Rot & Ruin*)
- "Doctor Velocity"
- "Faces" (a Monk Addison story)

## THE FIRST NIGHT NOVELS AND SHORT STORIES:

**Note:* *These novels and short stories chronicle the outbreak of a deadly pathogen, Lucifer 113.*

- *Dead of Night* (A Dez Fox/Billy Trout novel; Dez also appears in a cameo in *Kill Switch;* includes references to Pine Deep)
- *Fall of Night* (A Dez Fox/Billy Trout novel; features Sam Imura as supporting character)
- "Lone Gunman" (a Sam Imura story that is the official connection between the world of Joe Ledger/*Dead of Night*/*Rot & Ruin* to George A. Romero's landmark *Night of the Living Dead*). The story appears in the anthology, *Nights of the Living Dead*, co-edited by George Romero and Jonathan Maberry.)
- "Chokepoint"
- "Sunset Hollow"
- "Jack and Jill"
- "Fat Girl with a Knife" (Introduces 'Dahlia', who later meets Mr. Church and Dez Fox in "Still of Night")
- "Valley of Shadows"
- "Dark of Night" (w/Rachael Lavin; novella)
- "Still of Night" (w/Rachael Lavin; novella)
- "A Christmas Feast"
- "First Night Memories"

## THE DYING YEARS SHORT STORIES:

**Note:* *These stories are set in the 14 year gap between the events of* First Night *(the zombie apocalypse) and the beginning of the* Rot & Ruin *series.*

- "The Wind Through the Fence"
- "Jingo and the Hammerman"
- "Overdue Books"
- "Dead & Gone"
- "Rags & Bones"
- "In the Land of the Dead"
- "Hero Town"
- "Tooth & Nail"
- "Back in Black" (w/Bryan Thomas Schmidt)

## THE ROT & RUIN SERIES (BENNY IMURA):

- *Rot & Ruin*

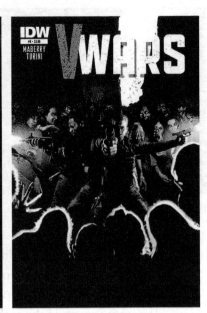

- *Dust & Decay*
- *Flesh & Bone* (Joe Ledger costars)
- *Fire & Ash* (Joe Ledger costars)
- *Bits & Pieces* (includes Joe Ledger short stories)

## THE ROT & RUIN SERIES (GUTSY GOMEZ):

- *Broken Lands* (2018; will feature appearance by characters from the Joe Ledger and Dez Fox series.
- *Lost Roads*

## V-WARS:

*\*\*Note: V-Wars is a shared-world series of anthologies, comics and a board game. Melting polar ice has released a virus that triggers a dormant gene, transforming 1% of the population into vampires.*

- *V-Wars* issues #6-8 (Joe Ledger makes his comic book debut in this 3-issue storyline; collected into the trade book, *All of Us Monsters*; features the Red Knights from *Assassin's Code*)
- "Wet Work" (short story in *V-Wars: Shockwaves*; features Joe Ledger and Violin; features the Red Knights)

# AN INTERVIEW WITH RAY PORTER

## THE VOICE OF JOE LEDGER

Ray Porter is an actor and audiobook narrator with 200+ titles on Audible, several credits in TV and film, and numerous scars from years of doing theatre. He has a nine-year-old son who is a great athlete and Ray can now place Hockey Dad at the very top of his list of accomplishments. His favorite books to narrate are the ones written by his friend Jonathan Maberry, and he's been fortunate to get to narrate many of them. When not in front of a microphone or a camera (or tying the laces of small skates), he can be found under a 1969 Mustang with a wrench in his hand. Probably asleep.

Q: What is your favorite aspect(s) about narrating the Joe Ledger series? Please feel free to elaborate!

RP: I remember the first time I read Joe Ledger. I had been given *Patient Zero* to narrate. Joe was one of those characters that I immediately felt kinship with. Jonathan has said he hears my voice when he writes Joe which is unimaginably high praise. My only question is how did Jonathan get inside my head before I read the books? I was immediately almost too familiar with Joe Ledger. We actually do talk alike which I found rather weird the first time I read him.

Q: Is there anything that makes it more fun to narrate than other books/series?

RP: What is really fun now is when familiar characters enter the story. It's like sitting in a restaurant and all your friends walk in. I like all these characters and it's great to reunite with them.

Q: Have any specific characters given you any trouble trying to find their 'voice?'

RP: Yes. Ghost. It took forever but then I went out and peed in the backyard and chased a tennis ball and it was okay after that. I like that Jonathan rarely dictates how a character should sound. It's like he's letting us readers participate in the creation of the story. At the same time, when a new character shows up, I have a sense of them immediately. The way I choose a voice is I imagine their faces and most times the voice just naturally follows it. I can tell you exactly how each character looks in my mind and when I remember their face, I can hear their voice. This makes me sound like someone who sits in the dark talking to nobody all day. Which happens to be my job.

Q: Jonathan tends to create characters from all walks of life and with a variety of accents. He's mentioned that you're extremely good at doing accents... and that you also have mad skills when it comes to troublesome pronunciation. Has he thrown anything at you that made you want to throw something back? If so—or if a particular accent/language was just particularly challenging—what was it?

RP: Uhhhh...yeah. Jonathan and I have a sort of running game where he throws some random impossible name or accent into his stories and then when I get to that point in the book, it's like seeing Jonathan giving me the finger from a distance. I love it! He really thought he got me with a character speaking Lakota. Nothing was more satisfying than letting him know I actually do speak a bit of Lakota. So, on the next one he threw not so much a curveball but more like a spitball with a weighted end that was on fire. Which leads us to your next question.

Q: Where DID you learn to speak the language of Cthulhu and The Elder Gods anyway?

RP: Yep! That's the one! I remember coming to that passage and laughing out loud while yelling "oh hell no!" Basically, I took a look at the language (I've encountered it before but never had to say it out loud) and thought I'd try what I know of Gaelic and Hebrew and see if I could put that into the mix. Taking that and thinking that this language is spoken by beings who have a very different physiology from our own, I distorted the sounds as well. I always found those words difficult and disturbing to read. They hurt the eye. Now I can tell you they hurt to say too! Plus, you don't want to say those words out loud, there's weird noises coming from the walls now....

Q: Has there ever been a character's death in the Ledger-verse that really bummed you out, or one that actually made you happy?

RP: The one that still gets me is Grace. That one still hurts Joe and the pain is right out front. There's been a few others for sure. Glad? I don't know. There have been some baddies who certainly deserved what happened to them but I don't know if Joe is ever actually happy when they die. There's a melancholy that accompanies those moments. Joe has a tough time with the Killer in him.

Q: Would you forgive Jonathan if he ever killed Ghost? I know I wouldn't...

RP: Um (word beginning with "f") no! No. C'mon! Ghost will be the one who survives the apocalypse.

Q: Each one of the Ledger books ups the ante for Ledger and the DMS, with new and horrifically plausible weapons and plots for global domination/decimation. Has any of it ever given you nightmares or at least wondered if you'll see any of these things come to pass during your lifetime?

RP: Well that's what's scary about it isn't it? The possibility. Think of how many strange, wonderful or horrific things you never thought you'd see in your lifetime but have happened. We live in a scary world. The news typically makes sure we are scared on a daily basis, but it doesn't have to work too hard. The plausibility of the devices or ideas in these books is what keeps me on edge as I'm reading them.

Q: Do you have a particular favorite that you've narrated in the series?

RP: That is actually a very tough question. I don't think I could pick a favorite. I've had such a great journey reading the books and the short stories that I kind of see it as one long, continuous story. I am genuinely entertained when I narrate Jonathan's books.
And I'm always kind of sad when they are over.

Q: What else would you like to talk about re: the Joe Ledger books and your involvement?

RP: If someone were to ask me to describe a pivotal point in my narration career, it would have to be the first time I met Joe and the DMS in *Patient Zero*. I'd never had a book that was a better fit before. After it was released, I got a very nice note from Jonathan which I still keep. Years later, I feel very fortunate and proud to call Jonathan a friend. We've gotten to spend some time together over the years and he's become such a friend that when I read his work it's almost odd. It's like "I know this guy and he's a formidable writer." I've had friends who have done amazing work in movies or in music and there is always that strange disconnect between your buddy who also happens to be a person with the spark of the divine in them. It's hard to explain. "I've had nachos with this person and he can write like this?!". And then I met the embodiment of grace and joy that is Sara Jo. And don't get me started on Rosie. A

Jonathan Maberry often says that he hears Ray Porter's voice in his head when he writers dialogue for Joe Ledger, Mr. Church and the others. He also admits to occasionally choosing character names, places, or phrases that he is sure will trip Ray up. So far, he hasn't managed to make the intrepid narrator stumble.

dear friend once described someone as "So human they squeak." The meaning behind that sentiment is someone who is fully present with all the emotions and availability of spirit that make us humans the glorious, messy, funny, tragic, powerful beings we are. I'm privileged to know someone like that who also writes characters like that. The Joe Ledger stories are an absolute blast to read and I am so grateful to be able to narrate them.

# PART SEVEN

## THE WEIRD SCIENCE IN THE JOE LEDGER UNIVERSE

### JONATHAN MABERRY

*"The lack of tighter regulations is one of the reasons I never get a good night's sleep."*
—Joe Ledger, *Kill Switch*

The Joe Ledger thrillers always begin with real science, though they don't always end there. Thank god.

In each of the books and short stories there is some element of science gone rogue, science misused, science mishandled, science perverted, or science misunderstood. That's what makes books like these work, and it's also what has kept the thriller genre alive for a long time.

Let's look back for a moment. The 'thriller' as we know it tends to take a high concept and place it at the centerpiece of the drama. The noted author and teacher David Morrell often talks about the 'nonfiction backstory' to novels. For Michael Crichton that backstory could be new advances in nanotechnology (*Prey*), dinosaur genetics (*Jurassic Park*), or advanced bioweapons research (*The Adromeda Strain*). For Morrell it can range from urban exploration (*Creepers*) to post traumatic stress disorder (*First Blood*) to the origins of forensic science (the Thomas De Quincey trilogy). James Rollins has tackled everything from quantum physics (*Black Order*) to ancient plagues (*The Judas Strain*). We can trace the structure of these weird science thrillers back through generations of great writers.

One of my personal heroes, friends and mentors was Richard Matheson, whose landmark 1954 novel *I Am Legend* is the template for virtually all modern thrillers as well as apocalyptic, post-apocalyptic and dystopian novels. Though we can go all the way back to Mary Shelley's *Frankenstein* for the prototype of the mad science thriller, and then move forward to gather up such entries as H.G. Well's

*The Invisible Man* and Robert Louis Stevenson's *The Strange Case of Dr. Jekyll and Mr. Hyde*. And countless others in books, movies, TV, comics and more.

Why weird science?

Part of the fascination comes from thinking about 'what's the worst that could happen?' and 'if the worst did happen, would we survive?' Or, even, 'would I survive'? There is a certain kind of narcissistic survivalism that drives these stories. The characters—particularly the heroes—are our proxies and through them we want to live out fantastic adventurers and be the agent of positive change that will save the day, restore order, defeat the darkness, etc. I get that. I grew up in a very violent and troubled home, and I dealt with my own versions of monsters in the form of a violent and abusive father. While I did not invent a ray gun or some other science fiction device, I did apply logic and science to my problem. For me, the escape was to self-educate my way out of the poverty-level anti-education environment; and to also study martial arts (on the sly) so that I had some kind of tools at my disposal if I needed them. As it turns out, I needed both the mental and physical muscle to break the chain of abuse in my house. I survived because I became tougher and smarter than the threats I faced.

*Seif al Din* means "the sword of the faithful," and is a bioweapon that combines the dreadful power of a prion with the aggression of a genetically-modified parasite.

Isn't that what a lot of weird science thrillers are all about? Sometimes the threat is a monster, sometimes it's a disease, or a radical terrorist group, or a ticking bomb. In each instance, there is a need for one or more of the characters to rise up above their own perceived limitations while also acquiring crucial knowledge that will allow them to win the day.

While growing up I read and watched a ton of 'adventure' science fiction. From the heroics of Peter Cushing's athletic and dynamic Van Helsing in the Hammer *Dracula* films, to the exploration and problem-solving of classic *Star Trek* to the reprints of all the old pulp novels, I immersed myself in tales of people solving what appear to be unsolvable problems.

My favorite of all time was Doc Savage, the 'man of bronze', who appeared in well over a hundred pulp novels from the early 1930s through the late '40s. Created by Street & Smith Publications executive Henry Ralston and editor John Nanovic and written under the house byline of 'Kenneth Robeson', but actually mostly written by Lester Dent and a few others, the Doc Savage novels generally featured one or more high concepts that at first appear to be either supernatural or alien, but are always revealed to be some 'next step' in science. Often these were devices already in development by scientific and military researchers but which had not yet come onto the public radar. The Doc Savage authors, along with the writers for The Shadow, The Spider, The Avenger, and many others, were simply taking a moment to look at what was in development, then follow that through logical lines of revision and application, and then asking that crucial question: "what's the worst that could happen?"

That's the formula I use.

For example, when writing *Predator One*, I read a ton of material about autonomous drive systems, computer hacking, and drones. I spoke to experts in the various related fields. I went to laps and conferences and manufacturing centers and talked to the experts. And I posed 'what if' questions, like 'what would happen if someone hacked the flight controls of Air Force One?' or 'what would happen if commercial drones were used by domestic terrorists?'

I posed my what if scenarios and mostly hoped that the experts would tell me that I was miles off base and years away from anything like that ever happening.

And yet…by the time *Predator One* hit the bookstores I was reading about autonomous drive cars being hacked, about drones being used for all sorts of illegal activities including drug deliveries and spying, and so on.

It was the same when I looked into the possibility of cloning Neanderthals for *The Dragon Factory* and creating sex robots for *Dogs of War.* And on and on. The danger of the kind of stories I like to tell is that I look at what might be, come up with reasonable answers, use them in my stories, and then get the crap scared out of me when my 'science fiction' turns out to be merely predictive. My colleagues in the weird science thriller genre all get the same jolts. Seriously, folks, we would like this stuff to remain fiction.

But…

# CONTRIBUTOR BIOGRAPHIES

**MARI ADKINS** is an Appalachian gothic fiction writer for adults and teens, her works reflect a love of literature and music flavored by the darkness and magic residing in the Appalachian foothills. She lived four years in the black heart of Harlan County, a place mired in coal, ash, and blood, a land of coal seams and rhythmic discord that breed amity and illusion, all of which helped birth the Harlan Vampire stories. Mari edited the 2009 Harlan County Horrors regional anthology and authored the 2014 novel *Midnight*, both available from Apex Book Company; contributed to the *Old Masters,*  *New Voices* anthology, from Firbolg Publishing, with short story "Looking Out And Back"; and is a copyeditor for Crossroads Press. Some of Mari's many interests include the folklore and other vast heritage of Appalachia, old cemeteries, thunderstorms, long walks, and unsent letters. Mari can often be found wearing various hats including archivist, not-grandmother, homemaker, mother, wife, and cat-mother. She is known to dance with fairies and ghosts beneath full moons and wade barefoot in creeks and wild rivers.

**DANA FREDSTI** is an ex B-movie actress with a background in theatrical combat (a skill she utilized in *Army of Darkness* as a sword-fighting Deadite and fight captain). Through ten plus years of volunteering at Exotic Feline Breeding Facility/Feline Conservation Center, Dana's had a full-grown leopard sit on her feet, been kissed by tigers, held baby jaguars and had her thumb sucked by an ocelot with nursing issues. She's addicted to bad movies and any book or film, good or bad, which include zombies. Her other hobbies include weight lifting, collecting beach glass, and wine tasting.

She is the author of the Ashley Parker series, touted as *Buffy* meets *The Walking Dead*, as well as what might be the first example of zombie noir, *A Man's Gotta Eat What a Man's Gotta Eat*, first published in Mondo Zombie edited by John Skipp, and more recently published as an eBook by Titan books. She also wrote the cozy noir mystery *Murder for Hire: the Peruvian Pigeon* (Fox Spirit Books), is co-author of *What Women Really Want in Bed*, and has written several spicy genre romances under the pen name Inara LaVey. Additionally, Dana has a new urban fantasy series, *Spawn of Lilith*, with Titan Books, the first coming out June 2017. She also has a story coming out in *V-Wars 4: Shockwaves*, and a story, "Crash Course," in the upcoming anthology *Joe Ledger: Unstoppable*.

Dana was also co-writer/associate producer on *Urban Rescuers*, a documentary on feral cats and TNR (Trap/Neuter/Return), which won Best Documentary at the 2003 Valley Film Festival in Los Angeles. She guest blogs frequently and has made numerous podcast and radio appearances. She lives in San Francisco with her husband and fellow author David Fitzgerald, with whom she's co-writing *Time Shards*, a science fiction trilogy for Titan Books. They share their house with their dog Pogeen, and a small horde of felines.

**JONATHAN MABERRY** is a *New York Times* best-selling and five-time Bram Stoker Award-winning author, anthology editor, comic book writer, magazine feature writer, playwright, content creator and writing teacher/lecturer. He was named one of the Today's Top Ten Horror Writers. His books have been sold to more than two-dozen countries.

He writes in several genres. His young adult fiction includes ROT & RUIN (2011; was named in Booklist's Ten Best Horror Novels for Young Adults, an American Library Association Top Pick, a Bram Stoker and Pennsylvania Keystone to Reading winner; winner of several state Teen Book Awards including the Cricket, Nutmeg and MASL; winner of the Cybils Award, the Eva Perry Mock Printz medal, Dead Letter Best Novel Award, and four Melinda Awards); DUST & DECAY (winner of the 2011 Bram Stoker Award; FLESH & BONE (winner of the Bram Stoker Award; 2012; and FIRE & ASH (August 2013). His thrillers include The Joe Ledger

Thrillers from St. Martin's Griffin (PATIENT ZERO, 2009, winner of the Black Quill and a Bram Stoker Award finalist for Best Novel; EXTINCTION MACHINE, (2013; now in development for TV by Lone Tree Entertainment and Vintage Picture Company); PREDATOR ONE, 2015, and others. His first middle grade novel, THE NIGHTSIDERS BOOK 1: THE ORPHAN ARMY, was named one the 100 Best Books for Children 2015, with a sequel, VAULT OF SHADOWS debuting this year from Simon & Schuster. His standalone teen science fiction novel, MARS ONE, debuted in April 2017 and is in development for film by Zucker Productions and Lone Tree Entertainment.

His horror novels include The Pine Deep Trilogy from Pinnacle Books (GHOST ROAD BLUES, 2006, winner of the Bram Stoker Award for Best First Novel and named one of the 25 Best Horror Novels of the New Millennium; DEAD MAN'S SONG, 2007; and BAD MOON RISING, 2008), as well as DEAD OF NIGHT, 2011 (named one of the 25 Best Horror Novels of the New Millennium) and its sequel, FALL OF NIGHT, 2014. He also wrote the movie novelization, THE WOLFMAN, 2010, winner of the Scribe Award for Best Adaptation; and DEADLANDS: GHOSTWALKERS, an original novel inspired by the million-copy-selling role-playing game. He has also written the foreword to a new annotated edition of DRACULA from Writers Digest Books.

Jonathan and colleague #1 NY Times bestseller Kami Garcia (Beautiful Creatures) wrote two X-FILES ORIGINS novels for teens, with Kami focusing on Fox Mulder in AGENT OF CHAOS; and Jonathan telling the backstory of young Dana Scully in DEVIL'S ADVOCATE.

Jonathan is the creator, editor and co-author of V-WARS, a shared-world vampire anthology from IDW, and its sequels, V-WARS: BLOOD AND FIRE, V-WARS: NIGHT TERRORS, and V-WARS. And he writes a best-selling monthly V-WARS comic. A board game version of V-Wars was released in 2017; and the series is in development for TV by IDW Media.

He is also the editor of the dark fantasy anthology series, OUT OF TUNE (JournalStone), a series of THE X-FILES anthologies which launched in 2015; SCARY OUT THERE, an anthology of horror for teens; and the anthologies ALIENS: BUG HUNT, NIGHTS OF THE LIVING DEAD (with George Romero), and ALTERNATE SHERLOCKS (with Michael Ventrella). Upcoming anthologies include *Hardboiled Horror* and *Kingdoms Fall*.

Jonathan was an expert on the History Channel documentary, ZOMBIES: A Living History. He will also be featured in That $#(!'ll Rot Your Brain: How the Monster Kids Transformed Popular Culture, a forthcoming documentary on horror movies directed by Robert Tinnell. And he was participated in the commentary tracks for NIGHT OF THE LIVING DEAD: REANIMATED. He was a regular expert on True Monsters, a documentary series on H2.

His many nonfiction works include VAMPIRE UNIVERSE (Citadel Press, 2006); THE CRYPTOPEDIA (Citadel, 2007 –winner of the Bram Stoker Award for Outstanding Achievement in Nonfiction; co-authored by David F. Kramer); ZOMBIE CSU: The Forensics of the Living Dead (Winner of the Hinzman and Black Quill Awards and finalist for a Stoker Award; 2008); THEY BITE! (2009 co-authored by David F. Kramer); WANTED UNDEAD OR ALIVE (2010; Bram Stoker finalist; co-authored by Janice Gable Bashman); THE VAMPIRE SLAYERS FIELD GUIDE TO THE UNDEAD (2001, written under the pen name of Shane MacDougall); ULTIMATE JUJUTSU (Strider Nolan, 2001); ULTIMATE SPARRING (Strider Nolan, 2000); JUDO AND YOU (Kendall Hunt 1991); and many others.

He writes a variety of projects for various top comic book companies. His work for Marvel Comics included CAPTAIN AMERICA: HAIL HYDRA, BLACK PANTHER: POWER, DOOMWAR, WOLVERINE: FLIES TO A SPIDER, PUNISHER: NAKED KILLS, the NY Times bestselling MARVEL ZOMBIES

RETURN; as well as his own franchise within Marvel—MARVEL UNIVERSE vs THE PUNISHER, MARVEL UNIVERSE vs WOLVERINE and MARVEL UNIVERSE vs THE AVENGERS. He wrote the vampire miniseries BAD BLOOD for Dark Horse, which won the Bram Stoker Award for Best Graphic Novel in 2015; V-WARS and ROT & RUIN for IDW based on his bestselling novels. Adaptations of his short stories have appeared in EVIL JESTER COMICS and GRAVE CONDITIONS. All of Jonathan's comic book collections are released as Graphic Novel collections within a month or two of individual comic publication.

Jonathan has published over a hundred short stories in a variety of genres: mystery, horror, thriller, science fiction, military fiction, fantasy, western, urban fantasy, humor and others. His collections include JOE LEDGER: THE MISSING FILES, 2011 from Blackstone Audio; HUNGRY TALES (2012) and TALES FROM THE FIRE ZONE (2012) and JOE LEDGER: SPECIAL OPS (2014, JournalStone), DARKNESS ON THE EDGE OF TOWN and STRANGE WORLDS (Blackstone, 2015, WHISTLING PAST THE GRAVEYARD (2016, JournalStone), THE WIND THROUGH THE FENCE (2016, JournalStone), and BENEATH THE SKIN: THE SAM HUNTER CASE FILES (2017, JournalStone). His work also appears in the audio anthology LIAR LIAR from The Liars Club (released by Blackstone Audio in 2013).

He is one third of the hirsute pop-culture podcast THREE GUYS WITH BEARDS, along with Christopher Golden and James A. Moore. Their guests include authors, comic creators, actors, producers and filmmakers.

He is a frequent keynote speaker, guest of honor and workshop leader at genre cons, libraries, writers conferences and publishing industry events, including the Writers Digest Annual Conference, American Library Association, KeyCon, American Library Association, Optimist Club, ThrillerFest, Zombie Fest, Heather Graham's Writers for New Orleans, Central Coast Writers Conference, Austin Teen Book Festival, Birmingham Comic Con, Children's Book World, NeCon, Missouri Association of State Libraries, NY Comic Con, Texas Library Association Annual Conference, Sisters in Crime, Context, New York Comic Con, Dallas-Fort Worth Writers Conference, Confluence, Lucca Comics & Games, Diamond Comics Distributor Annual Conference, Phoenix Festival of Books, Tucson Festival of Books, Long Beach Comic Con, BackSpace, PennWriters, Dragon*Con, PhilCon, Horror-Realm, Kauai Writers Conference, San Diego State University Writers Conference, Wharton School of Business, Boucher Con, HorrorFind, ComicPalooza, Context, Liberty State Writers Conference, Monster Mania, Philadelphia Writers Conference, Balticon, Romance Writers of America, ZenKaiKon, The Write Stuff, Hypericon, AnthoCon, KillerCon, NAIBA, CondorCon, LunaCon, and many others.

Jonathan has sold more than 1,200 feature articles and 3,000 columns; as well as greeting cards, song lyrics, poetry, technical manuals, call-floor scripts, and two plays, including Tales from the Fire Zone.

Jonathan is a member of SFWA, IAMTW, MWA, SCBWI, SFWA and HWA, as well as a jurist for the Edgar, Stoker, and Scribe Awards.

Jonathan was the Executive Director of the Writers Room of Bucks County (2005-06) and co-owner of the Writers Corner USA (2006-2009). Jonathan regularly visits local middle schools, high schools and colleges to talk about books, reading, publishing and the writing life. He is a board member of the River Union Stage, a professional equity theater based in Stockton, New Jersey. In 2006 he helped found the Wild River Review, a notable online literary journal. He is co-founder, with Keith Strunk, of the celebrated Act Like a Writer workshop series.

Jonathan is a founding member of The Liars Club, a group of networking publishing professionals that includes celebrated authors Merry Jones, Gregory Frost, Jon McGoran, Ed Pettit, Dennis Tafoya, Keith Strunk, Don Lafferty, Kelly Simmons, Marie Lamba, Solomon Jones, Stephen Susco, Chuck Wendig, Janice Gable Bashman, Cordelia Biddle, Christopher Golden, James A. Moore, Scott Sigler, Amber Benson, Kathryn Craft, Peter Clines, Jake Bible, Del Howison, Jeff Marriott, Nancy Holder and Michael Boatman. The Liars Club works to support booksellers, raise awareness and support for public libraries, and cultivate a joy of reading and books.

The late NY Times bestseller L. A. Banks was a founding member of the Liars Club.

Jonathan created the Writers Coffeehouse, a free three-hour open-agenda networking and discussion session for writers of all genres and levels of skill in multiple locations around the country each month. Jonathan has opened Writers Coffeehouses in Willow Grove, PA, Philadelphia, Asheville, NC, San Francisco, Los Angeles, San Diego, and elsewhere.

In February 2016 Jonathan had an award named after him and became the first recipient of The Jonathan Maberry Inspiring Teens Award, presented by the Canyon Crest Academy Writers Conference, the first free teen writers con in the country.

Jonathan has been a popular writing teacher and career counselor for writers for the last two decades. He teaches a highly regard series of classes and workshops including Write Your Novel in Nine Months, Write and Sell Short Stories, Revise & Sell, Experimental Writing for Teens, and others. Many of his students have gone on to obtain representation and/or publish in short and novel-length fiction, magazine feature writing, nonfiction books, TV, film, and comics.

In 2004 Jonathan was inducted into the International Martial Arts Hall of Fame largely because of his extensive writings in that field. He is the former Expert Witness for the Philadelphia District Attorney's Office for murder cases involving martial arts; and he's done extensive work for civil cases.

Jonathan and his wife, Sara Jo, to whom he dedicates all of his published works, and their dog, Rosie, live in Del Mar, California.

Visit his website/blog and sign up for his free newsletter at www.jonathanmaberry.com

www.facebook.com/jonathanmaberry, www.twitter.com/jonathanmaberry

**THOMAS RAYMOND** was born, raised and spent all but eight years of his life in California. With the help of wife 2.0 and his awesome daughter, he made a successful escape from L.A. and is now living somewhere in New Mexico with two dogs, three cats, and a tortoise.

**BABETTE RAYMOND** is a self-described nerd. She enjoys all things sci-fi and comedy, and reading everything she can get her hands on. She lives for Halloween, and the Haunted Mansion at Disneyland is her happy place. She's a 40-something married lady with two dogs... a wiener dog and a 1/2 wiener dog. The most two important things to know about her are that she loves s'mores and abuses ellipses.

**BRIAN L. BIRD** was born and raised in the Finger Lakes of NY where he cut his teeth designing role playing and tabletop games. A U.S. Air Force veteran, he currently puts his 20 years of Logistics Management experience to work as a Procurement Specialist with the University of Texas at San Antonio. Brian studied Art Education and Psychology at Our Lady of the Lake University. He enjoys reading, writing, tabletop gaming, making found object art, and spending time with his wife Juanita and their children Johan, Elihu and Yahaira; and their granddaughter Arianna at their home in San Antonio, Texas.

**KELLY POWERS** was born into a family of educators and high achievers, so it was really no surprise to anyone when she became a Library Media Technician for a Junior High School. Though Kelly loves her job and the school she works for, she realized that she wanted to finally shoot for her childhood dream of being an author. She expressed her desire to her family and found them to be supportive of that goal too. To date, this marks Kelly's first publication in the literary world, but she hopes it will turn out to be the start of a glorious career. She currently resides in Torrance, California with her husband, son, and stepson.

**BEN RAYMOND** has many different interests. He likes pro wrestling, weiner dogs, good scotch, country music and his wife but not in that particular order. He's very honored to be a part of this project.

CPSIA information can be obtained
at www.ICGtesting.com
Printed in the USA
LVOW05s2335200817

545751LV00006B/44/P